ACCLAIM *for david steece's PARADOX*

Most tough guys are conceptualized and wr... book worms looking for a window to express... Paradox is by the author who's been there and understands the nuances of the "Blue" mindset and it's counterpart – the thug mentality. With any luck, a rookie will use this book as a guideline on how to become a real cop, not just a punk with a badge.

Anthony Kallas, retired Mississippi, Louisiana, Cop

david steece's PARADOX gives an intriguing view of a life which most of us never experience. It's written by a man who truly lived that life. One of extremes from brutal gangster to law enforcement, but he always remained a loving father and loyal friend. It is a very illuminating read.

Claire H. Collier, Baton Rouge, Louisiana

I just finished your book *david steece's PARADOX*. It is incredible. I could not put it down, although I wasn't sure if I should hate you or love you throughout the book! EXCELLENT read, you've inspired me.

Amanda Suddeth, Author, of Fire & Ice

Wow! What a story. Can't wait until the movie hits the theaters, but who could play Blackie- but Blackie? If you missed *david steece's PARADOX* you missed an accomplished writer exhibiting his great book.

Carol Smith, Author, of Journey to Command

David, I hope you have great success with you book. You deserve a best seller, your good friend Pascal.

Pascal F. Calogero, Jr. Chief Justice of the Louisiana Supreme Court (retired)

Your book *david steece's PARADOX* is a fascinating story that eminently deserves a wide reception. Our entire group enjoyed your book.

Lester D. Langley, Author and President, San Angelo Texas Writers Club

The story of your life is remarkable even more special because it is true. *david steece's PARADOX* tells the story of a man who's life was out of control. You proved you could change for all the right reasons. Your selection for your title sums up your story.

Lucienne Gautier, Head Librarian Harrison County Library System D'Iberville, MS

Thank you for your transparency in *david steece's PARADOX*. Blessings to you.
Reverend Robert Scott, Pastor, Corinth, Texas

david steece's PARADOX is an outstanding and captivating story of a man that has many contrasting facets to his life. A must read book for those who want read about a man who literally has nine lives.
Steve Thornton, Pilot Atlanta, Georgia

david steece's PARADOX is a fearlessly honest narrative of perseverance and strength. His stark conversational prose brings the reader dangerously close to the realities of his past. Steece's dedication to telling this tale, no matter what retaliation it may bring, shows his true character and courage.
Claire E. Kowalick, reporter, Times Record News, Wichita Falls, Texas

...the book, *david steece's PARADOX*, casts a spell on the reader; in fact, once I started reading, I could not put it down. ...captivating, creative and very informative. This author has created a book that is worth buying just to see how an individual can reform himself from the underworld to an example for all. I recommend it to both adults as well as young adults.
Daryl Ross Halencak, author, STARING BLUE EYES

Getting to meet you in person and develop a personal friendship with you is a blessing. Your book *david steece's PARADOX* is an amazing story which I tell everyone I meet because it is so fascinating that you had such a life of stardom and excitement that is definitely fit for a movie. I'm sure I speak for the entire staff when I say I am proud to have met you.
Kristy Fomin, Community Relations Project Coordinator and Customer Service Manager, Sgt. Grid Marine Specialties, Oklahoma City, Oklahoma

I REALLY ENJOYED YOUR BOOK, *david steece's PARADOX*. YOU WILL KNOW ME AS JUDY'S MOM.WRITE SOME MORE.I KNOW THERE IS MORE TO TELL AS YOU JUST DIDN'T STOP BEING THE MAN YOU WERE.THANKS SO MUCH FOR THE BOOK AND THE GOOD READ.I WILL ALWAYS BE YOUR FAN AND FRIEND.
JEAN CORLEY, WINDSTREAM, KENTUCKY

Blackie, *david steece's PARADOX*, the book was brilliant! The detail, the pace, the humor, and don't forget all the redheads. Waiting to find out what happened to Sandy. The way you put your girls, the five loves of your life before anything or anyone.....you could be Al Capone's ghost and I'd have your back. Till your next book, take care.
Pat Steuben, San Francisco, California

david steece's

PARADOX

Photography credits:
Unless otherwise specified, all photographs are the courtesy of the author.
Every effort has been made to trace the owners of copyrighted material.

Cover by Shannon Anderson, Artisan Communications
Additional graphics by Metal Graphics, Inc.

Published by Paradox Sales
www.davidsteece.com

Steece, David
    david steece's PARADOX
    Includes index
    ISBN-978-0-9836-27807

Editor: Rossie N. Lucitt

1. Steece, David   2. Crime and Criminals-United States-Autobiography
3. Organized Crime – United States, 4. Political Corruption
5. Sexual Exploitation 6. Gangsters – United States, 7. Law Enforcement

The names of certain individuals, locations and dates have been altered to protect their privacy.

Printed on acid-free paper
by ECPrinting, Eau Claire, WI
www.ecprinting.com
Manufactured in the United States of America
10,9,8,7,6,5,4,3,2,1 Printing 2011

Books are available in quantity for promotional or premium use. Write:
Fabricators/Paradox Sales, PO Box 253, Midway, AR 72651

*In loving memory of
my daughter, Theresa Ann*

*my Godfather, Uncle Rolland and
my good friend, Herb Smith Jr.*
who all left this world too soon.

FORWARD

The man known as "Blackie" left us his legacy; a legacy left only to anecdotal accounts until now. In his book <u>Paradox</u>, David Steece peels back the layers of crime and corruption to reveal this harsh reality during a period of Louisiana's history overflowing with both. He gives a blow-by-blow account of the events as they unfolded. You read about it in the newspapers. Now get the facts from the man who lived it on both sides of the law.

Ronald P. Kincade
Prosecuting Attorney
Baxter County Arkansas

Like the two faces of the Roman God, Janus, David Steece's PARADOX describes Blackie, (Steece's street name) as a connected gangster; a nefarious, vindictive egomaniac with sociopathic tendencies. Then, conversely, as a kind, warm, humorous friend, family man and doting father, who through his daily actions so clearly shows he adores his "angel" daughters.

A man's life is a manuscript upon which he writes his legacy.

PREFACE

This book has been a long-time project with many starts and stops along the way. It began in journal form as a father's history to his infant son and, with much prodding, grew to unleash a darker side of the realities and secrets of crime in our society. I would be more than remiss not to credit the myriad people who influenced and encouraged its fruition.

With gratitude, the following is how this writing came to be:

In the late 1980s, I lay in a hospital bed recovering from a heart attack—a virtual prisoner of Southern Baptist Hospital in New Orleans. I was being guilt tripped by the angry mother of my very young son, David 'Chip' Steece, Jr., Delone Mariano. She prodded and begged for a written history of my exploits. I had been somewhat of an enigma from a street hood to an undercover law enforcement detective. Neither profession was known much for its longevity. "I want your son to know all about you—what you've done and what you became. The way you take care of yourself, you'll be lucky to live to hear him talk." After days of badgering, she said if I would just lie there and talk as I had many times at the dinner table, she would be my scribe, and my namesake could eventually know my story. She encouraged me to tell about this particular case because of the current news coverage. She wore me down and, thus, began a journal edition and that reminded me of the many *flashbacks* that created *Paradox*.

A couple of notebooks later, I was well again and back on the street. Chip was four. Things had changed after a court battle. I had full custody of him. I forgot about any need for him to know me through a journal. I was, after all, I thought, indestructible.

A few months later, I was rushed to the same hospital by my then Police Chief Max Rodriguez, after I had been found nearly unconscious by longtime girlfriend Barbara Gay, who called the Police Department. My daughters, Theresa, Gail, Alisha, Rachael, along with Chip and grandsons Trent and Kristian, all arrived at the hospital after a wild hundred-mile-per-hour drive. It was touch and go for a couple of days; when I finally woke up, there at my bedside was a very worried Gail, and a longtime friend and associate who had come in from Chicago, whose street name was (Joe-nose), holding Chip. I had only been in law enforcement for a short time, so the parade of associates was mixed with new friends and continued until Easter Sunday. Sgt. Swenson took me home and said, "That was close." He suggested I make some "provisions" for the little guy, not just financial, but some type of written history, so Chip would know who his dad had been. Swenson prompted me to do this because of his own early loss and his curiosity about his history. He added, "Your life is much more complicated than mine, so write something down." Thoughts of the journal I had started returned, and I contacted an old and trusted friend, Gina Duplantis. When she finished typing the notebooks, it was a scant forty pages. She said, "That's really interesting, funny, and actually pretty good. You should make it into a real book." But my feeling of indestructibility had returned and, once more, I blew it off.

A few years later, I had retired and moved to Houston, when the health problems returned. Chip was now a second grader and I was in a wheelchair, down to 147 pounds. This was well below the usual 235/240 I had carried since high school. I had been diagnosed with diabetes related polycythemia vera, and though I was taking thirty-seven medications a day, I continued to deteriorate. I had been a personal friend for a few years with the head pharmacist, Linda Pham, at Walgreen's on Hwy 6 in Sugar Land. Linda would push me out to the van because I was too weak to roll myself. With great concern for my worsening condition, she recommended, then insisted I see David P. Schauer, M D. Linda made the appointment and drove me there. I remember his receptionist, Jeannie Beard, who, from that day forward, made sure I was taken special care of. Dr. Schauer, after a brief examination, sent me straight to the hospital. In a few weeks, he was getting me under control and called in Pavan Grover, M.D., and a pain specialist, to treat me. Dr. Grover, a personable man, during one of our non-medical talks mentioned he was writing a book. I told him of my meager efforts to start one. He had heard some of my background and wanted to read what I had finished. After I was released, he kept on me until we met and, after he read the famous "forty pages," he said, "This is very good. You have to finish this." He then gave me some pointers and, once again, the book continued.

By now, I needed some dates and contacted my former partner, Herb Smith. He was still on the job and could dig through warehouse files for me. I reached Herb at the Bureau and, after some catch-up jawing, told him what I was after. "Sure, hold on," he said.

SURPRISE! In a few minutes, he came back on the line. "What do you want the dates for?"

I said, "I'm writing a book."

Herb said, "hold on," again. This time, when he came back, he said, "you can't do that."

"Why"? I asked.

"Don't do it," he warned. "They'll never let you get away with that."

"Who do you mean they?"

"You know we don't do the stuff that we do, and they're afraid you might be believable. Without the dates and times, if someone runs your name now, you'll just come up as a gangster and an alleged hit man, and who would believe you without explicit dates and details?"

"What the hell ya talkin' about?" I asked.

"I love you like a brother," he said, "but my hands are tied."

"You sat in my den in Picayune, with John, when I pulled the pin, and told my family how no one could have done the things that I did, nor took the risks that I took on many cases, including ones I worked on with you."

He said, "I know, but I won't be able to say that publicly. You know I'm taking a resident agent transfer to Alabama, mostly because you won't be working with me anymore."

I thought about it a few days and then called Harry Cabral, Jr., my life-long friend and attorney. Harry said, "you and Herb are friends and have worked closely for a long time, but you've worked with others. Aren't some of them still your friends? Why not ask them discreetly?"

I thought that was a good idea. I called Del Hahn, now a private investigator after he retired as a resident agent in Baton Rouge, where he went when he and I quit working together in New Orleans, back when Bob Rightmier was still Special Agent in Charge. I knew Del had been deeply involved in the investigation of the big narcotics dealer, Barry Seal, whom they flipped and who turned many cases for the Government including the Gotcha Cartel in South America. Two Columbians had gunned down Barry in Baton Rouge at the Salvation Army, where he had to spend the night as part of the parole requirements from a Federal Judge. Del and I had done some pretty heavy shit together. We were not as close now as Herb and I. I had never missed Carolyn, his wife's birthday (October 2nd). But when I was sick in Texas, I didn't send her a card for the first time in over thirty years. Del went to a lot of trouble tracking me down to make sure I wasn't dead. I still have the handwritten letter he sent, "in case his memory goes bad" also.

We met for coffee in Baton Rouge on College Drive at the Waffle House and just shot the shit. After a while, I mentioned I had seen the TV movie *Double Crossed* with Dennis Hopper and Adrienne Barbeau, about Barry Seal, adding, "I thought that might have been yours."

He didn't say anything for a couple of minutes, and then said, "yeah, I wrote it all out for a book, but someone beat me to it."

"How could someone beat you to it? It was your case!"

He shrugged and changed the subject.

I went to back to Harry with this information, and he said, "you have a young son to raise, and you, of all people, know how capable 'they' are, and you have plenty of time. Be smart. Write it and wait, and then at the right time, publish it."

I laughed. "You mean when I'm dying?"

He said, "write it down, wait, be smart!"

I went home and thought about what had happened, and you know me, I was well on my way to recovery, out of the wheelchair and walking with a cane and, of course, once again indestructible, so I just blew it off again.

By this time, Chip was ready for middle school in Houston. He was headed for an inner-city school where gangs and dope ran rampant. I contacted OSHA and was told that the best two counties for air and water were Bonner County, Idaho, and Marion County, Arkansas. Idaho was too cold, even though we visited it in the spring. So we moved to rural Arkansas on the Missouri border, where the chances of catching a stray bullet were remote.

There I met Rosie Lucitt. She was there with her partner, a retired cop, and we became friends. I knew her as a photographer because of the great pictures she took or "made" as they say. She moved to Buffalo, NY, after her man died, to be near her daughter, but we stayed in touch.

In 2002, about sixty people from the little town I lived in, asked me to run for Mayor. I did, and of course, sent letters to everyone I knew asking for money. Rosie, though hundreds of miles away, was one of the first to send a contribution with a letter asking me to let her know how it turned out. To shorten a long story, I lost and was subject to some of the most outlandish lies ever told. So, after the election, when Rosie and I were talking on the phone, the election was over and the lies were now funny. I said, "I should write a book about the election."

Rosie said, "One about your life/career would be better. You know that's what I do. I'm a magazine editor."

I said, "I didn't realize that. I thought you took pretty pictures."

"That's just a hobby," she said.

I then mentioned I had started a book many years ago at a couple of different times, and the one time when I really decided to get serious about it I was told, "you can't do that," by my former partner.

She asked some details and asked how long ago that was.

I said, "I think in the mid 90s."

"Do you still have a copy?" she asked.

"Yeah, somewhere."

She told me to send it to her, and I told her I would and then forgot about it.

She called back after awhile and reminded me, "send me a copy. I want to read it."

After a few more phone calls, I finally dug up the manuscript and sent it to her. About a week later, I received a letter from her that started out WOW! It went on to say how mad she was when the story just stopped. She said, "sit down NOW and finish it and to hell with everyone who doesn't want this stuff known." As we got into it, she said, "what a great movie it would make and, of course, if you're reading this, as Paul Harvey would say, "AND NOW YOU KNOW THE REST OF THE STORY."

Without each of these people, there would be no *Paradox*. They are listed in the order in which they affected this book, of course, starting with me!

A Bunch of Bad Guys and Crooked Politicians
DeLone Gladys Mariano (David Jr.'s mother)
David "Chip" Steece, Jr. (son)
Theresa Ann Steece (daughter, deceased)
Elizabeth "Beth" Steece (daughter, adopted)
Luann Gail Steece Grommon (daughter)

Alisha Louis Steece Massarini (daughter)
Rachael Elizabeth Steece O'Neill (daughter)
Barbara Ellen Steece (wife)
Gina Duplantis (friend and first typist)
Max Rodriguez (Chief of Police, retired)
Harry R. Cabral, Jr. (first attorney, deceased)
Linda Pham (head pharmacist at Walgreen's Drugs)
David P. Schauer, M.D. (saved my life)
Pavan Grover, M.D. (Advisor)
Lois Miller (friend and typist)
Rosie N. Lucitt (the editor)
Artisan Communications (cover graphics)
Metal Graphics (novelty graphics)
Black Willow Consulting (webmaster)
Ronald P. Kincade (attorney)
Sue Hall (Asst. Director, Bay City Library)
John C. Smith (Captain, USN Retired, advisor)
Carol Smith (author of *Journey to Command*)

Credit must also be given to the Houston inner-city school system that caused our move to Arkansas and the eventual meeting with Rosie and her RED PEN. Also very important, with loving thanks for the perseverance of my wife Barbara and son, Chip, Jr. Chip typed all the writes and rewrites, until I married Barbara who took it to the end. But, alas, they all had to deal with my fits of rebellion against sitting down to dictate, placing the pictures in the right locations, etc. Their hard headedness surpasses even my own. The journal is now complete. The son knows his father, and the father is lucky enough to know his son, now an honor student in college and making his way toward his own adventures.

Oh yeah, better give gratitude also for INDESTRUCTIBILITY.

David "Blackie" Steece
Somewhere in Texas

PARADX

"THE FLASHBACKS
OF
BLACKIE'S ILLOGICAL LIFE"

the true narrative of a real gangster

Chapter 1

The ringing phone stirred the afternoon heat as he walked up from the dock. He reached through the kitchen window and answered it.

"Yeah?"

"The deal's all set."

He recognized the voice on the other end as a long time political friend, Eddie D'Gerolamo. Eddie D's stature, of only 5'2" and about 125, did not project the power he really wielded. His olive complexion, dark penetrating eyes, and black curly hair were signatures of his pure Sicilian ancestry. Eddie D' had been the main liaison for family business to politics for as long as Blackie could remember. First, an elected councilman and then the Mayor of the City of Kenner, Louisiana's fourth largest city, he was now a state legislator who led the powerful Jefferson delegation, which, with its block vote, could usually control any bill presented. In addition, Blackie shared one of his metro offices with Eddie D' when he was home from Baton Rouge. His mind wandered as his friend rambled on. How long had he been in this godforsaken place? Ten months? It was only forty miles from metropolitan New Orleans but he felt isolated. The closest town a couple of miles away was a quiet, sleepy place of country folks, and that dullness only increased his isolation.

He looked around his temporary prison through the heat ripples. Acres of beautifully manicured rolling grounds were bordered by the Ponchatoula River on the North. The water he had just left was so clear he could count the tadpoles swimming between the polished rocks. A guesthouse sat empty on the bank beyond the three-car garage. The rustic main house was enormous and held all the amenities an estate could offer—fireplaces, an indoor atrium, sunken tubs, wet bar, and cedar closets. The double front doors opened to a place built of windows and peaceful country views designed to bring the outdoors in, comfortably controlled.

There had been a power struggle back in the city between two families. Even though his side had won, there had been a lot of heat, and he was out here cooling off. This was his cooler. With only a half a dozen people who knew where he was, communication was at a minimum. This wasn't life as he knew it. This place was dead and he was bored.

At 6'3 and 235, his muscular upper body and wiry legs required that his clothes be custom altered, in addition to the coat adjustment to hide the .44 Magnum that was always on his right hip. His natural dark complexion was copper colored from the southern sun, accenting his high cheek bones and making his distinctive black eyes menacingly that of a predator when angered. His nose had been broken a couple of times but, hell, Sicilian noses were big and crooked anyhow. He had a scar on the edge of his chin where a pistol sight had cut him in a fight. There was an indention over the right eyebrow where a shotgun pellet had dented the skull permanently. He had a three-and-a-half-inch scar on his throat from surgery. A knife fight had left him with a scar crossing the middle, ring, and little finger on the left hand. The beads of sweat on his forehead, mixed with his natural body oils, made his coal black hair seem even blacker than it was.

Eddie D' said, "you have to call the Commissioner in Baton Rouge today and set up an appointment for Monday. You got the number?"

"Yeah," he said, "whasa dis guy like?"

"You know, he's a virgin," Eddie D' responded. "It's his first time out and he don't know shit."

His mind wandered again. Would this be the one? Would this be the guy who figured him out?

"How are the girls?" Eddie D' asked.

"Okay, getting big."

"Call me Monday and let me know how it went."

"Alright, man, thanks a lot," he said, as he stood there holding the telephone with the dial tone buzzing in his ear.

Looking across the backyard where his three daughters, still at home, played in the water of the small river. His oldest daughter, Teri, was away at college and Bitsie was getting ready to go, honing up her studies at a private girls school. None of them liked it here, either, but they were his girls and they were tough. As he gazed at the girls, he remembered how all those big brown eyes had stared at him and asked, "What do you mean, dad? We're moving and we can't tell any of our friends or our teachers where we're going?" Street life had been tough on them. He was married, but you really couldn't say he had a wife. He married her so that he could get custody from the children's mother after the divorce. Even when he and the stepmother were together, the relationship was at best strained. He pondered calling the Commissioner from his home phone, but his instincts told him no. He packed the girls up in the pick-up and drove the hour to Baton Rouge to call from a local pay phone. As they drove along Interstate 12, he started missing his black Caddy. His signature, or logo, or trademark, or whatever you wanted to call it, was one of the reasons that got Blackie his nickname. Since 1960 there had been a black Cadillac with the red leather interior, which he acquired new each year. Everyone who was anyone knew that when the black Cadillac pulled up in front of their house or business, it was Blackie, delivering either help or trouble, depending on which side of the fence they were on, and those who didn't know found out fast.

Blackie was a strange dude. Friends described him as a humorous, warm guy, who was, for the most part, kind. Family saw him as a loyal friend with a heart of gold but very private. Others saw him as a tenacious, vindictive egomaniac who had a mean streak a mile wide with all the traits of a sociopath. Occasionally, the press had depicted him as something of an enigma, or a paradox, best left alone. Law enforcement, on the other hand, was always trying to figure out what side of the fence he was really on. Although he had had several criminal arrests and spent some time in front of Grand Juries, he had no convictions.

Reproduction of criminal rap sheet:

Bureau of Identification, SHERIFF OFFICE,
Jefferson Parish, Louisiana

NAME: David Warren Steece
ALIAS
NO. 40282 SID #471 666

Contributor of Fingerprints	Name & Number	Arrested or Received	Charge	Disposition
P D Atchison Kansas	David Warren Steece #2968	11/10/55	Fraud Solicitation	Printed for Atchison, Co. Charge Reduced Cost Pd & REL.
P D Baton Rouge, La	David Warren Steece #105	5/24/57	Appl. FP.	PRT. RET
P D Baton Rouge, La.	David Warren Steece #18653	3/26/58	BURG & THEF	REL NO CHARGE
P D Baton Rouge, La	David Warren Steece #18653	5/8/58	Disorderly Conduct 13:300	5/12/58/case Cont. With Out Date
P D Shreveport, La.	David Warren Steece# 68386	11/2/59	Suspect	REL. 11/3/59
P D New Orleans, La.	David Warren Steece #SO7435	7/20/67	APPL. F.P.	F. P. RET.
S O Gretna La.	David Warren Steece #SPD-421 Residence: 5024 Haring Court, Metairie, La.	10/22/69	APPL. F.P.	PRT. RET.
S O Gretna La.	David Warren Steece #40282	7/9/70	Public Bribery	AFF#70-1101 Case was Nolle Prossed 9/14/71
S O Gretna La.	David Warren Steece #40282	8/25/73	Att. Murder	No Record in Clerk Office As of 8/7/77

Jefferson Parish, La. Sheriff's Office 3/9/78 Updated by Sgt. Reggio

No one knew just where he came from. He just kind of fell out of the sky in the fall of 1955, living and going to school from Nofia Pecora's home, an alleged high-ranking Mafia member and seen much of the time associating with the family and playing with Nofia, Jr. It was obvious he was connected, but you never heard him drop any names. The next traceable thing about him was that, when he was in his early twenties, he either owned, or appeared to own, two nightclubs, allegedly mob controlled.

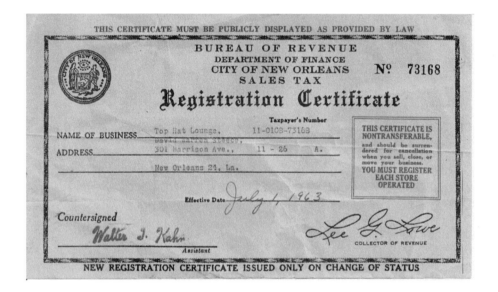

The Top Hat Lounge, New Orleans, LA

One of the clubs, The Top Hat, was in New Orleans, and the other, the Joy, a reputed gambling casino, was in Gretna, just across the Mississippi River and long known for its fast and loose lifestyle.

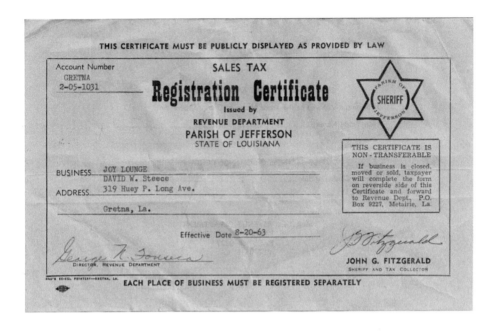

The Joy Lounge Casino, Gretna, LA

That came to light in a 1963 story in *The Saturday Evening Post* with a picture of Blackie and his daughter, Teri (then six years old) walking out of the club in Gretna on a Saturday morning. The story claimed that drugs, vice, and gambling were wide open in this club and that only a direct descendant of a high-ranking Mafia figure could ever hold that position with that club in Gretna. That publicity put him out of the nightclub business, but he was seen regularly driving alleged Mafia figures, usually Peter Marcello. Many times they were accompanied by Peter's younger brother Pascal. This added to the enigma of Blackie, because two of Marcello's younger brothers, Vincent and Anthony, owned and operated Jefferson Business Machines, which handled pin-ball machines, juke boxes, etc., throughout Jefferson Parish, and both of Blackie's clubs sported "TACS," John "Tac" Elm's machines and Anthony Tucia's New Orleans cigarette machines. Undercover detectives had photographed his connections when Blackie had been to their homes and businesses. In the mid 1960s, he surfaced again with a private detective agency and, for many years, purported to be just that. But anytime you looked at his investigators, it was obvious that they could go bear hunting with a stick.

Blackie pulled into a self-service gas station in Baton Rouge and dropped a dime into the pay phone. He dialed the number and counted

On six, a child answered. Blackie said, "May I please speak to the Commissioner?"

"Who's calling please?"

"He's expecting my call."

A few moments passed and a booming voice said, "This is the Commissioner speaking."

"David Steece here. Someone told me to call you for an appointment tomorrow."

The Commissioner said, "Who?"

Blackie repeated, "David Steece."

"Oh, yeah, I'll be in the city tomorrow. Meet me at the Roosevelt Hotel, Suite 910 at 7:00 a.m. sharp."

"Okay," Blackie said and hung up the phone. He got back in the pick-up and drove across the street to Dairy Queen and got his girls some ice cream. When they started back east on Interstate 12, he wondered if the Commissioner was as arrogant as he sounded. What the hell, most elected officials were arrogant assholes. In his many years, he had dealt with about a thousand, and he could only think of a few that he could depend on for anything.

Chapter 2

Blackie lay in bed looking past his fireplace and out into the yard, when the alarm sounded at 5:00 a.m. He rolled out of bed, went to the bathroom, and turned on the shower. Maybe this would make him feel like he was alive again. When he finished his shower and began to shave, he wondered, *will the people in the city still remember me without my famous beard?* He'd shaved it when he moved to the country. "The Man" had told him to, so that he wouldn't scare any of those old country folks. He dressed in a black mohair suit, white on white shirt with diamond stud cufflinks that Dr. Frank Minyard had given him for his birthday a few years before, white on white tie, gold nugget bracelet, diamond "pinky ring," and black alligator shoes, the standard dress for his image.

As he slipped on his Rolex, he realized it was time to wake the girls for school and supervise the morning bickering while they dressed and ate. Not knowing what time he would be home, he gave them instructions to only answer the phone on the prearranged code and for Lu, the oldest of the girls at home, to keep a piece with her at all times, and to let no one, NO ONE, in the house, except family. At 6:15 a.m., he strapped on his ankle gun and put his pet .44 magnum on his hip, kissed his girls goodbye, and left. As he turned onto the interstate, he looked at his watch. The time made him wonder why he always left so late. He decided that he liked to drive 80 or 90 mph, because it gave him a rush. He arrived in New Orleans and pulled into the hotel parking garage at five minutes to seven, tipped the regular attendant a *fin($5.00)* so that he wouldn't park upstairs where it would take forever to get it back, went to the elevator in the Roosevelt Hotel, and pushed number 9. When he arrived at room 910, he had a little over a minute to spare. He watched his second hand sweep the dial of his Rolex for exactly 7:00 a.m. and then rapped loudly on the door. Several seconds passed, and then the door opened. He recognized the Commissioner from political ads and said, "Dave Steece."

"You're not so big," the Commissioner replied.

"Neither are you. Who'd you expect, Goliath?"

The Commissioner looked him up and down, appearing a little bit surprised at Blackie's sharp tone. Blackie was sure he wasn't used to being talked to like that. Tough shit, he'd better get used to it or change the way he talked to him. The Commissioner was about 6'1" and 185/190, he guessed, in his early forties, with gray hair, and obviously thought himself a pretty boy. Blackie had done some background on the Commissioner and knew that he came from the western side of the state near DeRidder, had been something of a basketball star in a 1-AA college, had flown jets in the military, a little above average attorney and, even though he had lost, had run a pretty good race the first time he tried his hand at politics. Now he had won the state-wide race against the twenty-year incumbent Dave Pierce who had taken his office for granted. Other than that, Blackie would have to learn about him as he went. As they went inside the suite, a pretty lady in a green negligee came out of one of the bedrooms. Blackie looked at her and thought, *well, things are looking up.* The Commissioner introduced his wife Jean and asked if Blackie wanted coffee. "No," Blackie replied, and then added, "I ain't got no vices," to which the Commissioner snickered. After some small talk, Jean excused herself, leaving the two men to talk.

The Commissioner immediately opened the conversation. "I understand you're the man to see if I need anything done?" The emphasis was on "*anything.*"

"Maybe."

"Well, I've asked a lot of people about you and they say you're loyal, you're well organized, and connected."

"I'm loyal to who pays me."

"Well, I'm putting you on the payroll right now, and I have a couple of small jobs for you to do today."

"Wait a minute, how much payroll?"

"Oh, whatever the job pays."

"I don't operate like that. The money thing has to be settled up front."

"Okay, here's $400.00," the Commissioner said, having taken the bills out of his wallet. "Take my state car and go see this disc jockey in Lafayette, who's saying bad things about me on the radio. Handle that for me today and meet me at the Capitol tomorrow, and we'll work out all the details."

"What is this, a fuckin' test?"

"Whatever," the Commissioner shrugged.

"What kind of car?"

"It's a white Buick. Here's the parking ticket," the Commissioner said, separating the ticket from the bills.

With that Blackie got up and left. When he reached the lobby, he stopped at a pay phone to call Eddie D' to let him know what had happened. "How'd it go?" Eddie D' said, without preamble when he answered the phone.

"I think this guy's been watchin' too much T.V."

"He'll be o.k. You settle the money thing?"

"No, tomorrow."

"Well, you can make a good deal because you're controlling the legislative votes that he needs to make his office run."

"I understand. I just don't think I'm gonna like the dude too much," Blackie said.

"You'll be alright. You know you gotta get back in circulation."

"Yeah, yeah, you're right. Well, let me go. I gotta go to Lafayette and kick some coonass' ass who the Commissioner don't like."

"Okay, you be cool," Eddie D' said.

Blackie hung up and called Zap, quickly brought him up to date, and told him where his pickup was and to bring it home to him.

Blackie hung up. He walked across the street to the parking garage. As he waited for the Commissioner's Buick, he knew he would have to tell "The Man" that he'd been hired. He guessed he'd have to call him to see when they could meet. Anyhow, he'd deal with that tomorrow. Blackie tipped the valet again, climbed into the white Buick, and wheeled it out onto O'Keefe. As he crossed a fork at I-10 and I-55, about twenty miles north of New Orleans, which was the exit to his sister Patsy's home, he thought about the story she liked to tell about his daughter Lu.

A few years ago when he was involved in a power struggle for one of the mob's areas, his men were running in and out of his house day and night, all armed and everybody and everything was in turmoil. Each of his girls had a personal bodyguard twenty-four hours a day. Sis had told him that Lu, eight at the time, would clutch a little tiny piece of paper with the telephone number for his car phone in her hand and never put it down. Alley, who had just started school at the time, had one of Blackie's best and most trusted soldiers, a black, "Big John," who was as tough as a company of Marines. He took her to and from school and watched her every minute. She was really too small to understand what was going on. Blackie remembered the many times he had tried to explain to the girls the WHY and BECAUSE, only to be met by a bunch of big brown sad eyes, and the standard question. "When can we go outside and play again, Daddy?" Then he'd just take them all in his arms and rock them in the rocking chair and they would all cry. Blackie was crying because the life he had inherited from his father, though it was his choice, left him no way out until it was ended, and the girls, because their daddy was crying and they loved him. Sometimes this life just sucked.

As he crossed through Baton Rouge on the elevated expressway, he thought about another good friend, Gus Weill, whose office was nearby. A man he would do anything for, without hesitation, a man who had taught him a lot about life and someone he could always trust and depend on. He hoped someday to be able to serve him in some manner, since this man was one of only a handful who had never asked him for a favor in the many years they'd been friends. Thoughts of Gus brought back memories of their mutual friend "Big John" McKeithen, a two-term governor, and one of the few politicians Blackie respected. Like everyone in public life, good, bad, or indifferent, he'd had his turn with the media and was now a country attorney, while numerous other people not half as good still served in elected positions. The media! What a pain in the ass! They were kind of like kids shooting off their mouths when they only have half the facts. But Blackie had a couple of reporters he liked, so maybe there was hope for these jerks too.

As he crossed the twenty-mile-long Atchafalaya Basin Bridge, he started to think about how he was going to handle this dude he was going to see. He turned south off I-10 and soon saw his destination, a fertilizer company. He drove by once to check out the cars in the area then pulled up beside the office and parked.

Blackie went in the front door and saw a blonde, thirty-fiveish woman, sitting at the reception desk. "The Commissioner called. Lefty's expecting me," he told her.

Blackie surveyed the reception office as the secretary disappeared into the private office. She reappeared almost instantaneously and held the door open for Blackie to enter. He strode inside pulling the door closed behind him. It was a large, expensively furnished office with sofas on two walls, a bookcase with a T.V. on the other, and two high wing-back chairs in front of a huge mahogany desk. He crossed the room, as Lefty stood up from behind the desk and came to meet him. Lefty was late forties, kind of a squat ruddy-faced man, obviously of French descent. The mousey brown hair had receded enough to leave a round shiny spot. He was dressed in a white open-collar shirt, slacks, and cowboy boots. Blackie, looking past Lefty's shoulder through the window, noticed a bright yellow, small private airplane behind the building and wondered what and who it was for. Was this guy a pilot? Deciding he probably was, since the Commissioner had been a pilot in the military, he thought that was probably the tie between these two, some kind of old military buddy loyalty-thing.

As they shook hands, Blackie said, "the Commissioner told me you have a name and address of someone who's having a mouth problem." Lefty picked up a small piece of paper off his desk and handed it to Blackie. It had a name, address, apartment number, a car model, make, color, and license number.

He glanced at the paper. "Can you give me a physical?" he asked.

Lefty responded with a nod. "He's about six feet, a hundred-ninety pounds, dark hair, and a smart ass."

"Does he live alone?"

"I guess he does, unless he has some one-night stand with him."

"Does he carry?"

"I don't believe."

"Okay. The Commissioner appreciates this, ya hear. He'll be in touch with ya."

They shook hands and Blackie left. As Blackie walked back through the reception office and thanked the blonde, he wondered if she had been any good when she was twenty. Cellulite, bleach, and too much make-up had taken its toll, and he figured if you unsnapped her bra and skirt at the same time, she'd roll out like a broken dam in all directions.

He got in the Buick and headed south at about eighty, for ten minutes, abruptly pulling into the median and making a U-turn back north; he now set the cruise control at fifty so he could easily survey all the southbound traffic. He had made his U turn just outside of New Iberia, a small town that brought back memories of many years ago. *Amusedly, he reminisced on that phone call he had got back in the early 1960s from the millionaire in Oklahoma. He'd called to tell Blackie that he'd just wired him a grand, and to meet him in Little Rock. It was like yesterday to Blackie when he met the dude, how he just looked rich, smelled rich, and acted rich. The guy from Oklahoma had rented a whole floor of the then pretty-new and fancy round hotel in downtown Little Rock. As soon as Blackie walked in his room, he nodded to a young weight lifter, who looked like Tarzan in a suit. Tarzan got Oklahoma's jacket, which looked as rich as the rest of him. The Oklahoman was in his late fifties. You could tell by the tailored silk shirt he wore that he was still in good shape. Tarzan went to bring the car around. He got up and Blackie followed him to the elevator.*

On the way down, Oklahoma asked, "you from St. Louis originally? How'd you end up in New Orleans?"

They walked out the front door and Tarzan opened the back door of the Limo. As they pulled away from the curb, Blackie thought he'd better give him some kind of answer. "My dad had a freedom problem in St. Louis, and his friends in New Orleans took me in. I've been there ever since." Oklahoma nodded and lit about a three-foot cigar. Twenty minutes later, they pulled up in what looked like a private airport to Blackie. Over to one side of the tower, they climbed aboard what looked like an old C-47 World War II military plane that Blackie had seen in the movies. But wow! When they walked inside, it looked like the Presidential Suite at the Roosevelt Hotel. Blackie had never seen anything that looked like that before. They ate and talked, seemed like Oklahoma had a lot of different businesses, and there was this dude that had worked for him, that had not been too good with math and geography. He forgot how much he was supposed to take to the bank and then he got lost and ended up three states away, hidden in this little town in south Louisiana, New Iberia.

The Oklahoma man didn't care so much about the money; he just wanted to make sure everybody knew that when you danced to his tune you had to pay the fiddler. He told Blackie he had the greatest respect for the people from St. Louis who had recommended him. Then he offered Blackie a ride back south in his airplane. Blackie declined, saying the only things he flew on were Goodyear tires.

When they got back to the Hotel, Oklahoma gave Blackie another grand from a roll that would choke a big horse. Blackie walked down the hall toward the elevator and thought, there's more tits and ass here than there is in the Sands Hotel in Vegas.

He left the city immediately and drove the four-hundred plus miles without stopping. By the time he pulled into a little tourist court about ten miles from his destination, it was after 4:00 a.m. and he flopped down on the bed and slept until 3:00 p.m. the next afternoon. He showered and dressed and went to a pay phone in town to check in and see what was going on. He told a couple of his men to bring a rental car and a hot car with stolen tags to him along U.S. Hwy. 90. They would all meet at 7:00 a.m. the next morning. After the conversation, Blackie found a little local grocery store and bought himself a big ham and cheese Po' boy sandwich on French bread, a gallon of milk and a half dozen Twinkies, which he downed on the bench out front of the store while listening to the old timers bullshit and watch him eat.

At seven the next morning Blackie and his two men discussed strategy. While Blackie was checking out the dude's hideout in the hot car, his boys would stash his Caddy north of town alongside a small bayou. Then they would come back to town and back-up Blackie. If the cops got involved and a chase ensued, they would be the blocker car. Time for everything to come down was 9:00 a.m.

Blackie's men parked in an intersection, half a block from the house on the inside corner. Five minutes later, Blackie drove up from the opposite direction in the stolen Oldsmobile, parked in front of the house on the wrong side of the street against traffic, leaving the driver's door open. He was dressed in his traditional black mohair suit, white on white shirt and white tie. He went through the gate and jammed it back against the grass to make sure it would not swing shut, thinking to himself that he never was much of a hurdler in track. The screen door was hooked. He slipped a knife through the crack, knocking the hook off, entered, and crossed the porch.

Standing just slightly to the side of the door, he knocked hard and called out, "bill collector." He heard some movement inside and a young woman with dirty blonde hair, barefoot, and in shorts and a baggy T-shirt came to the door. Blackie said, "I'm from the Spiegel Catalog people in Chicago and I want to talk to Al Rogers. He bought a portable radio from us and never did pay, is he home?"

"No Al Rogers lives here," she said.

Blackie unbuttoned his coat and reached into his inside pocket with his left hand, pulled out a card, and said, "here's the contract he signed and this is the address he gave. Are you sure he's not hiding in there?"

Then Blackie saw a man peering around the corner of an inside room. He could also see that he was holding a shotgun beside his leg. The man from Oklahoma had failed to mention someone had already tried to get this dude.

"I told you, you have the wrong address," the girl said loudly.

"Look lady," Blackie shouted, "I'm gonna have to go get the sheriff with a warrant to search this house for that radio. You people think just because you buy through the mail and sign somebody else's name, you ain't gotta pay for nothing. But it ain't like that, I'll be back."

With that, Blackie stormed off the porch, scratching the back of his neck with his left hand signaling trouble to his men on the corner. As he went down the steps and crossed the yard, his men began driving slowly toward him.

When he went through the gate, he heard one of his men shout a warning, and instinctively dove toward the rear of his car, away from the open door. There was a thunderous roar, breaking glass, then screeching of tires. As Blackie rolled over on his back, his .44 in hand, his men were sending a barrage of shots toward the man on the porch with a raised shotgun. Blackie added three rounds from his .44 mag in the same direction, leaped up, and jumped into the Oldsmobile. Its driver-side windows and dash had been torn apart by the shotgun blast. The engine roared to life and he tore down the street. He heard the shotgun go off again but he didn't hear it hit anything. When he turned the corner half a block away, his men were right on his bumper. He looked back, could see no one, and could only hear the woman screaming. A block away, with broken glass flying all around, Blackie was sure that the gunfire, especially the shotgun and the .44 mag had alerted everybody in the neighborhood, so he decided to abandon the plan and the car. He pulled the Oldsmobile to the side of the street, left it, and jumped into the car with his men. They drove north through town to where the Caddy was hidden. When Blackie's men dropped him at the Caddy, he told them to go toward Texas, maybe Lake Charles (they had plenty of broads there) spend the night, and then head back to the New Orleans area.

Blackie headed east and, in a little over an hour, pulled into the Trailways Bus Station in Baton Rouge close to the old state Capitol building. There he changed his gun for a spare one that he kept in the bus locker. This was a trick he had learned from his dad, to have a place to stash a hot gun and pick up a cold one. He had several such locations in the city and in some other towns he frequented. As Blackie left the bus station, he thought he noticed someone following him, but he shrugged it off and took the Airline highway bypass to a pancake house. He ordered a large stack of buckwheat pancakes and four basted eggs. He didn't eat regularly, but when he did, it took a lot to fill *that frame. Then he drove on to a truck stop and called the man in Oklahoma.*

"Hey man, the dude was hot. You forgot to tell me that."

There was a long pause before Oklahoma asked, "What happened?"

"I'm sure you'll be happy, when you read the newspaper. But there could be some heat and heat costs money, sometimes lots of money."

"Okay. I'll wire a bonus to the same place, okay?"

"That'll work."

Blackie told Oklahoma to call him if he needed him. As he drove from the truck stop to the Belmont Motel to check in, he again thought he noticed a tail, but after watching a few minutes, he changed his mind. Why would they be tailing him this soon? From his room, he called a local chick he knew, but Kathy said the old man was at home and it would take her a couple of hours to get out. So while he was waiting, he turned on the T.V. and lay down on the bed. He must have dozed off, because the loud banging at the door woke him up at midnight.

He jumped up, grabbed his piece, and hollered, "who is it?"

"POLICE! Turn on the lights, open the door, put your hands on your head."

"Yeah, yeah, how do I know you ain't robbers? Don't get trigger happy, and put some kind of I.D. up to the window so I know who you really are. If you're the police I'll let you in."

"Okay hard ass," said the voice outside that Blackie recognized as a lieutenant. he knew. "Here!" yelled the voice, holding a police I.D. up to the window.

"So you really are the cops! You can't be too careful in these times you know." He opened the door and, as he stepped back, detectives swarmed all over the room. "Where's your piece?" hollered the short, fat lieutenant, letting everyone know that he was in charge.

"Right on the nightstand, man, What's this all about?"

"We'll ask the questions," snapped the lieutenant, adding, "where you been all day?"

"Shacked up, why?" said Blackie.

"With who?"

"A good looking chick that goes all day for fifty bucks."

"What's her name?"

"Hey, I was into her sex, not her heritage. Ask me what size tits she had and maybe I can answer you."

"I think you're a lying smart ass. Where is she now?"

"I dropped her off down near the old Capitol around four this afternoon," Blackie said, remembering that he had suspected a tail earlier.

"That's right, Lieutenant, that's about the time we picked him up downtown," said one of the other detectives.

Dumb cop, *thought Blackie, now he knew they didn't know where he had been or who had been with him. The Lieutenant turned beet red, gave the cop a look that would kill, and yelled. "Shut up!" Turning to Blackie, the Lieutenant fumed, "Steece, you're gonna fuck up, and I'm gonna find out what you're doing and how."Blackie thought,* Yeah, yeah, you couldn't find your ass with a real crew, a flashlight, and a pair of binoculars.

As the local fuzz pulled away, Blackie wondered if it might have been a mistake for him to eat that po'boy on that bench back in New Iberia with those old geezers. He bet one of those dudes remembered him and ID'd him as the stranger in town for the local fuzz. Maybe that was why the Baton Rouge heat was on him so fast. Oh well, too late to worry on it.

Just then, Kathy pulled up in the parking lot, and Blackie thought to himself, "well the night might end up o.k. after all".

His memory took him all the way to Lafayette and, as he turned into the apartment parking lot, he wished he wasn't in the Commissioner's white Buick. It was like waving a red flag in front of a bull, and he didn't need that. He parked and went to check the mailboxes for the dude with the bad mouth. No mail in his box, which meant he was either already home or he didn't know anybody who knew how to write. Blackie walked through the apartment complex and by the window of the dude's apartment, but he couldn't see anything. Damn! Why weren't these assholes more cooperative? Bad mouth could just come outside so Blackie could kick his ass and get it over with. He went back to the Buick and found a parking place with a better view and waited. After a little while, his luck turned. The dude's door opened and he came out. Blackie got out of the car with a piece of paper in his hand, approached the man, and asked him for some dumb name. The dude said he never heard of him and, as he turned away, Blackie drove a hard right shot into his left kidney that doubled him over. Blackie spun him around and drove another into the pit of his stomach, and out came the rest of his wind and most of his last meal. It's hard to yell with your wind knocked out, but just in case, Blackie put his left hand behind the dude's head, and right hand over his mouth, and drove his knee up between his legs and the dude lurched and slumped to the ground. Blackie bent over him and snapped the switchblade open and pressed it against his neck.

"Hey asshole," Blackie said, asking quietly, "you ever try to talk with your throat cut? Cause if you make one peep, that's what's gonna happen. Got it?"

Fear was shining in the man's eyes as he nodded. Blackie rose up and looked between the parked cars. Even though it had only been a few seconds and almost no sounds, you could never be too careful. Leaning back over the dude, Blackie said, "listen to me good, boy, cause I'm only gonna say this once. You gotta bad mouth. Someone I know don't like it over in Baton Rouge. You think you're a bad ass, but you're just an asshole. You say one more word on that radio station you work for or anywhere else and, when you least expect it...poof! You're gonna disappear. Now I know after I'm gone you're gonna think about this and figure I got lucky this time. You think that the police, or the feds, or that somebody else will protect you. You'll get big and bad again with that bad mouth. But while you're thinking, remember how well they protected Jimmy Hoffa, and how quick they caught the guys who did him in and they had a lot of people lookin' for him. An asshole like you, the fuzz will stop after a couple of days. Even if my man goes to jail, or gets hit by a car, or is unlucky and lightning strikes him, you're still gone, see, cause I already got my bread and I got a reputation to keep. I'm gonna go now. Don't move until you hear the car drive away, and after I'm gone, you can get up, go tell the apartment manager you fell down in the parking lot and sue 'em, and your night won't be all bad after all. Be seein' ya."

With that, Blackie closed the knife and left. He drove straight back to his country hideout in Hammond, wanting to get there before the girls went to bed.

As he sped along the interstate, he thought of his daughter, Teri, and how quickly she had grown to be a beautiful young lady. His "little princess," with the enchanting almond-shaped brown eyes was already in college—time does fly! He remembered teaching her to drive and wondered if she drove her new Mach 1 Mustang around the college campus as fast as he drove. He hoped not.

He wondered if he'd ever find a woman who could love him and his girls, so they could all live some semblance of a normal life. As the miles sped by, he thought about Bitsie, his angel, away at a private school in New Orleans now. Even though she was adopted, she was so much like him you would have thought he spit her out. Coal black hair, passionate, big brown eyes, always filled with love and happiness at the sight of him. He remembered well, a few short years ago, when she got her first bicycle, a purple one with a big flowered basket. It was her seventh birthday. She ran to him and threw her arms around him, eyes sparkling with joy, crying, "Thank you, Thank you!"

Lu, his heart, was just a year younger and didn't have that same black hair, but she had even bigger brown eyes. She followed him around constantly with total admiration, sort of a female Dennis the Menace, but definitely a Daddy's girl.

Alley, his eyes, was just starting school, and he was awed by her ability to suddenly pronounce words on highway signs as she began to learn to read. She was the one that most people said was the "apple of his eye." And she definitely had his black expression-filled eyes.

Rae, his love, the baby, was still into pushing her doll around in the carriage and had almost perfect features like her mother. Copper-colored complexion like daddy, but she had her mother's petite build and soft, warm quality. Not loud like the others (he wondered, chuckling to himself, where they got all the loudness from) and she had those eyes that could melt you at a glance. Yeah, he would definitely have to worry about her when she got older.

As he turned into the long driveway, the strategically located floodlights switched on automatically. Blackie realized, as he rolled down the drive, that no one would recognize the Commissioner's white Buick, and he blew the horn in a "daddy's home" code so as not to alarm the girls. He scanned the area close to the house wondering where his 120-pound German Shepherd attack dog Rommel was lurking. He knew Rommel would be waiting somewhere to find out who this stranger was, so he could jump on his back and chew his ass off. Blackie noticed the Doberman, Gretchen, over near the garage. Gretchen, not as big as Rommel and still a pup, was something like a young soldier in training. As he pulled up by the garage, he let the window down a couple of inches and called, "Rommel, its daddy, where ya at?" Rommel had been around for over ten years and had taken his mother's place when she died. He was the pick of the last litter of Bridget, the granddaughter of Pard. Pard was the well-known, decorated shepherd that had served with the U.S. Marines in the South Pacific. He had made his bones many times, and once leaped in front of Blackie taking a direct hit in the chest from a .38 round that was meant for his master. He was still tough as iron, but he was old. God, how Blackie was going to miss Rommel.

As he looked out the window, he saw Rommel standing by the back fender wagging his tail…that little shit…as if to say, *I know you said it was you, but I was just makin' sure.* When Blackie got out of the car and spoke to Rommel, Gretchen recognized his voice and came bounding across the yard like a little kid expecting ice cream, jumping all over him. Rommel just rubbed his head against his leg as they walked toward the house. He had gotten Gretchen because his brother had a Doberman, Victor, who was mean enough to kill a lion. Blackie hoped that Gretchen some day would grow up like that. The door opened and six big brown eyes peered out, first with love and admiration, and then with the curious look of what-did-you-bring-us-good-to-eat. Blackie thought, *kids and dogs, do they ever grow up?* The baby crawled up his legs like a monkey while Lu pulled on his right arm telling him that Zap had brought the pickup and went and got them McDonald's hamburgers and cookies. Alley jumped up and down in front of him screaming, Lu wouldn't let her have any ketchup, and Rae ate half her cookies, while she was doing her homework. Hell, Blackie thought, he needed a bodyguard just to come home, to protect him from the dogs and girls. But the excitement of his return cooled down, and discussion of the day's activities created a more normal atmosphere. Blackie reviewed Lu's homework and Alley took her bath. He watched the baby playing with her Barbie dolls in the middle of the floor, and silently thanked God for such good, healthy children. He hoped He would not look upon them too harshly for the kind of life their father led.

Chapter 3

Blackie woke up to a buzzing alarm at 5:00 a.m. Looking outside to see the rising sun, he thought, *it's going to be another hot one.* He showered and dressed quickly. He wanted to check with his neighbor to see if they would look in on the girls, until he decided how he was going to handle being in Baton Rouge or traveling around the state so much now. He could always move them back to "The Fort" in New Orleans. That's what everyone called the big house in town. It had no windows facing the street, full steel gates with sheet steel behind the brick wall, and an eleven-foot-high fence bordering a common yard shared with his sister Patsy's house next door, all patrolled by guard dogs.

"THE FORT" 5024 Haring Court, Metairie, (New Orleans) Louisiana

His mind wandered as he thought about that house*, remembering not too long ago when the telephone had rung at 3:00 a.m., and one of* his capos, Frankie, on the other end said, "man, there must be at least thirty cops cars in front of your house."

"Jesus, call in an air strike."

Frankie laughed but said, "I'm serious."

Blackie went down to the study to listen on the police monitor and recognized the voice of a Lieutenant he knew well, and who was supposed to be his friend.

The Lieutenant Roy Jacob was saying, "Be careful, this is a bad dude; don't take any chances. Remember we want him for a signal 30 two times", a police code for murder. Was he dreaming? Blackie pondered the radio transmission as he heard the doorbell ring.

He flicked on the floodlights in the forty-foot hall and felt the deep red carpeting under his feet. He walked barefoot with only a pair of white jockey shorts on to the gates. No reason to give some trigger happy cop a chance to make his bones on him.

When he reached the gate, Blackie yawned. "Hello officer, can I help you?" feigning sleep as though he'd just woken up.

"You David Steece?"

"Yeah, why you want to know?"

"We'd like to talk to you. Please step outside."

"I don't have any clothes on; if I step outside like this, all the neighbor women will attack me. Can I go get dressed?"

"No, just step outside," said the police officer.

"O.k.," he said and opened the gate.

As he stepped out and saw the police cars he said, "my God! What's going on?"

"Where have you been tonight?"

"Right here since about four-thirty this afternoon."

"Anyone else been here?"

"Some friends left ten or fifteen minutes ago. My lady and four daughters just went to bed, why?"

"Do you own a black Cadillac?" the officer asked.

"Yeah."

"Where is it?"

"In the garage."

"Do you own a gun?"

"Several," was Blackie's retort.

"Are they in the house?"

"Yes."

"We'd like to look at your car, do you object?"

"No," Blackie said. "Do you want to buy it?"

With that, an entourage of police trooped into the garage with Blackie. Parked side by side, facing the door, as though ready to bolt from a starting gate, was Blackie's black Cadillac, a red Corvette, and a red Kawasaki motorcycle. The police seemed shocked at the way they were parked. One officer pointed at the motorcycle. "What do you use that for?"

"To take my girls riding."

The officer opened the hood on the Cadillac and felt the engine. "How long since this car's been driven?"

"About 4:30 p.m. Why?"

"Where do you keep your guns?"

"I have two in my bedroom. Why?"

"Where?" said the officer.

"My two-inch is on the night stand and my .44 Mag is on the shelf in my closet," Blackie said,

"Can we see them?"

"Sure. Can I go tell my lady to dress?"

"No. If you have to go in the bedroom first, we'll get a policewoman to go in and wake her up."

"Oh, what the hell, let's go." They walked into the bedroom and flipped on the lights. Toots, startled by the light, looked up and saw all the police and asked, "what's going on?" Blackie said, "be cool, baby, they're into feeling engines and guns tonight; you're safe." Two of the cops went into the closet as another one picked up Blackie's .38 caliber Chief off the night stand and smelled it to see if it had been fired. The two officers came out of the closet with his .44 mag. "This one hasn't been fired."

"Neither has this one," replied the other cop.

Blackie thought to himself, these cops sure need a lot of help from dumb street people before they would ever be able to make an arrest, or they been watchin too much T.V. If they think anyone would let them search their home without a search warrant if they had anything to hide they have to be stupid.

One officer told Blackie, "go put some clothes on," and then followed him into the closet while he was getting dressed.

"You're not gonna hit on me are you? Blackie asked, "and why can't I have a policewoman?" Then he wondered if policewomen were any good, or were they just cops with tits.

As soon as he was dressed, they all went outside. That was an amazing sight; there were police cars all the way to the corner. Blackie thought, I'll bet the burglars and bad guys are having a ball tonight. There can't be another cop on duty anywhere. *When they got near one of the cars, right in front of the house, the officer that had been inside told the Sergeant sitting in the car,* "the engine's cold on his car and the guns he showed us haven't been fired."

The Sergeant in the car relayed the statement over the radio and a voice at the other end said, "stand by."

Blackie recognized the voice of the same Lieutenant he had heard earlier on the monitor. Blackie just stood in front of the police unit waiting for something to happen. He saw one of his soldiers drive by about a half a block away. He knew his men would be swarming all over the neighborhood and hoped that none of the cops would notice them and get nervous.

The radio cracked in the Sergeant's unit and the Lieutenant's voice came on. "The Major said not to arrest him but ask him if he would mind riding over to headquarters with you. Another officer from Kenner wants to talk to him."

Blackie answered the radio question before the Sergeant could relay it to him by saying, "not at all, but I would at least like to know why it takes thirty police cars and sixty cops to ask me a few questions and not arrest me?" *The Sergeant relayed the message back to the Lieutenant.*

"Tell him that he and his car were identified in a double signal 30 at 2:45 a.m." *The Lieutenant responded.* "Be careful when he's in the unit with you, he's a bad ass and could turn on you at any minute. The two of you would have a hard time with him without having him in handcuffs. You can't handcuff him because the Major don't want him to be able to sue us for false arrest just in case it's not him, which I'm sure it probably is."

Newspaper Article:

THE STATES – ITEM

Saturday, February 23, 1974   New Orleans A-7

Jeff Report

By Tom Fraser
Playing Hard Ball

In Jefferson Parish it takes mental toughness to play the "hard ball" brand of politics practiced there.

Take for instance, the recent Parish Council meeting in which the hearts of all the councilmen thudded to a halt when a man named David Steece stepped into the council chamber carrying a briefcase.

Suffice it to say, Steece seems delighted to be known as a mysterious figure who could walk into any dark alley in the world—from Tunis to Rangoon—and not only get you to put your money on him, but also have you feel sorry for the other guy.

In any case, Steece beckoned silently to Councilman Lawrence W. Heaslip, Jr., then handed Heaslip the briefcase. Retaking his seat next to Council Chairman James J. Donelon, like Heaslip, a candidate for Lieutenant Governor, Heaslip, whispered to his foe, "Jim, there's supposed to be $100,000.00 in here for my campaign. Do you think I ought to trust that guy, (Steece), or would you like to help me count the money?"

With that, Heaslip opened the briefcase, disclosing stack after stack of fresh bills. All that could be seen were $100.00s and a few $50.00s.

Donelon, who learned to his dismay about Steece in his own unsuccessful 1972 race for District Attorney when Steece served as armed bodyguard for his opponent Mamoulides, reportedly opened his eyes to dinner plate-sized at the sight of all that dough.

Donelon may *never* know how much money was in that briefcase.

The Sergeant spoke into the radio mic. "Lieutenant, he's standing right by the unit and can hear everything you say."

There was a long pause and the lieutenant said, "oh shit!" And then silence. The Sergeant in the car looked nervously out at Blackie and said, "are you ready?"

Blackie smiled. "Yeah. Are you ready?" he cracked. "If you're scared with me riding behind you, I can always drive and you can sit in the back." He laughed loudly as he got in the back of the Sergeant's car.

As they rode along the street, Blackie asked, "who am I supposed to have killed?"

The two cops looked at each other and one finally said, "a couple of people in Kenner."

"Oh," Blackie said, "and you got an eye witness, huh?" He continued, "all this is more bullshit. They got thousands of black Cadillacs and hundreds of thousands of dudes with black hair. The Sheriff is just trying to make headlines again. If he heard someone farted at the Vatican, he would have some cop ask me if I ate red beans and rice last night. It blows up his ego and sells newspapers. He probably owns stock in the Times Picayune."

As they pulled into the Sheriff's East Bank headquarters, Blackie wondered what excuse they would use to book him, feeling sure they would think of something. Anyway, he went up to the front counter with the two cops, not to the booking area.

The cop from Kenner walked up smartly. "This my killer? What did you do with the gun, Steece?" Blackie's hot Sicilian temper flared. The hate that flowed through his veins was like cold liquid mercury and showed through his piercing black eyes, causing the cop to step back. "Look into my eyes asshole and figure out what I'd do with a gun if I had one right now." The Kenner cop dropped his eyes and mumbled something unintelligible and walked over to the other side of the room.

Still smoking mad, Blackie looked at the desk Sergeant, whom he knew well. "Hey, Jack, they think I shot somebody less than an hour ago. Get your Captain on the radio and tell him I want a paraffin test right now."

The Sergeant came back in a couple of minutes. "The Captain is off and the Lieutenant on duty said it's not necessary."

Blackie wondered why this lieutenant who had been on the payroll for so long was suddenly playing ball on the other side of the tracks.

Repeating to the Sergeant, Blackie said, "then call the Sheriff. I want the test now; you know they're just trying to fuck me."

Just then, two of Blackie's soldiers walked in and asked, "hey boss, what's goin' on? You all right?"

Blackie quickly briefed them and told them to go to Judge Floyd Newlin's home, a long time friend, to tell him what was going on and maybe he could force the paraffin test. Blackie knew after several hours the test would prove nothing and figured that's why they were stalling. And they called him crooked! Shit! He had never bum rapped anybody in his life. The phone on the Sergeant's desk rang and, as the Sergeant spoke, he looked at Blackie and shrugged his shoulders.

When he hung up, he said, "Sorry man, I gotta book you with attempted murder."

"What happened to the dead people? They come back to life?" Blackie asked.

"Hey, man, you know where I stand. Don't hassle me. I don't know."

"Okay, sorry" Blackie said and walked over to let himself into the booking area.

The Sergeant started the process. "Empty your pockets."

"Don't have anything."

"Take off your belt and shoe laces."

"I don't have any."

"Name?"

"David W. Steece."

"Address?"

"5024 Haring Court, Metairie, Louisiana."

"Phone number?"

"It's unlisted and I don't know it by heart. I never call myself."

"Age?"

Blackie laughed. "In years or miles?"

"Come on, man."

"Thirty-one."

"Height?"

"Six-foot-three," Blackie answered, as he wondered if he'd ever get back that inch Dr. Klein had taken out of him after he had been run down in an attempted hit a few years ago and got his neck broken. Hell of a doctor, David Klein, smart, quick, calculating. Shit, he could have been a Sicilian!

"Weight?"

"Two-thirty-five"...another problem. He thought he was skinny at 235, down from his many years of 245 to 250. But one of his best friends, Dr. O'Meallie, was on a health trip and wanted him to weigh 190, which seemed as farfetched as Blackie's fantasy of making love to Susan Hayward.

"Eyes?"

"Two," Blackie responded and laughingly added, "black."

"Complexion?"

Blackie laughed. "Very pretty."

"Sex?"

"Never too much!"

"Next of kin?"

"Why, you think I'm gonna hang myself in the cell? You already asked for my belt and shoe laces."

Just then, the Sergeant's phone rang and Blackie could tell by the conversation that it was about him.

"That was a judge. He said to parole you on a five-thousand-dollar recognizance bond."

"Which one was it?"

"Which one did you call?"

"None," Blackie said.

"Oh, that was Judge Charlie Gaudin."

"Shit, I thought he liked me better than that," Blackie said.

The phone rang again. In a few minutes, the desk Sergeant hung up. "That was Judge Doug Allen. He said to parole you on a $1,000 recognizance bond."

Blackie thought, "what fun. Pretty soon they'll pay me to leave."

As soon as the Sergeant started to type the release papers, the phone rang again and, after a few words, the Sergeant hung up and said, "wanna guess?"

"Yeah it was either Susan Hayward, and she wants to make love to me, as soon as I get out, or your wife and she just wanted you to know that her and the car note are both one month past due."

"Funny. That was your friend, Judge Newlin. He said let you out of here on your signature, and he was calling back in five minutes to see if we were hassling you or still holding you, and you'd better be gone. I wanted to tell him, if I didn't have to keep answering all your phone calls, I'd already be finished. You really didn't call those Judges, Blackie?"

"Nahh! It's E.S.P. They love me and know I'm innocent."

Just then, Blackie's driver walked in. His street name was "Wonder Animal" because of his size and his ferociousness. "You o.k., Boss?"

"Yeah, be cool. You got my wheels?"

"Yeah, your old lady called me." Wonder then walked over to the other side of the room and leaned on the wall near the pay phone looking menacingly at anyone that would look back at him. Blackie thought he looked just like a caged animal. He might really be an animal. In a few minutes the desk Sergeant brought some papers over for Blackie to sign and pushed a release buzzer to let him out of the booking cell.

As Blackie and Wonder walked out into the parking lot, Blackie noticed the lieutenant that forgot who he really worked for on the other side of the lot. "Have a nice night, Lieutenant, I'll be seeing you," Blackie called out to him. He settled back in the big leather seat in the Caddie and leaned his head back and watched the red lights go up the highway like electronic salmon going home to spawn. Wonder wheeled the Caddy out into the traffic to take Blackie home to his girls. God, he hoped he wouldn't make the paper so the girls would be embarrassed and his sister would be bitching. Fuckin' cops.

Blackie thought to himself, *"am I gonna be able to have a straight life and a regular job while I try to get this guy or will I be a street dude again and just doin' muscle work for him. Agriculture must have some legitimate work I can do so that I can raise my girls in a safe environment. If the commissioners' as dirty as it appears, but I do a good job at the same time, I catch 'im why wouldn't the new guy keep me and let me out of the street life that I've been in all my life."* Blackie decided he'd get to Baton Rouge early and do some regular work so everybody wouldn't think he was just another political hack, but hell, he wasn't even assigned to a division yet. Who was he going to do regular work for? Shit!

Chapter 4

"No! Gimme."

"Mine!"

Blackie's reverie ended quickly when he heard Alley screaming. Lu had taken all the Twinkies for her lunch. From murder to mayhem, quickly making peace, he promised to stop for more Twinkies on the way to school in return for their promise not to fight. He sent them off to make their beds while he went next door to see if his neighbors, the Drudes, would look in on his girls this evening after school. Great neighbors, warm and friendly, not Italian, they were white but good people. The husband, Ray, came to the door and said they would be glad to check on the girls. Blackie thanked him and returned home wondering where to leave Rae today. Yesterday it was easy; he had to go to New Orleans, so he just dropped her off with his sister in LaPlace. She brought her home after the girls came home from school. But today, he was going in the other direction. He guessed he'd better get his act together soon and make arrangements for his girls if he was going to get this show on the road to get the Commissioner. Oh well, he'd make that decision tonight after he and the Commissioner talked. When he got back in the house, he called Jamie Veverica, a female attorney, who not only was one of his lovers, but he also trusted her with his girls. He quickly relayed his problem and asked her to meet him at the I-55 and I-10 exit for Hwy 51, his turn off to Baton Rouge. In fifteen minutes, he had Lu, Alley, and her Twinkies at school and was flying down I-55, the eighteen miles to the junction, where his attorney friend would take Rae for the day. As he pulled up behind Jamie's car and took his baby in his arms with her bag, which he was sure was packed with more toys than clothes. He checked the time and wondered if he could make it to Baton Rouge in twenty minutes. Kissing both the baby and the baby-sitter goodbye, he dashed back to the Buick and raced up I-10. Boy, he wished he had a Chrysler 440 under the hood; he knew he'd make it then.

He thought about the Chryslers' 440 as it roared along. He had been a Caddie nut for so long until a friend, now his brother-in-law, talked him into buying three 440 power packs a few years ago. He bought two Plymouth sedan Furies and a GTX convertible for his kid sister, Patsy. He got so hung up on Plymouths that he left the Caddy in the garage a lot. His sister wasn't too crazy about the GTX, but she fell in love and married Ed and then they bought a Caddy...weird huh? A few years later, Ed bought a Chrysler-Plymouth dealership and then Blackie and his soldiers all went Chrysler crazy. Hard to beat a Chrysler, Blackie thought. He remembered when two of his men were on a case and not too alert. They ran off the end of an unfinished expressway at McArthur Boulevard and the West Bank expressway, in one of those Plymouths at 100 mph, fell fifteen feet, tore off the muffler, and kept right on going.

There was another time when one of Blackie's former men had a vendetta, because he had been bounced and told a wild story to one of Blackie's women. So in fear and total stupidity, she grabbed what she thought was a money bag and split with one of his cars. Well, the bad part was she got the bag with the collection books and not the cash. Blackie could only keep this quiet for a short time and then all hell would break loose. So, he started a wide search for the nutty broad. By noon the first day, the car had been seen in Mobile, Alabama, but before anyone could get to her, she disappeared. Late that night, she was seen again in Birmingham but again eluded the pursuers. Blackie's people next spotted the car in Anderson, South Carolina. This time, they put a tracker and a bug in the car. Blackie was contacted after she was followed to Cedar Rapids, Iowa, when they had learned she would fly to St. Louis arriving the next day about 5:00 p.m. They didn't have much time to cover six hundred seventy miles. Blackie couldn't fly because one of them had to drive the car back, not to mention airlines kept a record of who was flying, and there was always a chance he'd run into someone who knew him. The nutty broad could maybe be a problem, and they surely didn't want any record of them being in the same state. Blackie called D.D., one of his most trusted capos. They left the Crescent City at 9:10 a.m., driving a 1977 Chrysler New Yorker, with a 440 engine. They arrived at the St. Louis airport at 4:55 p.m. averaging over 100 mph. Now that was hauling it, considering gas stops and a small run in with the Missouri State Police in New Madrid, Mo. Blackie doubted if the Commissioner's Buick would have made it to the next town, and it could never get close to the 140 mph that the Chrysler could pull.

Letter from Mayor Freddie Wilcox:

City of Harahan

Fred Wilcox	**6437 Jefferson Hwy. Harahan, La 70123**	Fred Barocco
Mayor	**P.O. Box 23545 Harahan, La. 70183**	Alderman
Mrs. Barbara Butera		Alton Bourg
Sec.-Treas. & Tax Collector		Alderman
J. Hugh Martin		Hermann Dutreix
Attorney		Alderman
George Picone		Robert Prado
Chief of Police		Alderman

September 18, 1975

Judge J. Bailey
Courthouse
New Madrid, Missouri 63869

Dear Judge Bailey:

I am writing you concerning one of our officers, David Steece, who was issued citation #207257 on September 7, 1975, in your county.

Mr. Steece's daughter had taken his car and run away from home a few days before this incident. The car was located in Cedar Rapids, Iowa. He and Lt. Dauphin (another policeman) in a borrowed car, were rushing to Cedar Rapids hoping the child would still be there.

David has been in law enforcement for eleven years and I know of no time he has acted foolishly or carelessly.

I am confident had he not been under this emotional strain concerning his daughter, he would not have received this speeding ticket. Acknowledging that this is not an excuse, but hoping with all of the facts before you and knowing, as a judge, you have both the authority and compassion to help him in whatever way you might. Please let me know what your final decision will be.

If I can ever be of service to you in Louisiana, do not hesitate to call.

Respectfully,
Freddie Wilcox /S/
Freddie Wilcox
Mayor

Enclosure
FW/ja

Dear Sir:
The traffic violation against Mr. Steece has been dismissed by Hal E. Hunter, Jr., Prosecuting Attorney. Yours very truly, Lorene Marsh (Clerk of Magistrate)

As Blackie arrived at the State Capitol parking lot, he had less than a minute, and the Buick felt like it would die any second. He pulled into the Commissioner's reserved parking place and walked to the elevator. As he rode up, he looked at the other people and thought, *State Government sure is full of losers and hangers on.* Oh, he knew they had some good, dedicated people, but they had more than their share of dead beats and bad guys. Oh well, that's why he was here. When the elevator door opened on the 8th floor, the first thing Blackie saw was a beautiful chick at the reception desk. She was about 5'6" and 118 lbs., with long black hair and sparkling blue eyes. Her skin looked like porcelain, and he was sure it felt like silk. She had full red lips and a perfect smile that could be interpreted as inviting by a player like Blackie.

With a grin from ear to ear, Blackie rushed over to the desk. "Hi, I'm lost. Will you take me home with ya?"

The chick blushed but smiled back and asked if she could help him.

He grinned again. "I'm sure you could, all the way to heaven," adding he was there to see the Commissioner.

She asked his name. "David Steece, but you can call me anything as long as it isn't too late, and, by the way, do you insist on marriage or are you into short term affairs?"

She blushed again as he chose a seat.

In a couple of minutes, a door opened and another knock-out appeared. This one looked almost like her sister, with long black hair, creamy white skin, bright blue eyes, and built, man, I mean built!

The knockout said, "Mr. Steece, would you please come with me?"

Blackie thought *I'd love to* but responded with, "Darlin', I'd come with you anywhere in the world" He thought the Commissioner might be a virgin in politics, but he sure had good taste in women.

They went into the private office, and she asked, "can I get you anything?"

Blackie grinned. "What are my options?"

The Commissioner's secretary's name was Jeannie. He read it off the name plate on her desk. "What do you mean?" Jeannie asked.

"Well, you'd be my first choice, and then the chick out at the front desk, second, if I have a choice."

Jeannie smiled. "We heard you were bad, but we thought they meant physically."

Blackie flexed his muscles. "See I am," he said. "Are you married or happy?"

Jeannie grinned. "Would you like something to drink?" she said, changing the subject.

Blackie's eyes beamed with devilment. "Yeah, with the chick out front. By the way, what's her name?"

"Oh, you mean Vicki? She is very pretty isn't she, but you must not touch. That's the Commissioner's right hand man's personal property."

"So, maybe he don't need a right hand anymore; maybe he's got a whole body now," Blackie said, flexing his muscles again.

Jeannie smiled. "You're a very interesting person; we were expecting some big, ugly, giant, obnoxious guy when the Commissioner said he hired a trouble shooter to handle his problems."

Blackie grinned. "Ain't you glad you got such a handsome, good lookin' dude instead?"

Jeannie said, "don't forget modest and shy."

"Oh, yeah," said Blackie. "I always forget those qualities."

Then the door opened and yet another looker came into the office. This copper-skinned, 5'8" woman had shoulder-length red hair, dark almond-shaped eyes, and her body looked like the Mercedes ad "Precision Built." She wasn't beautiful; she had more of that Angie Dickinson look. Jan was country-city, if you know the style. Strong, hard, efficient exterior but with a soft, warm quality about her that, once you got to know her, was very genuine.

She threw her shorthand pad on Jeannie's desk, and in seaman's language said, "if that mother-fucker thinks I'm gonna screw him to keep this job, he'd better learn how to type!" She lit a cigarette, sat down on the corner of Jeannie's desk, and said to Blackie, "who are you?"

"I'm afraid to answer you. I can't type."

Jan laughed a deep rich laugh. "I bet you do other things well."

"I'm afraid to answer that too. I still can't type." She laughed again and asked Jeannie, "who is he? The Commissioner's new muscle we've been hearing about?"

When Jeannie didn't respond, Blackie said, "you can answer her, Jeannie, I know you can type. I've been watchin' you."

And with that, they all laughed.

The inner office phone rang and Jeannie picked it up. She spoke briefly and hung up. "Mr. Steece, the Commissioner will see you now."

"Call me Dave," Blackie replied. "I'm not old enough to be a mister," he said, as he entered the Commissioner's office.

The Commissioner was on the phone. "Tell the Governor I'll be there for lunch."

Blackie wondered how you talked on the telephone without having a line light on and figured the Commissioner was trying to impress him. Shit, he didn't care who the Commissioner ate with; all he cared about was his bread and his daughters. Blackie stood until the Commissioner hung up and told him to sit down, asking him what happened. Blackie shrugged. "We'll have to wait and see."

"What do you mean?"

"Just what I said," Blackie answered.

The dark glare from the Commissioner told Blackie he didn't like his smart-ass answer. *So, I'm two for two,* Blackie thought. *Tough shit.* He wasn't into kissing ass, especially an ass on an ego trip, which the Commissioner obviously was.

The Commissioner paused a moment and then picked up the phone and dialed another office number and said, "come in here."

In a minute, a very short young man came through a rear door. Gerald Kidder was about 5'2" and 120 lbs., with an acne-scarred face and raggedy blond hair that looked like a bird or animal had built a nest in it at one time. His shifty eyes made him appear more frightened than he probably was, as he nervously played with a pencil and pad in his hand. Blackie thought he looked like a little fruit and thought, *what a combination, a nervous fruit and the Commissioner and all these gorgeous chicks.*

The Commissioner didn't introduce them; he just said, "Gerald, Steece here needs a car and credit cards, and find some place to put him on the payroll."

"When do you want him started?" Gerald asked.

"Put him on in an unclassified position, any one that's open where his time won't be accountable, and he'll have an excuse to run all around the state."

"All right, where do you want him domiciled?"

"Why?" asked the Commissioner.

"Because, wherever he's domiciled determines how he gets his expenses. If he's domiciled here, he'll get paid expenses when he is outside of this city." The Commissioner thought a minute and looked at Blackie and said, "where do you think?"

"How about Hammond where I live?" Blackie said. "That way I can get expenses regardless of which town I'm in."

The Commissioner OK'd it and Gerald left the office. The Commissioner told Blackie to go back to Jeannie's office, that he was busy. Blackie thought, as he left the room, that at least the scenery was prettier in there. Jeannie was typing away, but Jan was gone when he got back. He sat down and put his feet up on the desk.

Jeannie looked up from her typewriter. "Want a coke?"

"No, how about a diet anything?"

"A Tab ok with you?"

"Yeah."

Jeannie picked up the phone, dialed an interoffice number, and told someone to bring the drinks. When Paula walked in with the sodas, Blackie wondered if every chick on the Commissioner's payroll was a knockout.

Paula at 5'4" was put together like another Mercedes TV ad, "engineered to perfection," with beautiful, long, dark hair, gorgeous eyes, and a lovely mouth, and she bounced in with a big, "Hi. So you're the guy who made my boss so nervous."

Blackie said, "who's your boss?"

"Gerald."

"You think he'll ever grow up? He sure looks like a little fruit to me," Blackie quipped, and everybody laughed. Paula left, and the noon hour finally arrived.

Jeannie covered her typewriter. "Do you want to go to lunch?"

Blackie responded with a menacing look. "What do you want to eat?"

Jeannie blushed. "You're bad. Come on, I'll show you where the cafeteria is."

"Wait a minute darlin'," Blackie quickly cut in. "Who's payin'?"

"You can just bully the cashier when we leave, o.k.?"

As they waited for the elevator, a young dude walked up with Vicki.

Jeannie spoke to them and then said, "Dave, this is Cuz, Vicki's fiancée and the Commissioner's good friend and right-hand man." Cuz (Cornelius Dupree II) was about 5'8", 150, and carried his French ancestry in his looks and build. He had recently passed the bar exam as reflected in his dress and action.

The two men shook hands and Dave said, "let me know if you ever get tired of her, hear?" He grinned at Vicki.

He couldn't tell by Cuz's expression if he was offended or flattered by the crack. As they boarded the elevator, Blackie nodded to Charles Romer II, the Governor's top assistant. CRII (Charles Romer II's nickname) Governor Edwards Administrative Assistant was in his late fifties with graying hair and skin that looked like he had been in an office all his life and had a serious Vitamin D deficiency. His 5'8" frame was carrying at least thirty-five pounds more than it was designed for, causing his clothes to give a disheveled appearance. He was one of the wealthiest men in the State of Louisiana, and his position made him the second most powerful man in state government. Hard to tell by just lookin at him. They'd met before. Blackie wondered to himself if CRII ate in the cafeteria with the peons. But when the elevator stopped again at 4, the Governor's floor, CRII got off, answering that question.

When they reached the basement and were walking toward the cafeteria, Cuz asked Blackie if he knew CRII.

Blackie's reply was "Sort of." To which Cuz said, "he and the Commissioner just don't get it."

The cafeteria line wound out to the hall and, as they stood in line, several legislators from metropolitan New Orleans stopped, shook hands, and exchanged greetings with Blackie.

Jeannie said, "you seem to know a lot of people here."

Blackie smiled. "It helps," he said.

By the time they got to the cashier, Blackie's bored morning showed on his tray. He had cottage cheese, salad, mashed potatoes, peas, roast beef, two pieces of corn bread, a dish of peaches, a half dozen pats of butter, two cartons of milk, and a piece each of apple and cherry pie. He said he couldn't decide if he wanted to eat the cherry for truth, or the apple to show he was an all-American boy, so he got one of each.

Jeannie laughed. "You're gonna need a table all by yourself just to hold all that food."

"If you think I'm gonna give up sittin' with a good lookin' chick like you," Blackie said, also laughing, "you're crazy or you been smokin' them funny cigarettes. I'll just throw all this food on the floor, gaze into your eyes, and fill up on your beauty."

Jeannie blushed and rolled her eyes. After they sat down, Blackie wondered if Cuz ever talked or if he had offended him with the crack about his girl friend. *Oh well, you can't win them all*, he thought, as he tried to decide which dish to inhale first.

When they finished eating and were ready to leave, Cuz commented to Blackie, "that's a good looking ring."

Blackie looked down at the ring. It had three crystal-cut diamonds weighing almost two carats, set in a fourteen-carat-gold mounting that wasn't even available to today's jewelers. He told Cuz that his father had given it to him.

He almost choked up, thinking to himself how he had gotten the ring. His daddy had given it to him for graduation. He remembered how his father had been out of town the day he was supposed to bring the $10.00 to school for his class ring. When his father got back, it was too late to order one. Blackie had never told Pop, but his brother did. When the old man found out about it, he went and paid a bunch of bucks for this ring so his kid would have something better than anybody else in the school. God, how he loved him. He was tough and strict and had knocked Blackie on his can a few hundred times while he was growing up, but he loved his kids and would push a hand cart through Hell for any one of them without batting an eye. Blackie always felt it was a love that only a Sicilian could feel for his kids. Blackie remembered the time when he first got his driver's license. He was fifteen years old, going on thirty.

As soon as the old man came home that night, Blackie grabbed him and said, "Pop I got my driver's license today and there's this Halloween dance in October. Can I use the Packard for a date that night?"

Now this was only four and a-half months away, but being the kind of father he was, he wasn't going to let his kid's bubble get busted on this happy day. He patted Blackie on the shoulder and said, "sure, son." This was Blackie's main thought until that October date. He had bragged about it all summer and every day in school up through the day of the dance. Rushing home from school, he first soaked in a hot tub, then showered, washed his hair, and shaved both whiskers, one on each cheek, put on his suit, and soaked in cologne and then he sat nervously on his bed from 5:15 p.m. until 7:45 p.m. the time to leave for his date.

When Blackie walked into the living room, he noticed Pop was dressed in a tuxedo, but it didn't really register.

"Where are the keys to the Packard, Dad?" he blurted out with excitement.

The old man looked a little surprised and asked, "why?" "This is my big date, Dad," Blackie responded. "Don't you remember? I asked you about it in June."

Daddy said, "Oh yeah, I remember. Here's the keys and a fin so you can take your chick out for something to eat after the dance."

Blackie hugged his Dad and kissed him goodbye and, as he bounded out the door, he heard Pop call out after him, "midnight sharp and no drag racing."

Blackie's head was so big driving that Packard, he thought he was in heaven. He didn't even notice his date Andrea.

He got home one minute early and, when he came in the house, his brother said, "man, I didn't think you were going to get the car tonight."

Blackie looked a little astonished and said, "why?"

"Dad had an important meeting tonight and he had to have someone pick him up."

Blackie sat on the couch. He couldn't decide if he was flattered or embarrassed that he hadn't been more considerate. But he was sure of one thing, Pop really loved him. Blackie must have drifted off to sleep because about 1:15 a.m. he felt a hand on his shoulder and he looked up and saw that giant standing over him. The old man was a big man, 6'9", and 295 lbs. He'd been a US Marine in the Second World War and still looked like he just came out of boot camp.

Blackie jumped up and put his arms around his dad. "Pop, I didn't know you needed the car. I'm sorry I put you out, you should have told me."

His Daddy hugged him and said, "it's all part of being a father. Always remember, there will be some things I can do for you, some things I can't do for you, some things you won't understand that I do, and some things you won't agree with that I do. Maybe like when I divorced your Mother, but I always want you to remember, I love you and I'll always do what I can for you." Blackie hugged his daddy hard and said, "I love you too, Daddy, and I'll always love you."

As Blackie got up to leave the cafeteria, he hoped he was as good a father to his girls as his Dad had been to him and that they would understand him too.

When they approached the elevator, they saw Gerald, Paula, and some fifty-year-old-looking redneck that Blackie had not met.

Gerald made some comment to the man, and Blackie knew it was in reference to him when the man changed directions and came toward him sticking out his hand. "You David Steece? My name's Charlie, I'm the Commissioner's cousin."

Charlie Darnell was about 5'7" and, without the gut, about 150 lbs. With the gut that too much Jax Beer had made and also turned his face bright red, he was probably close to 200. He looked sixty years old, but Blackie guessed he was in his mid forties. This was definitely a redneck.

Blackie thought B.F.D. as he said, "good to see you," and kept on walking, thinking to himself "as good as the Commissioner's taste was in women, it appeared to be just that bad in men, except for himself of course."

Back upstairs, Blackie amused himself by looking out the window of the capitol down at the Mississippi River and hoped two tug boats would run together and cause some excitement.

At 4:00 p.m., Gerald came in and handed Blackie two credit cards and said, "I won't be able to get your car until Monday."

Blackie's hot Sicilian temper flared again, and he jumped up towering over the little man and shouted, "look, jerk, I don't know what your job is here but I'm not big on patience. I've been sitting around this joint all day picking my nose. I want my car and I want it NOW! If you can't find one then you'd better shit one, because if you don't, your next job is going to be a paratrooper," and he dragged the little man over and pushed him up against the window of the 8th floor.

"I'll ask the Commissioner what to do," Gerald whimpered.

"I don't care if you ask God. I want my fuckin car now." Then he turned Gerald loose, and Gerald left the room at a run.

Jeannie said to Blackie, "Wow! Don't ever get mad at me."

In his typical fashion, Blackie changed back to his loving, grinning self. "I never get mad at beautiful women, especially if they can type."

Jeannie smiled but didn't look too convinced.

In a couple of minutes, redneck Charlie and the Commissioner came in the room, and the Commissioner said, "Dave, come drive me home. There's been a mix up and Charlie has to stay at my house this weekend so you're going to use his car until Monday when they get yours ready."

As they left, Blackie winked at Jeannie. "Give my love to the dwarf." She just smiled.

As they boarded the elevator, it was packed with state workers including CRII. Blackie noticed that, when the Commissioner spoke to him, he only got a slight nod in reply. When they got off on the legislative floor, Blackie and Charlie followed the Commissioner from the House to the Senate and back again like two little puppies. Blackie again spoke to several legislators as the Commissioner looked around like he was lost.

Finally in the car, they drove across town to the Commissioner's house. "Don't be so hard on Gerald," the Commissioner said. "He's afraid of you, but he does a good job for me in what he does."

"O.k., I'm just not into dwarfs," Blackie said.

A few minutes later, the Commissioner asked, "you think you can teach Charlie anything?"

Blackie thought to himself, *what do you want him to be, a redneck? That shouldn't be hard.* "What do you want him to learn?" he said, instead.

The Commissioner just looked out the window like he was trying to think of something that Charlie would be smart enough to learn.

The Commissioner's house was near the southeast edge of Baton Rouge not too far from the L.S.U. campus. It was a mixture of frame and brick. You could see that it had been added onto several times and sat on about two acres of land. In the rear was a large guesthouse and, beyond that, a tennis court. Charlie and Blackie were left sitting on the front porch of the main house watching the grass grow. In a few minutes, Jean, the Commissioner's wife, came out with two big bowls of ice cream and Blackie wondered how she knew he was an ice cream nut. While they ate, Charlie talked steadily. He had done everything in the world and owned almost the whole state and had single handedly gotten the Commissioner elected. Charlie flashed a card of some kind and said it was a state police commission that he carried a gun, and he wasn't afraid of anyone. Blackie figured if he was on a dark street and someone farted, he would probably faint, shit his pants, and then die of a heart attack.

After listening to an hour of that bullshit, the Commissioner came out. "Charlie, give Dave the keys to your state car."

The Commissioner handed Dave a piece of paper. "This is a man who called me. He works for the head of the Mafia in New Orleans. They offered me money for my campaign, but I could never get together with them then. Now, I don't know where he is anymore, or what his phone number is. Find him and let me know what they want. Let me know Monday."

Why in the hell would Vince Marinello the "alleged Mafia member"
want to talk to an egomaniac like the Commissioner? Blackie thought,
as he was leaving. He walked around to the rear of the Commissioner's
house for Charlie's car and saw Cuz sitting at the breakfast area in the
main house. He wondered just how close he and the Commissioner
really were. There were three cars parked in the rear: a yellow Ford
Mustang, a green Chevrolet, and a green Plymouth. The Chevrolet must
be Cuz's state car. Blackie checked the window as he walked by and
saw the police radio. He guessed the Mustang was the wife's or one of
the kid's.

He climbed into the Plymouth, cranked the engine, pulled out of the
driveway, and headed south on Highland Road. He flipped on the
police radio as he turned on the state road that would take him to the I-
10. He slammed the accelerator to the floor. Might as well see what this
thing would do. The Plymouth shot ahead as Blackie watched the two-
lane road narrow down so it looked like a telephone line as it raced
toward him. When the speedometer needle passed the 100 mph mark,
he took his foot off the gas and said to himself, "not bad, must be a 383
with a four barrel." He thought one of his soldiers, Mel in Slidell, could
really make this engine scream with a few changes.

He laughed to himself about the first meeting between the Hulk and
the Mechanic. They were all at the pistol range. Mel's, street name was
"The Mechanic" and Mike, "The Hulk." The Hulk always carried as
his number one piece, a .45 automatic and his backup, a .25 Berretta.
He had a Bowie knife in his boot, and Blackie used to wonder why they
didn't call him Jim Bowie, he was so good with that knife. Everyone
was lining up to shoot twenty-five yard silhouette targets, and the Hulk
said to Blackie, "Boss, you make everybody come out here and shoot or
you just got the Mechanic here in case one of our cars breaks down?"

Blackie smiled and said to the Mechanic, "quick fire from the
bench." The Mechanic placed his old .38 Smith and Wesson M&P on
the bench. Before the whistle's sound had left their ears, the gun was in
his hand and he had rapid fired six shots. When they went to check the
target the pattern told the story. Five rounds had struck the kill area,
and the sixth pierced the head. Any one of them alone would have been
fatal. Clearly, The Mechanic had talents beyond tuning an engine. Few
people knew he had been a member of the Gallopin' Gooses'
Motorcycle Gang.

The Hulk just raised his eyebrows and never said another word all
day.

As Blackie cut the Plymouth off the state road and headed east on I-10, where it would intersect with I-12, he thought, *what a wasted day. No wonder people bitched about state employees. The boss didn't even act like he knew what was going on.*

As he turned into the estate driveway and gave his horn signal, he noticed Jamie's car parked by the garage. She must have waited for him to come home when she brought Rae home from the city. When he got inside, he was surprised but glad to see a nice home-cooked meal on the table. Everybody was just waiting for him to get there. He thought to himself how nice it would be if he had a woman sharing their lives. When they sat down to eat, Alley said Grace and then they talked about the day's activities. After dinner, Jamie cleaned up the kitchen, Lu and Alley did their homework, while the baby played and Blackie dozed in the chair watching T V. About 9:30, he felt a tug on his arm and realized he had fallen asleep. When he opened his eyes, the gorgeous petit redhead was standing in front of him nude. Jamie took his arm and led him into the bedroom. She sat down on the edge of the bed and undressed him. Her white skin glistened when she lay back onto the black silk sheets. As she pulled him into her, her red hair and emerald green eyes were the last thing he saw as she buried his face into her shoulder. They were awakened about 2 a.m. to loud rolls of thunder and flashes of lightening, as a heavy storm passed over. Jamie got up and dressed, kissed him goodbye, and drove back to Metairie, to her own family.

Chapter 5

They got up late the next morning, at 7:30 a.m., and Blackie decided since it was Saturday he would take the girls to Metairie to see Mom and Pop. Though these people were not his birth parents, they treated him like one of their own. Their oldest son, Lynn, was as close to him as any real brother could be, and their oldest daughter, Deanie, was just like his own sister. The baby Rae, whom Mom and Pop idolized, was ecstatic when she found out they were going to town so she could play with Victor, Lynn's Doberman.

As they rolled leisurely along Interstate 55, in Redneck Charlie's state car, Blackie wondered what was going to happen Monday when he saw the Commissioner again. They arrived at Mom and Pop's around 10:30 a.m. Pop was really into cooking and was already fixing dinner. Mom was scouring around the house, and all the kids were in and out. They were a modest couple, who lived in an average house and had worked hard all their lives. These people were the exact image of the ideal American family life. They were God fearing and full of love and support for all. No matter what kind of bad publicity Blackie got, and they had no idea who he was really working for, when he would call and say, "Mom, I hope I haven't embarrassed you," she would always answer, "you can't embarrass me, heart. I love you." God, how he loved them.

Blackie used their phone to call The Man to set up an appointment to fill him in on what had happened with the Commissioner. Blackie and The Man were to meet at the Howard Johnson restaurant on Veterans Boulevard in about an hour. He then called Eddie D' and caught him up to date. About fifteen minutes before the meeting, Blackie told Mom he had to take a ride for a little while—would the girls be o.k. there?

In her usual understanding way, she said, "of course, heart; you know we love to have them."

Blackie kissed everybody goodbye, got in the car, and wheeled away.

At the restaurant, he went into the coffee shop where they often met, and ordered a small orange juice while waiting for The Man. He watched the door and, in a few minutes, saw the car enter the lot. His friend was a big man. He guessed around 6'2" and 220, well built, with coal black hair with slight streaks of gray at the temples. He was an assertive, overpowering figure, knowledgeable, street smart, and quick witted. His mind was always thinking a block ahead of everybody else. Blackie figured that, deep down, he might have been an introvert who forced himself to do many of the things he did. Blackie knew The Man was a devout family man and somewhat of a loner. In Blackie's long relationship with elected officials, he had seen the worst—promiscuity, gambling, graft, incompetence, stupidity, and every type of flaw a human being could have. This man was not tarred by flaws. He was different. Blackie had known and respected him for fifteen years. Their friendship ran deep and was one that many people had never understood. Maybe it underscored why this man was "The Man." He was not like other politicians. Even when he was double crossed by another elected official, the small flare of anger he would show did not have that deep-rooted hatred or vindictiveness that was normal, or at least Blackie thought was normal. His friend's eyes swept the room and picked Blackie out of the crowd. He smiled and walked briskly to his table. They shook hands, then he sat down, took off his glasses, and laid them on the table. Blackie wondered why he wore glasses. They spent most of the time off his face, usually in his hand or on the table, but seldom near his eyes. Maybe he thought glasses made him look distinguished...who knew?

In the scores of meetings that these two men had had, Blackie knew what the first words would be. "How have you been? How do you feel? How are your children?" Blackie used to think he was just programmed to say those things but, as the years wore on, he realized that this man was sincere and was deeply concerned, not only about what you could do for him, but he was concerned about you. Many people say, "have a nice day," but when he said it, he really meant it.

They small-talked about their children and then The Man asked, "how did the meeting go with the Commissioner? He has no idea who you are or why you're there?"

Blackie kind of smiled and leaned back in his chair. "No. I think the guy's on such an ego trip and such a womanizer and is so self centered he can't see anything but himself," Blackie said.

His friend smiled. "Good, this is perfect for you to do your job. When are you going to meet him again?"

"Monday morning. He's supposed to give me some new assignment. You don't even want to know about the one he already gave me."

His friend asked if they had settled his pay, Blackie said no, they were trying to put him in some unclassified position.

They chit-chatted some more and his friend said, "whenever you need votes at the session, be sure you go to Eddie D' and have him arrange to deliver our whole delegation to your bill. That will strengthen you with the Commissioner, because he had a bad time in the legislature last session."

Blackie nodded. "He doesn't seem to be too popular on the floor of the House or the Senate. I been down there with him one time. Whenever someone asks what I'm doing there and I tell them I'm working for the Commissioner, they kind of raise their eyebrows and smile. No one has said anything positive to me about him yet."

His friend said, "that will come with time; right now, he's new and nobody trusts him."

"I think he's nuts." They discussed some local politics and agreed to meet in two weeks for further discussion on the Commissioner and his plans for Blackie.

Blackie reminisced as he drove back across town, how he and his friend had been involved in a bitter campaign years ago. He laughed to himself as he thought about the antics that had been blamed on him by his friend's opponent. His friend had come to him in the wintertime, told him of his plans to seek this particular office, and asked for his support and loyalty. Blackie committed himself and, several months later, as it got closer to election time, Jim Donelon came to him and said, Blah, blah, blah, you're gonna be this, you're gonna be that in my new administration. Blackie listened and then gave Jim the "good news" that he was already committed, committed to the other man. Jim with his usual arrogant attitude leapt up and said he would go get Lewie Johnson to straighten Blackie out.

Lewie had been a friend of Blackie's for many years. Blackie had been on and off his payroll many times. In a few hours, Lewie and Jim came back to his house and they had a tremendous argument. First, Lewie offered money, all kinds of money, and then promises of all kinds of jobs. When Blackie stood fast, Lewie threatened him saying he would make sure certain people heard some of his alleged dealings, and whether they were true or not, he would be investigated and his family ruined. Blackie held his temper and reminded him that a few years before a Supreme Court Justice had tried to buy him unsuccessfully. That man no longer sat on the Supreme Court. He told Lewie they could be friends after the election (which was bullshit) and told Jim they could never be friends (which was true) and asked them both to leave. Smiling to himself, Blackie thought about the things that happened as the election got under way, how Jim would run down to the Times Picayune *every day and tell the newspaper that his friend had a gangster and the Mafia working for him, and that they were doing this and doing that. Like the time when a tremendous billboard on I-10 was cut down overnight. Another time, the metal building where they stored their 4'x8' signs was loaded onto a truck by a cherry picker and hauled away during the night, supposedly with ten thousand signs inside. Rumor had it that the signs ended up in a barn in Simsport, a small town about 140 miles north of Jefferson Parish. Then more bad luck, one of the sign trucks loaded and ready to go caught on fire in the parking lot of the AAA building on Causeway and burned up. This supposedly was some of Blackie's doing.*

Blackie reminisced about the T.V. debate and wondered if Jim ever figured out how his friend got the illegal letter that Jim sent to bail bondsman requesting money and donations for his campaign. He remembered how, as the election drew to a close, one of his friend's top assistants told him that Jim came strolling into headquarters with a three foot section of telephone cable cut from his telephone line. Supposedly, the line was to his telephone bank and, of course, he alleged that too was done by Blackie. And, of course, they were trying to catch Blackie in a promiscuous situation and spent most of their time at the newspapers condemning Blackie and his men for everything, taking away from his campaign time, which probably had a lot to do with why he lost the race.

Even on election eve, Jim and Lewie tried to have Blackie arrested for kidnapping some little kid, which showed the world what dummies they were. Blackie thought if he had done all of this stuff, he'd have been so busy he wouldn't have had time for sex, or even to go to the bathroom, much less take care of his little darlin's, which were always number one on Blackie's list.

Chapter 6

When Blackie got to the Capitol Monday morning and told the Commissioner he had not found the alleged Mafia connection, the Commissioner was obviously agitated. He slammed himself down in the chair and dialed for Gerald to come into his office.

Gerald arrived though the back door, and the Commissioner said, "I need to get this thing settled. Where's his car? What payroll is he on? How much does he make? I want it done now!"

Gerald, looking just as frightened as he had Friday and like he hadn't had any sleep since then, hustled out the door to get things done. Blackie figured he had gotten the Commissioner's attention, but he was a little surprised. He hadn't thought the Commissioner was smart enough to figure out why he had not been able to find the Mafia guy. The Commissioner gave Blackie a speech about trust, saying that he must trust Blackie, so Blackie should trust him and should have gone ahead and done what he wanted him to do this past weekend. Blackie nodded in agreement and shrugged thinking donkeys should fly. He replied that he didn't have the money to do much looking. The Commissioner looked at him and said, "you have two houses; one is an estate worth several hundred thousand dollars, and you don't have any funds?"

Blackie said, "check the record. I don't own anything. I have friends who let me live there, because they like me. Whatever I've earned goes to my girls. I have to earn my way every day."

The Commissioner mumbled something and dismissed Blackie as he started to fumble through the papers on his desk.

Blackie went back to Jeannie's office and propped up on the desk again. At 11:00 a.m., the guy called Redneck Charlie came into the office and told Blackie, "come on, I'm taking you to pick up your car."

As they left, Blackie said to Jeannie, "I don't get to go to lunch with you today darlin', but don't forget me, I'll be back."

Charlie and Blackie went downstairs to Charlie's state car and drove to the edge of town. At Charlie's directions, he pulled into a big white building on Florida Boulevard. They went inside and back to one neck. The small deep-set eyes sat on a ruddy complexion. He was divisions under the Commissioner. Blackie was introduced to Holmes of the divisions under the Commissioner. Blackie was introduced to Holmes Johnson, a fat man whose shoulders slanted down from his thin neck. The small deep-set eyes sat on a ruddy complexion. He was probably in his late sixties. He was supposed to be the director of the Weights and Measures Division.

"We want the keys to your car," Charlie told him. The guy looked up in shock and asked, "why?"

"We're giving it to this man," Charlie answered. "He needs it to travel all over the state."

Blackie thought, *what tact these people have*. The man reluctantly gave Redneck Charlie the keys, told him where it was parked, and they left. It was a green Plymouth, exactly like the one that Blackie had driven that past weekend. But it didn't have a state police radio.

Blackie immediately asked, "where do I get my state police radio?"

Charlie gave him an address and told him to just go there. "Tell them who you are and who it's for, and they'll put it in while you wait." He added, "the Commissioner then wants you to come back up to the Capitol so he can talk about what he wants you to do."

Blackie acknowledged Redneck Charlie and left. When Blackie got to the radio shop, he discovered that nobody knew he was coming, and they had only one old tube type radio in stock. Blackie made friends with a guy there who installed it anyhow and said he would hustle him up a new one. After about an hour tinkering, it finally worked a little. Blackie left and headed to the Capitol.

It was after 2:00 p.m. when he took the elevator to the eighth floor. He spoke to Vicki and started to enter Jeannie's office, when he noticed the same old man they had got the car from sitting in the lobby. Blackie was sure he recognized the old man from the other office in the white building. Blackie sat down in Jeannie's office and asked, "what's happenin' doll?"

Jeannie just smiled and kept on typing. Blackie thought if she was as good a lover as she was as a typist, she would really be something.

The door to the Commissioner's office opened and Cuz stuck his head out. "Dave, come here a minute."

Blackie got up and strutted into the Commissioner's office, thinking Vicki must have let Cuz know that he was back. Cuz was alone and motioned Blackie to close the door. When the door closed, Cuz asked Blackie, "you see the old man in the lobby?"

Blackie nodded affirmatively.

"The Commissioner has put you in his division," Cuz said, "and that's why he's up here for the Commissioner to give him the news. He's been around for over twenty years and really knows the ropes. The Commissioner wants to put him out to pasture but doesn't know how."

Blackie just shrugged.

Cuz added, "the Commissioner told me to tell you to finish the job he gave you Friday and he would see you in the morning."

Blackie shrugged again and went back to Jeannie's office. Jeannie looked up when he came in and mouthed the words, "what happened?"

Blackie just rolled his eyes and blew her a kiss. "See you tomorrow if you're lucky," he said, as he walked out into the lobby.

He stopped by Vicki's desk so he would have an excuse to look at the old man. When he finished talking to Vicki he went to the elevator. As he waited, he looked back across the lobby and noticed that the old man chain smoked but, otherwise, he looked alert to everything around him. The elevator was full of Girl Scouts taking a tour of the Capitol. He was glad to make his escape from all those giggling little girls.

Blackie headed east on I-12 for almost an hour before he turned north toward U.S. 190 on State Road 434. It was only a few miles before he drove through Robert, the small town just west of Covington. He turned back west, then north on a gravel road to an ex-hooker he had known for years. He was sure Betty Asselli would know where to find the guy he wanted. As he pulled up to the house, Blackie wondered if all old hookers moved to the country and lived a quiet life to the end. He parked the Plymouth, walked to the front door, and knocked. In a few moments, a blonde in her fifties opened the door. Though she had a lot of miles, you could still see that Betty had been a looker. She was about 5'9" and still only carried 130 pounds. In her younger days, she had been Uncle Rolland's number one squeeze. When he moved on to Beverly, Betty sort of became a Capo of a crew of girls for Ms. Kay. Though she was in her late fifties, you could tell her pride still had her in high heels, a deeply unbuttoned blouse, and short skirt. They exchanged greetings and Blackie told her the reason for his visit. She told him she thought Vince lived on an estate near the Tangipahoa River about twenty-five miles south of there, but she didn't know the exact address. He thanked her and left. As he turned south again through the countryside, he decided to drive by all those big estates; just maybe the name would be on a mail box.

His mind drifted back over the years to the time two police officers assigned to organized crime had come to see him. They said that they didn't believe the rumors about Blackie being involved with the Mafia and that their boss, Captain Freddie Roth, who was later sent to prison for fraud or something at Avondale Shipyards, wanted him to come and work undercover for the police. Blackie thought, me, Ha! It's just more of the Sheriff trying to figure out what I'm up to. *Anyhow, they went through the whole spiel, left a ten-page application and told him to be sure and answer all the questions. Blackie and an agent friend of his filled out the application so well that it would check out perfectly. When Blackie turned it in, they told him he would have to be fingerprinted and mugged.***(Reference Reproduction of Rap Sheet Chapter 1 Page 4 entry 8 on column 07/09/1970)** *About two days later, the same cops came to Blackie's office and told him he had an appointment with their Captain at 2:00 p.m. the next day and told him where to go. After they left, Blackie wondered what they were really after. Oh well, he guessed he'd soon find out. When he got to the Captain's office, it was obvious that everyone knew he was coming. The Captain tried to be cordial, but Blackie could feel the tension in the room. The Captain placed a chair in front of his desk for Blackie and started asking questions that had nothing to do with work—just nosey. After about five minutes of vague answers, he noticed the top drawer of the Captain's desk was open and realized the conversation was being taped.*

He waited for the right opportunity in the conversation, then he said to the Captain, "I understand you think your boss is a homosexual and you want to run against him next year, and you think I can get you some votes, and after you're elected you'll get off my ass."

The Captain sputtered, turned red, and slammed the desk drawer shut.

Blackie smiled and stood up. "Be sure your boss hears the whole tape, because if you try to edit or erase any part, I'm sure he'll hear a rumor, and he's so paranoid, he'll fire you just in case the rumor is true."

The Captain got enough of his composure to spit out, "you son of a bitch!"

"Let's not get our families involved, Captain. You know Momma wouldn't like you talking to her illegitimate son like that. Not to mention calling your own mother a bitch."

As Blackie walked out of the Captain's door, he called over his shoulder, laughing, "let me know when I start work."

As he pushed the elevator button, Blackie thought the Captain must really be stupid if he thought anyone would fall for that. He wondered when the Sheriff would stop trying to find out what Blackie really did and get back to fighting crime.

Blackie turned the Plymouth off the state highway and onto the winding drive along the Tangipahoa River and Flowers Estates. As he rolled by the beautiful homes, he checked mailboxes and driveways for something he would recognize. The road wound back to Highway 21, and Blackie had not recognized anything; he sighed as he sat at the stop sign looking at his watch. It was late. He'd try again tomorrow, he decided, and turned the Plymouth north toward I-12. When he finally headed east, he pushed the Plymouth to the floor. Suddenly, he was in a hurry to get home to his girls.

As Blackie turned off on U.S. 51 and into his driveway, the setting sun cast an aura of tranquility over the whole area. It was good to be home. As he approached the house, he saw a strange car parked near the garage and his mind began to race. There were no lights on in the main house. The heavy dusk that suddenly settled over everything made his heart pound. He jumped out of the Plymouth, unbuttoning his coat, as he ran toward the door, to free up access to his .44.

Just then, the door opened and outburst the girls and an old friend from Chicago. Blackie blew out his breath, thanking God, as relief flooded his body until his legs felt weak.

After everyone hugged and kissed, Blackie asked Joe Nose, "how did you find me?"

Joe smiled. "Same way you find people," he said.

They both laughed, and Blackie thought, as everyone went inside, how shocked people would be to realize that Joe Nose was actually the grandson of Frank Nitti of Al Capone fame. Joe was 6'2" and 220 pounds with square shoulders and the face of a bar brawler. In fact, the nickname "Joe Nose" came from the many times it had been broken. Everything was Sicilian on him but his eyes, which were almost navy blue, they were so dark blue, like many of the northern Italians, which many times elicited the joke, "there must have been an Italian in the woodpile."

It was late by the time all the old stories had been rehashed and the girls put to bed. Blackie threw himself down on the bed, hoping he could get up on time. As he lay there looking at the ceiling, he wondered if he could ever get used to punching a clock, then slowly drifted off.

On Thursday morning, Joe Nose and Blackie drove to New Orleans and met Uncle Rolland for breakfast at A & G. Uncle Rolland, not really Blackie's uncle, but his Godfather, not Catholic type, but family type Godfather, and in their relationship, Rolland and Blackie were more like brothers, Rolland being the older brother. Rolland, a 6'1" 180-pound string bean with a hatchet face, had been acting under boss for the last several years. Although he loved to project a passive demeanor, he was as deadly as a rattler with the rattlers cut off. You would never know he was coming. Blackie spent more than one sleepless night worrying about Uncle Rolland. He owned a Cash Register Business plus several apartment houses, the Bourbon Orleans Restaurant in the French Quarter, and many people thought an interest in Sol and Chris Owens' famous 809 Club in the Quarter. Almost every business that was anybody had the Sweda Cash Register, exclusively distributed by Uncle Rolland. You could also buy discount mink coats, loose diamonds, and gold nuggets that had obviously been melted down from some other jewelry. Blackie knew that, besides Uncle Rolland's fencing ability, he might be the one to tell him where he could find Vincent. Blackie asked Rolland, "have you seen Vince lately?" After a bit of inquiry Uncle Rolland said, "I think he's got a place over on the West Bank."

"That's cool. I'll look for him tomorrow. Today, me and Joe Nose are out playin' old times."

After breakfast, they headed east on Hwy 90, over the Mississippi River on Huey P. Long Bridge, and back into the West Bank on the expressway, eventually ending up at Churchill farms, hoping they would run into Vince Marinello, but smart enough not to ask for him. No luck. After a day of reminiscing with Joe Nose, Blackie dropped him at the airport and returned home to his girls. He was a little earlier than usual, which meant they would all have a good night.

Chapter 7

At 5:15 a.m., the damned alarm clock was ringing again. Blackie stretched, rolled out of bed, and started dragging screaming little girls out for breakfast. He had to get something done today or the Commissioner would think he was as big a dumbass as he was. After arrangements for the girls were settled, he headed to New Orleans to look for Vince, not quite believing that he had ever offered a deal to the Commissioner. But, hell, he would find him and get the real story. As Blackie drove over the Manchac Bridge on I-55 toward New Orleans his mind wandered.

He remembered especially the 1969 mayor's race, when Jimmy Fitzmorris, Jr., then a second term Councilman At Large, was in a race with half a dozen assholes for an open mayoral seat. After leading substantially in the first primary, he got into a pissing contest with his opponent Moon Landrieu, over the fact that John "Tac" Elms was supporting Landrieu. Tac had alleged connections with the Marcellos and the Gambinos, distant cousins of the New York mob, or maybe their competitors, the Confortos or one of those other wanna-be's that thought they were real gangsters. Tac Elms had the biggest music company (pinball machines, jukeboxes, vending machines) next to Jefferson Music, which was owned by the Marcellos and probably had a note for a loan on every beer joint and bar in New Orleans, and there was a lot of them. Jimmy criticized Moon's support from Tac Elms and, as a result, Tac put the arm on all the bars in New Orleans, and that left about three nuns and a priest to vote for Jimmy. What started out to be the saddest night of his life that December night in the St. Charles Hotel ended on a high note. When those returns came in, Jimmy got crushed. But then some of Blackie's men brought his red-head up there to cheer him up. The next September, Rae arrived. So hell, Jimmy lost the Mayor's race and Blackie got a beautiful daughter.

Blackie arrived at the Lieutenant Governor's office in the State Office Building on Perdido Street. He hoped Jimmy Fitz, his good friend, would be in. All the while, Blackie was still searching for Vince without asking for him. Blackie obviously did not want Vince to know he was looking for him before he found him, since he never really trusted the guy. Vince probably didn't trust Blackie either. If he found out Blackie was looking for him, he might do something stupid and get himself hurt. As Blackie walked into Jimmy's office, the first person he saw was plain-clothed State Police Officer A.J. Kehoe and realized that Jimmy must be in because this was one of his bodyguards. After Blackie spent about ten minutes hitting on the receptionist, to no avail, Jimmy finally opened his door and invited Blackie inside.

Blackie and Jimmy discussed his daughter and Blackie's tribe and how well they were doing. Blackie asked about Jimmy's wife Gloria and his brother Norris, whom Blackie respected. After visiting with Jimmy for about thirty minutes and dropping every hint on earth, Blackie realized that Jimmy was smarter than he'd thought. Blackie walked back to the car without any new information on Vince. He drove across the Greater New Orleans Bridge heading west on Hwy 90 toward Bridge City and Estella's restaurant where all the good Italian people ate, figuring that if Vince wasn't there he was either dead or had left town.

After stuffing himself with a five-pound plate of angel hair and seeing everyone on earth except Vince, Blackie gave up for the day and headed home. As he flew down the interstate, he decided that if he hadn't found Vince before Monday, he would go straight to Carlos Marcello, a.k.a. "the little man" and try to set up the meeting himself.

As Blackie reached for the phone, he noticed his watch. The day was almost gone.

He recognized the voice on the other end as Jim Knotts. "Have we got something goin'?" Jim asked. Blackie had known Jim over the years as a long time politico, who worked behind the scenes, who always seemed to come out on top of the pooh-pooh that hit all the elected officials. Jim was a big 6'4" blond-headed German who, unlike the Commissioner, really was a ladies' man with those steely blue eyes and that Arian complexion, plus he was smart.

"I believe it will be together by Monday or Tuesday."

You could tell by Jim's tone he was very pleased, especially when Blackie added, "to make it work, I think you're gonna have to come with the Commissioner. They know you're solid and they don't know him. So they'll want someone to hold his hand."

They exchanged some chitchat, and Blackie dropped the phone back on the hook. He thought to himself, *if this guy don't slow down, he'll get his ass put in jail before I can make a case on him.*

Sunday had the opportunity to "fly by." It was a flying kind of day, and Blackie ran his legs off teaching the girls to fly kites.

"Add some tail, Daddy!"

"No, Daddy, take some off!"

Whatever the girls learned he wasn't sure. But he knew that he felt like he'd run off fifty pounds while trying to get three goddamned kites up at the same time.

Who the hell invented kites? he wondered, *and what's the deal with running just to watch them crash into the ground? Now there's a guy who needs his ass kicked—more than some dumb radio announcer. Of course "Mr. Radio" could probably get a kite up just runnin' his mouth.* It had been a long time since their Burger break at Wendy's, and he wondered if he'd be strong enough to look for anyone tomorrow or not.

On Monday morning, Blackie called Jeannie and told her that if the Commissioner asked for him, to make up some story that he was looking for a place to live in Baton Rouge, and if his state police radio hadn't been invented during Huey P. Long's time in the 1920s, he would be able to call and find him whenever he wanted. After getting off the phone, he drove to the Town and Country motel in Metairie, which was where Carlos' daytime office was located.

As he pulled into the parking lot at the Town and Country Lounge, he thought about the time Frankie, then only a soldier, had wanted to straighten out a problem. There was a guy who had a little trouble with names and numbers. He kept calling Beverly, which was Frankie's phone number and Frankie's lady. So Blackie and his men casually walked into the lounge in pairs and took strategic seats around the place. After about ten minutes, Frankie came in. Frankie said he was just going to talk to the guy and didn't want anyone bothering him during the conversation. Anyhow, Mr. Tactful (Frankie) walked in, picked up a pitcher of beer, dumped it on top of the guy's head, and then smashed the pitcher over his head creating a beer and blood waterfall. The guy was a tutor for one of Carlos' men's kids and Carlos became highly offended at this act in his place of business. Blackie and his men had to hold everybody at bay, while Frankie beat the shit out of the tutor with what was left of the beer pitcher. The next day, Blackie had to go apologize and make amends with "the little man" or it would end up in a damn shooting war. The outcome was the tutor left Beverly alone, and Frankie finally married her, and they lived happily ever after. At least they didn't have any more trouble at the Town and Country.

Blackie walked in, asked to see "the little man" and was surprised to see one of Frank "Buster" Wortman and Francis Touche's top men, Bob Bergman, sitting in the lobby, and Blackie wondered to himself, what the hell were the St. Louis people doing in town? Bob was a good dude. He was as close as you could get without the blood. They exchanged pleasantries, and when he came out of "the little man's" office, Blackie went in. Blackie, not known for his tact, told Carlos he was working for the new Commissioner. The Commissioner said Vince had contacted him during the campaign and wanted to do some Monty Hall stuff. Blackie said he didn't know whether it was true or not, but he wanted to tell Vince in person that the Commissioner was trying to make contact, and Blackie was the mailman. If he didn't want to meet with him he'd brush him off, and if he did, tell him when and where.

"The little man" asked Blackie a couple of questions and said, "bring the commissioner to the farm next Thursday night about seventy-thirty or eight, and make sure you're not followed."

"You remember Jim Knots?" Blackie asked. "He's left over from the Michot régime, and I think he can be trusted. He's one of the Commissioner's top people now and he'll surely be with him. Is that a problem?"

"Not a problem."

Blackie thanked him and left.

Now that Blackie had done his bullshit duty for the day, he could screw around the rest of the week and pretend he was working. He headed back home to his girls and dogs. He decided he would clean house, cook, and play the rest of the week with those little angels, well…almost angels. Oh well, his angels for sure.

That evening during dinner, he told them he was going to have some free time that week. "What do ya'll wanna do?" he asked.

Rae wanted to go to Texas and ride horses. Alley wanted to go to Disneyland. Lu wanted to stay home and have fun; she called *fun* destroying the house. Blackie thought, *isn't it fun having kids, especially when they all want to do the same thing?*

Blackie thought that tomorrow morning they'd go to Grandma's for breakfast and then to the Audubon Zoo. Later, they'd go over on the Gulf Coast and feed the deer. Since the deer were brown, that'd take care of the horses, and Bambi was part of the Disney project, so that'd take care of Disney, all within forty miles of home. *How bout that shit?*

he thought, proudly. *Daddies aren't as dumb as they look. Then we'll go by Aunt Patsy's and hustle dinner, then a movie. By then they should be tired enough to sleep until at least eight the next morning.*

Blackie thought it was weird being a parent. When they're in school he felt like he'd never have enough time with them. When it was summer vacation, he'd be making novenas for school to start. He either missed them too much, or he thought they were a pain, but every night, when he tucked them in and kissed those little foreheads, it was worth all the bullshit they'd put him through. Then he'd realize that they were girls, and they were gonna grow up and get married to some idiot and he'd have to pay for the damn wedding.

At two on Friday afternoon, Blackie called Jim Knotts in Baton Rouge. He said he'd finally made the connection, and would give him the details Monday in the office. Jim thanked him and said, "take the rest of the week off and I'll pass the information on to the Commissioner." Blackie hung up the phone, thinking, *shit, I've been off all week already, and he headed back down to play with the girls as they splashed around in the river.*

On Monday morning, Blackie walked into the reception office, looked at Vicki, and grabbed his chest. "Quick!" he said. "I'm having chest pains. I need mouth to mouth. I'm gonna die!"

"You're not gonna die," she said, "and I don't know how to do that CPR stuff anyhow."

"I do," Blackie said. "I can teach ya, and a whole bunch of other things you can do with your mouth."

Vicki turned bright red. "Would you like some coffee?" she asked, changing the subject.

"Well, I wanted something hot, but it wasn't coffee I had in mind. I'm gonna go pester Jeannie."

When he entered Jeannie's office, Jan was sitting on the corner of Jeannie's desk, bitching about the Commissioner.

Seeing Jan reminded Blackie of the time she called him in New Orleans and told him she had a speeding ticket and asked if he could help.

Blackie asked, "how fast were you goin'?"

"I don't know. I guess about seventy. But can you believe, I'm in white halter top and short shorts, and this son-of-a-bitch could concentrate enough to write a ticket? Either I'm getting old or he's gay."

"Darlin' with a body like yours, the son-of-a-bitch was blind, not gay!"

"What's up ladies?" Blackie asked, as he flopped in the chair in the corner. "Where's el-Hitler at?"

"He's not in yet," Jeannie said, and Jan added, "he's probably in the bathroom with *Playboy* magazine."

"Hell the way you're sittin' on that desk, he could be in his office and peak through the keyhole and get more from you than a *Playboy* magazine."

"Don't be a smart ass!" Jan snapped back.

"Okay, I ain't sayin' nothin' else. I still can't type."

Paula came in with coffee for everybody and, right after that, El-Hitler showed up. The look exchanged in the office said everybody agreed they would be fucked up now. After hollering a few unimportant orders at people while pretending to be important, the Commissioner called Blackie inside. Jim was already there. He must have come in the back door, the Gerald route.

After Blackie and Jim shook hands, Jim said, "tell the Commissioner how this is gonna go down."

"I'm gonna escort the two of you to the meeting place Thursday about 7:30 p.m. There's only one way in and out by land. Once I get you on that road, I'm gonna block the road, so no one can follow you in there. I don't know if either one of you carry any toys, but I would leave them home that night, because there will be somebody there watching to see if you walk with a limp or sit down funny."

The Commissioner asked, "what did you tell them we wanted?"

"I didn't. I told him a member of his organization contacted you during the campaign and wanted to make a deal."

"Why did you tell them that?"

"What do you mean, why? Cause that's what you told me."

"Well I don't know for sure if Vince represented him," the Commissioner shot back.

Blackie, getting a little hot said, "well, you shouldn't have told me that, 'cause I told the man just what you told me."

Jim said, "now calm down, Blackie. It'll all work out."

The Commissioner, looking confused and half scared, sat there like the idiot he was, while Jim got the details of the plan.

Blackie, still pissed, said, "by the way, when am I gonna get my radio? What's that little worm Gerald do besides say he can't?"

The Commissioner, seeing a chance to break the tension, picked up the phone and told Gerald, "you gotta get Blackie's new radio today!"

From the background, Blackie added, "and, I'd like a new Cadillac too, and an unlimited expense account, and a weekend with Vicki."

The Commissioner rolled his eyes.

Jim laughed. "Anything else you need?" he asked.

"Yeah, a million dollars in small bills."

Blackie went into Jeannie's office. Damn, Jan was gone already, and he couldn't really figure Jeannie out. He guessed he'd go roam around the streets and try to stay out of trouble until Thursday.

From a pay phone in downtown Baton Rouge, Blackie called The Man and told him, "we need to talk."

"You'd better meet me Tuesday or Wednesday morning, at our regular place."

"7:30 a.m.?"

"Fine," The Man said.

Chapter 8

Blackie rolled out of bed an hour later this morning, since he didn't have to meet The Man at Howard Johnson's in Metairie, until 7:30 a.m., and he could surely get there in about thirty-two minutes if he could average 100 mph. He wondered if Chrysler's 383 would perform like the old 440 or the Hemi. Yawning, as he spread shaving cream on his face, he figured that he'd find out when he turned south on I-55 and stood on it.

Later, from his seat at the Howard Johnson's, Blackie watched as The Man stopped to pick up the *Times Picayune* as he walked through the lobby door, which served both the hotel and restaurant. He walked briskly to the corner table in the rear, and they shook hands. The waitress brought Blackie's orange juice and a coffee almost before they sat. Blackie thought, *Jesus, she knows our habits pretty well. I hope I'm not that predictable in other areas, or somebody will be giving me more than orange juice in the morning.*

"They're getting to know us pretty well, in here," Blackie said, giving voice to his thoughts. "Maybe we should change meeting places."

To which he received an affirmative response. The Man asked, "Do you feel like you're gaining his trust?"

"Yeah, the Commissioner's so eaten up with himself, he don't really pay much attention to anything."

"We need to start getting serious about this guy. Some of my contacts in the State Legislature are introducing a bill that will cause Agriculture, Education, the Department of Transportation, and all the other State agencies to reorganize and cross-train all their employees to make better use of the tax payers' money. By late fall, early winter, you've got to make him want to choose you as the head of his Regulatory Department. You will have to devise a plan, and I don't want to know about it...I only want to see results."

Blackie rolled his eyes. "People in Hell want ice water, too, but they ain't gettin' none."

The Man smiled, "You've done it before, and you can do it again. Just put your nose to the grindstone and get it done."

"You know, mean as hell and growing. They take after their mama, not sweet like their daddy."

Blackie asked him how his children were doing. His oldest daughter was away at college, and his son was a senior in high school.

"Okay, and yours? "Did you get your money worked out?"

"Yeah, I think so. We're still waiting on the radio and a few minor things like that. But it'll all work out. He's just so eaten up with himself it's hard to get anything done. He's what my daddy used to call, 'a self made man,' and he loves his maker. Good thing; I bet nobody else does."

With that, Blackie flipped a coin and said, "Heads I win, tails you lose, for the breakfast check. Oops, you lost...see ya." Blackie laughed as he left.

He turned the Plymouth onto the ramp and headed west on I-10 through Kenner. He headed onto the Twelve Mile Bridge rumbling different options around in his head. As he whizzed by the Sorrento exit, he thought *of one of his very best Capos ever, Bobby Alito, and* Pulse, *the paper they worked on together. Blackie, Bobby, and Roy Wilson, Jr., had decided to publish a paper to get their political views out. Blackie had gone overboard and gathered together another twenty-five people, formed a corporation, elected a Board of Directors, and began publishing the only wholly political newspaper in the history of Louisiana. In just a few short months,* Pulse *gained the respect of almost all the politicians and even some of the media. Other, less respectful, media showed their colors and tagged its endorsements with the usual cliques. It was the typical dumbing-down type of newscaster unable to see the candidate's position without a ready-made label.*

As Blackie thought about the beautiful home Bobby had built near Sorrento, he wondered if, with that big winding staircase that led down into the huge living room Bobby had his daughter's wedding in the back of his mind when he built it. Blackie remembered when he and Pam Guidry had gone to Lisa, the oldest girl's wedding and rolled up in that big black limousine. The straight-laced, uptight guests didn't know whether to shit or go blind until the bride and bride's maids ran out to greet him, jumping around and hugging him.

Blackie said, "Shit! Aw damn! I feel like Frank Sinatra in the Godfather movie and, Hell, I can't even sing. Good thing Pam ain't jealous with all these fine young chicks hanging all over me. Love them dago weddings, man!

The food is fantastic, the music's great, gets your lady in the right mood for on the way home, hmmm." Those were the good Sorrento memories—then there was the other...Back at the beginning of the family trouble that caused Blackie to go hibernate in the country, Blackie and one of his soldiers, Louie D'Amico, had just explained some of the territorial changes the night before to the other side. Evidently, they didn't, couldn't, or wouldn't understand the changes. Blackie and Louie had cut through from Ponchatoula to the French Settlement and Port Vincent and then on to Sorrento to explain there'd be new juke boxes, pinball machines, and cigarette machines coming and to throw those other people's shit out. After leaving Port Vincent on the way to Sorrento, there was no traffic on this country road. As they approached the red light in Sorrento and Hwy 61, preparing to turn right, Blackie was writing directions on a pad for the deliveries, when he dropped the pen. When he leaned forward to pick it up off the floor, he slacked his foot on the brake and the car rolled forward a couple of feet. Simultaneously a tremendous explosion tore through the back driver's side window and door from a shotgun blast. Blackie reacted by slamming the accelerator to the floor while Louie emptied a clip into the shooter's car. It apparently had been the other family's plan to cut off the head of the snake, so the rest of the body would wither and surrender. It didn't work. All Blackie and Louie got were some glass cuts and more determination to win the war.

THIS PICURE DEPICTS THE BULLET HOLES IN THE WINDSHIELD AND REAR SIDE WINDOW OF THE SHOOTING INCIDENT AT THE INTERSECTION OF HWY 22 AND US HWY 61 IN THE TOWN OF SORRENTO, LOUISIANA

Blackie exited onto Foster Drive, turned onto Florida, and pulled up at the agriculture building where he'd gotten his car from Holmes Johnson.

As he walked by Holmes' secretary into his open office, he said, "Hey boss, I come to do my job. I know you got a cab crossways because of the way I got hired, but I really ain't no hack. I know you're the Director and I'm only the Assistant Director, but I'm going to clean up all the shit that hasn't been cleaned up. You can just lay back and take it easy. You got your time in. I ain't gonna rain on your parade. I don't like the Commissioner no more than you do, but I got a bunch of kids to feed and I need the job and I'm gonna do it. Word on the street is, you can't do shit unless the Commissioner says you can. I ain't afraid of him. You tell me what to do and I'll get it done."

Holmes looked at Blackie. "You must be his boy, you took my car, and you run all over the state and don't do nothin', and you want me to trust you? I might be old, but I ain't stupid."

"Hey, I appreciate where you're comin' from. Gimme some inspectors that you trust and we'll go start checking shit out and you'll see if I'm straight or not."

"You got the same employee list I have. Pick your own inspectors. And I would appreciate it if you don't walk into my office without an invite. You just walked by my secretary like she wasn't even there."

Blackie said, "Sorry. By the way, I'm not going back to the Capitol; I'm going to be out here. Which one of these offices can I use? And do we share secretaries, or do I get my own?"

Holmes said, "Pat will find you an office, and assistant directors don't get secretaries."

"Good, I'll share yours." Blackie walked out to Ms. Pat Stamper's desk.

She was a pleasant white haired lady in her mid fifties, who looked shocked when he plopped on the corner of her desk and said, "Hi darlin'. I'm the new assistant director of Weights and Measures. I bet Holmes forgot to tell you that, and I need an office."

Looking somewhat intimidated, Pat said, "We have this room over here. It's got a lot of stuff in it, but I guess you can move it around and make it work. The only two real offices we have are mine and Mr. Johnson's."

Blackie gave her his best grin. "What the hell. I'll take his," adding, "just kiddin'," after she looked like she was going to have a heart attack.

Pat went back to her office and Blackie looked at the mess. Desks, chairs, file cabinets, all kinds of junk; it looked like a storage locker. Without even a thought about the shoulder holster, he removed his coat and got to work. As he pushed and shoved desks around, Pat came back to see how he was doing. She saw the gun and damn near had a heart attack again. Hell, it was such a part of him, it took him a minute to understand her shock. Oh well, he figured they'd all just have to get used to it.

After a half hour of pushing and shoving, Blackie sat on Pat's desk and used her phone to call Jeannie at the Capitol. "I don't think this guy likes me."

"Who?"

"Holmes Johnson. I'm supposed to be his assistant."

"He's been there since the beginning of time and you probably scared the old man. What do you need?"

"Typewriter, telephone, business cards, stationary, a chair with four legs, paper clips, pencils, pens, you know…stuff."

"Holmes should give you that stuff, but if he won't, Gerald's in charge of everything. Call him."

"Come on, Jeannie!" Blackie said. "He'll just crap in his pants again, and I'll be waiting like I waited for the car. Be a sweetheart. You call him for me, and I promise the next time you ask me to make love to you, I won't turn you down."

"How 'bout if I promise to do it," Jeannie replied, "if you promise not to ask me?"

"I didn't ask you. I said *when* you ask me," Blackie responded.

"Alright, I'll call."

As Blackie hung up Pat's phone, he saw the stunned look on her face. Blackie thought to himself, *wouldn't she be surprised to know that I'm a sweet loving father of all those little girls, who cooks breakfast, makes beds, vacuums floors and, ugh, even changes diapers.*

He decided it was time for lunch and walked out, calling over his shoulder to Pat, "I'll be on the radio if you need me." Laughing to himself as he left, he thought, *they don't even have a radio here.*

Blackie started out Airline Highway to the Chinese Inn, when the antique radio crackled, requesting him to call the Commissioner. He pulled off to a pay phone, when Vicki answered, "Commissioner's Office," Blackie panted into the phone and said, "This is a pervert callin'. Where is your car parked? Na, it's really only me. I got a message to call El-Hitler."

"He said when you called in, to transfer you to David Martin."

Blackie thought about that name, realizing that he was the son of Wade Martin, long-time Secretary of State, and married into one of the biggest real estate families in Louisiana.

A moment later, David came on the phone. "Hi, Dave, we haven't really met yet, but I'm sure you know who I am. I'll be doing a lot of stuff with you for the Commissioner. He wants you to run up to Alexandria and check on some disgruntled woman employee, left over from the Dave Pierce era who won't retire, resign, or quit, and won't come to work. In addition to that, we think she's the one blabbing to the Rapides Parrish Press about all the alleged bad stuff the Commissioner's been doing since he's been elected."

"Yeah, I'm on the way to eat lunch, when does he want this done?"

"Well, hopefully this afternoon." David said.

"Shit, Alexandria is 170 miles away!"

"Ah, from what we've heard about your drivin', that's like a two hour drive for you."

"Yeah, but that's when I'm chasin some fox, not some old beaver. Gimme the address."

Martin supplied the name, address, and physical description of the woman.

"Jesus, if she's sixty years old, why don't we just wait a few weeks, and maybe she'll die!"

David said, "Jeannie told me you were funny."

"Yeah, did she tell you I'm on the make? And, by the way, do you have a wife or sister who's not busy? They could ride up there with me."

David laughed and said, "You know I have a sister, 'cause you know my father. And yes, I'm married. My wife's name is Mary. Hopefully, we'll have you over for dinner soon."

"Are you shittin' me, Mary Martin?" Blackie exclaimed " God damn, I'm going to eat with Peter Pan. I don't believe it!" They both laughed and hung up.

Blackie called Millie Odom, Redneck Charlie's secretary, at the Brand Commission. Blackie had met her a few days back when he'd returned Charlie's state car. As usual, Blackie had hit on her. Although she was older than the Capitol girls, she was a looker and flirted back, which made him think she might like to take a ride and keep him company. Millie was a 5'8", a stunning blonde with deep blue eyes, with a peaches and cream complexion. She had a big chest and long shapely legs. Millie answered the phone.

"This is your secret lover," Blackie said. "Is that redneck in there, or are you alone?"

"He's gone for the day," Millie responded.

"Great," Blackie said. "I got to run up to Alexandria for a few minutes and come right back. Not only do I hate riding alone but I haven't been able to get you off of my mind since I saw that beautiful sweater when I brought that redneck's car back."

Millie laughed. "I thought you were observant. I knew you were looking at my chest. You must not have noticed it was a blouse and not a sweater, and I'd love to take a ride with you if I thought I'd be safe."

"Hey darlin', not to worry, I'm on the pill."

Millie laughed again. "Slow down, big boy. What if I get in trouble for leaving early?"

"Not to worry. I'll cover your butt. In fact, I want to."

"Alright, but I'm gonna trust ya, no funny stuff," and, after a long hesitation, she added, "this time."

Blackie said, "I'll pick ya up in about fifteen minutes."

"Ok, I'll be on the side of the building; the front has too many eyes."

When Blackie pulled up to let Millie in the car, he was excited to see how good she looked. She also smelled like lilacs, vanilla, or something. It really was great. As Millie got in and they pulled away, he said "I don't think that seat belt works over there. You can sit in the middle and that way if I have to stop quick, I can put my arm out like I do with the kids and keep ya from hittin' the windshield.

Smiling, Millie said, "I'll be just fine over here, and I'm sure you'll find a way to get that arm on my chest without you stopping quick."

"Awww, I wouldn't do that," Blackie said.

"Right," Millie said, "and the Pope's not Catholic."

You're right, Mill, he's a Polack. How'd ya know?"

Millie giggled again and settled back as they roared out onto Airline Highway. Blackie cursed the Commissioner, the crooked-ass highway to Alexandria, and the fact that it would be late before he got back. He would also miss dinner with his girls, which was important. Neither was going to make him a happy camper, or the woman in Alexandria that he was going to see.

It was after 3:00 p.m. when he knocked on the door of Irma Tucker's house in Alexandria. She was a little old, a little wrinkled, and looked pretty harmless. Blackie said, "you don't know me, but I just got hired by the new Commissioner guy, and when I was sittin' in that little room next to that fancy office of his, I heard him and some other guys talkin' about how they were goin' to rig up some books that you were responsible for and get you indicted and sent to prison. I thought that was kind of chicken shit, and I asked the lady who's office I was sittin' in, I think her name was Jennie, or Jeannie or somethin' like that, if she knew you, cause I know she used to work for the other Commissioner too. She said, yeah, she wished there was a way to warn you, cause she didn't want to see nothin' happen to you. So I asked her where you lived, and she looked in some kind of file and gave me your address. So here I am, the good Samaritan. I just don't have a camel. The lady in the Capitol said, the people that had resigned, they ain't done nothin' to, so I figured I'd let you know and give you a chance to get away from these crooks. The lady said tell you Hello for her, and you could call her and check out this story if you want, but be careful what you say on the phone, cause the phones are bugged."

She looked a little stunned, but thanked me and offered me a cup of coffee. I declined and said I had to get back, and that I had snuck away to warn her. "I have five girls to raise so I can't afford to lose my job." Blackie waved and left, thinking, *Shit, that's easier than beatin' up radio announcers.*

Blackie got back into the car. As he pulled away, he tapped his forefinger on his cheek and said, "I deserve a kiss for getting her out of her mess with no violence." As they pulled up to a stop sign, Millie said, "Ok," as she leaned over expecting to put a soft peck on his cheek. At the last second, Blackie took her face in his hands and softly kissed her mouth, letting go after a second and driving away.

"Whew!" Millie exclaimed, "when you grabbed me, I expected you to ram your tongue down my throat, but that was really nice."

Blackie said, "Hey, I ain't no animal. I respect ya. I ain't just tryin' to get laid. I like ya."

Millie blushed and looked out the side window, probably trying to figure out if Blackie was believable or not.

As he crossed the Huey P. Long Bridge, the sun was starting to set, and he was getting aggravated that the girls had already eaten. If he didn't wind this thing up, they'd be asleep before he got home. He had to get that new radio—because with the 1976 version he would be able to call State Police Troop A dispatch, and they could patch him into the telephone to talk to his girls. This would be his priority tomorrow morning, right after biscuits and gravy, hugs and kisses from his girls, and morning coffee with Jeannie, and, oh yeah, what about a smile from Vicki to get the motor running right? Hmmm. Embarrassed as he realized Millie was there with him, he decided he was going to spend more time looking at Millie than Vicki since Cuz had her locked up anyway.

He dropped Millie to go to her car. He watched her ass as she walked across the parking lot. She knew he was watching and twiddled her fingers at him. By the time he turned into the driveway, daylight was fading fast. He watched as Rommel stood by the garage glaring the message, "damn good thing it was you. I felt like biting ass tonight."

Blackie rubbed his head as they entered the house. He would take over protecting the girls the rest of the night. Rommel deserved a rest.

"C'mere, girls!" he called, while holding out his arms to hug them.

Chapter 9

Blackie rolled into the radio shop on Foster Drive. Jumping out of the car, he spoke to Jay, the asshole mechanic, telling him that the Commissioner wanted the radio in the car today.

Jay said, "Well, you'll have to leave it here."

Blackie walked inside and picked up the phone, called dispatch, and asked, "What weights and measures inspector is on the air in the Baton Rouge area?"

After a few moments, dispatch replied, "The only one answering is LAD14."

"10-19 to the radio shop on Foster and meet me."

Too much coffee and a long thirty minutes later, a blond-headed man in his late twenties stepped out of his unmarked Plymouth and went into the lobby.

Blackie gave him his best grin. "Hey, man, you my ride?"

"Dispatch told me to come pick up our new assistant of Weights and Measures, if that's you, then I'm your ride."

"That's me. I'm Dave Steece," Blackie said, and the men shook hands. "My friends call me Blackie. Some of my enemies do too, I guess," he said with another grin.

"I'm Woody Norris. Glad to meet you." Woodrow Norris was about 5'11", 175-180, obviously in good shape. He was wearing jeans and a polo shirt, and Blackie noticed that his hands were a little cleaner than most men's, including his fingernails.

Blackie asked, "How do you know? I might be an asshole."

"I've already heard that, but I like to make my own decisions."

Blackie knew right then that he and Woody were going to get along.

As they pulled out on Foster Drive and then over to Airline Hwy, Woody asked, "Where to, boss?"

"How 'bout Rick's Pancake House, so we can get some breakfast?"

"Sounds good to me."

Rick's was on the corner of Airline Highway and Plank Road in Baton Rouge, once a busy truck stop before the interstate moved the truck traffic from Airline Highway to I-10. What was left was a huge restaurant that had been converted to a 24-hour pancake house.

As the waitress approached their table, Blackie noticed Woody was undressing her with his eyes.

"You married?" Blackie asked.

"I used to be, but she'd been airmailed to me straight from Hell. You?"

"Sort of. Mostly I got a house full of kids. I had a good woman once, but she couldn't stand the stress of the life I lead. So now it's me and the girls and whoever I can get to cook for a day or two. I don't need nobody to help clean house. I know how to do that."

"How many kids you got?"

"I got three girls at home, one at the college, and one in a private girls' school in New Orleans. She comes home nearly every weekend and holidays."

"Damn, that is a bunch of kids. You think it was the water caused that?"

"I don't believe so," Blackie said. "I think it was the red hair. I fell in love with Susan Hayward when I was young and never got over it. The little woman looks like her." They both laughed as they looked up at the waitress at the table, with flaming red hair.

"Oh shit, you're in trouble now!"

The waitress asked, "What's wrong?"

"Nothin, but this fella here just got out of Mandeville State Mental Hospital," Woody replied. "He was there because of his obsession with red heads."

Everyone laughed.

Blackie said, "The only way to control me is to feed me huge stacks of buckwheat pancakes, lots of slices of ham, a bunch of basted eggs, and ice cold milk, and put your phone number on the back of the check."

"You can eat all that?" Woody asked.

"Yeah, and whatever you leave on your plate too."

Blackie asked Woody about the Division and Holmes while they ate. Woody's response was pretty general. They were usually just given orders and didn't have much contact with the Director. He said the Division kind of ran itself. Holmes had been around since the First World War and maybe before that. When Dave Pierce was

Commissioner, Holmes did whatever he wanted. Now, with the new Commissioner trying to give orders, Holmes bowed up every time he heard the Commissioner's voice.

They left Rick's Pancake House and drove down Scenic Highway to the Capitol. After two passes through the parking lot, Blackie asked, "What the hell you doing, Woody?"

"I'm looking for a parking space."

"Shit. Park the damn car and put your red light on the dash, we're the *Po*-lice. I'll be ready to retire and you'll still be lookin for a parkin' space."

As they walked into the Rotunda at the State Capitol, Blackie greeted a couple of old friends, Senators Sammy Nunez, Jr., and Francis (Hank) Lauricella of St. Bernard and Jefferson Parrish, respectively, both members of the powerful Jefferson delegation. They chatted a few minutes, and when Blackie started to move again, Woody caught him and asked, "You know a lot of people?"

"All the ones I need."

They entered the elevator, and CRII was already on, probably coming up from the Senate meeting rooms in the basement. They nodded politely, but didn't speak.

As the elevator stopped on the eighth floor, Blackie made a beeline for Vicki's switchboard with Woody tagging along behind.

Grinning, Blackie indicated Woody and said, "Vicki, this is my doctor. I was having real bad chest pains on the elevator, and he said I need mouth-to-mouth resuscitation right away. Then I'll be all sweaty, so I'll need a rub down, and after that I'll be too weak to drive, so you'll have to take me home."

Blackie glanced at Woody and was surprised to see he was blushing, as he heard Vicki ask, "You want me to tell Jeannie you're here?"

"Hell no, I'm just gonna go in there. I might catch her with her clothes off. Oh, that's right, she doesn't have to do that. She can type."

With that Blackie said, "Come on, Woody," and they burst into Jeannie's office.

"Hey darlin', where's El-Hitler?"

"He's at some meeting, somewhere."

"You know Woody Norris?" Blackie asked. "He's my new assistant."

Jeannie said, "No, we've never met."

"Well, we're gonna go out and inspect somethin'. If anyone is lookin' for me, they can call me on the radio. We'll be in LAD14."

Woody noticed the devilish grin Blackie aimed at Jeannie. Back in the lobby, he asked, "You messin' with her?"

"Come on," Blackie said. "I'm nearly a saint. Next time the Pope's in the U.S., he's gonna canonize me. Plus, I'm really gettin' stuck on a different chick in another area of AIG."

Woody laughed as they boarded the elevator.

As they left the Capitol, Blackie recognized a man he knew to be one of Governor Edwin Edwards' biggest supporters, Lewie Johnson.

He thought back to the time he'd seen Lewie and his driver putting up signs at Transcontinental and West Esplanade on a foggy morning, when Edwin beat Bennett Johnston in the runoff for the post he now held. Lewie had been a player at most levels of government for years. He had literally bought his son-in-law Rick Speeg a seat on the Jefferson Parrish School Board and spent bushels of money to elect people like Eagan, Pilney, and Molaison. He was supposed to be a builder, but he owned huge tracts of apartment complexes. One had over 700 units on the West Bank at Barataria Boulevard; another mammoth on the East Bank, called Park Manor was adjacent to Lafreneir Park. He had holdings in banks and finance companies. You name it, he had his finger in it. One time a few years before this, he got into a pissing contest with the LaHays family, up near Mamou, and Ville Platte over a flying service that he had bought 51% of. They were horsing him around and he thought screwing him out of his money, so he hired Blackie and some of his troops to go up and take over the joint.

Mamou Newspaper **Article No. 1:**

The Mamou Acadian Press   **Thursday September 19, 1974**

Tri-Parish Flying Service Under New management

In a shake up Monday, at tri-Parish Flying Service, located in Vidrine, the Board of Directors of Tri-Parish were relieved of their duties upon the request of Mr. Lewis E. Johnson holder of 51% or 9,650 shares of Capitol Stock of Tri-Parish Flying Service, Inc. They were replaced with a new board of Directors designated by Mr. Johnson, namely, Lewis E. Johnson 1342 Robert E. Lee Blvd., New Orleans, La.,

John J. Maxwell 1012 Veterans Blvd., Metairie, La., and J. Y. Fontenot of Ville Platte, La. In an interview with Mr. Dave Steece, interim manager, it was learned that Mr. Johnson took over to give better service to the people of Evangeline Parish and surrounding area and to expand operations to serve a greater number of people. The little farmer as well as the big farmer.

New Manager At Flying Service

Dave Steece new manager of Tri- Parish Flying Service in Vidrine is shown with his living quarters the mobile camper on the grounds. Steece is also editor of "Pulse" Louisiana Political news paper. (Staff Photo) **(continued next page)**

Mamou Newspaper **Article continued from page 1:**

The Mamou Acadian Press   **Thursday September 19, 1974**

Tri-Parish Flying Service Under New Management

Mr. Steece said that Mr. Johnson plans to extend the business of Tri-Parish Flying Service to entertain more business and better service to farmers regardless of how rich or poor. The service will be the same on a first-come first-serve basis, Mr. Steece stated. He also stated that service was above everything else, and that Mr. Johnson had a Bank in this area which will help finance loans to farmers until their crops can be sold at a reasonable market price. Mr. Steece also stated that a training program had been signed with the state and expected approval within the next 10 days, where "on the job Trainee" will be earning $5.00 per hour to help provide for his family while in training. Applicants may apply at Opelousas Unemployment Office and the Eunice Chamber of Commerce. Again Mr. Steece stressed the need for better service and more help for the farmers and better revenue use for our Parish.

Johnson Arrives To Attend To Business

**Lewis Johnson Tri-Parish Flying Service owner of 51% is shown with his manager
Dave Steece Friday afternoon. Johnson is from New Orleans.
(Staff Photo)**

Blackie remembered he took Emily Gremillion and Betty Trahan, who spoke coonass French better than them local boys, Zap, Big Paul, and Wonder Animal. They swooped in with an affidavit from an attorney, appointing them as Mr. Johnson's representatives and, with 51%, threw the people out of the office and took over. The locals had been having their way for the last hundred years, and as Blackie moved them out of the main office, they trotted into the other area where Blackie's girls, who looked like floozies instead of what they really were, were understanding everything they said in coonass French, about what they planned to do. Betty and Em would take turns going to the bathroom and transmit to Blackie's ear receiver a constant update of their plans.

The flying service had a half a dozen Tiger Cats, and the previous management planned to taxi them off to hide them. Without them, the business couldn't function. They figured they could steal it back from Johnson for almost nothing. Blackie sent Big Paul, Zap, and Animal out to pull big trucks across the runway about every fifty yards, and said, "let's see you taxi them mothers outta here now." He also bought and brought in a pilot named Mike Soileau, and as soon as the runway was blocked, Mike and the boys disabled the planes so they couldn't be confiscated or screwed with during the night. After a couple of days, Blackie ran a special in the local paper about crop dusting rates, and the local paper came out and took pictures of Blackie, his motor home, and his essentially hired thugs, whom Blackie referred to as business associates. Business got really good at the lower rates and the 49% owners realized they were up to their waists in doo-doo that was rising steadily. They decided they'd better buy out Mr. Johnson while they still could. Blackie negotiated a deal at about twice what the stock was worth, with promises of peace if they signed, and the repercussions if they didn't would be that Blackie and his guys would cut their fuckin' legs off with a chain saw. When the agreement was settled, and Mr. Johnson flew in, the local paper photographed his arrival and reported the situation. Blackie and his crew got the hell back to New Orleans.

Lewie Johnson was a character. Blackie had been both for and against the same candidates on occasion. This week, they were on the same side. For years, Blackie had gotten a $300.00 check every week from Lewie. When the IRS and Treasury indicted Johnson, they found a stack of endorsed checks by Blackie, and trotted out there to nab him for tax evasion. They were shocked to find out that Lewie had been *loaning Blackie all that money. Since it was a loan, instead of a payroll, it wasn't taxable. Duh!*

Blackie and Woody headed out to pick up the car with the new radio.

They pulled into the radio shop and saw Blackie's car parked out front. Realizing it must be finished, they went inside, signed the repair order, and headed for the Weights and Measures office and Holmes Johnson on Florida Boulevard. As they got out of their cars in the parking lot, Blackie said, "If you wanna wait a few minutes to come in, so you don't get on Johnson's shit list for bein' with me, I don't have a problem with that."

"Hell no, I'm either with you or not, and I'm with you!"

"Let's go then," Blackie said. Pat was at her desk looking as nervous as ever as Blackie and Woody barged in.

"Where's the boss?" Blackie asked.

"He had to go up North to check on something."

Blackie said, "Yeah, if he was a little younger, I'd figure he had a squeeze, but as old as he is, he might not even have memories."

Blackie asked Pat for an employee list, and he and Woody sat down in his makeshift office to figure out who they were going to make part of the team to get the job done. Woody said, "There are several people who would do a good job if they had a good leader but, as it is now, no one cares whether they do or not and, as a result, most of them do little or nothing."

Blackie asked Woody about a thousand questions on how to check scales. Blackie hadn't realized, until Woody explained to him, that just being out 100th of an ounce on a pre-price weight and packaging machine in a high volume store, could amount to thousands of dollars a year. Not every scale got checked within their calendar year, and when the year rolled and new checks began, it was conceivable that some scales were missed. Woody told Blackie, "this is 1976 and the inspection law was passed in 1952, and it was possible that some scales have never been inspected." After their earlier conversation, that made sense to Blackie. Blackie decided that, while he was figuring out the Commissioner, he might as well get this outfit on the right track, too.

After an hour of going over names, they decided to call Ronnie Harrell from Greensburg and Archie Seals from Bogalusa for an interview the next day. Then they went out to check a few scales. They picked a couple of stores at random, a Winn Dixie and an A & P.

They walked in, asked for the manager, identified themselves, and unannounced, went to the back of the store. There, with a weight kit, Woody checked the scales in the meat department.

After checking the two stores, it was late afternoon. Blackie told Woody, "I'll see you tomorrow." He was ready to get home to his girls. It was still early enough to take them to Dairy Queen. Damn, working a regular job really was hard.

As he rolled into the driveway, the sun had not yet set. There were little mops of black hair, with big brown eyes bouncing around the swing set and the playhouse and acting like they were in their right mind, until they saw the car, which caused a mass rush, necessitating Blackie to stop the car and disembark far from the house, or have a grill full of little girls. Clamoring all over him like a bunch of ants in a honey pot, he told them, "Let me get out of these clothes, and we'll go to Dairy Queen and get ice cream," which was met with cheers and yeas and more climbing and hugging.

After ice cream, then hamburgers, then ice cream again, and baths, Blackie flopped down on the bed and said, "Wow, I think I'm mad at their mother for leaving." But he was asleep before the thought could take more form.

Chapter 10

As Blackie fixed breakfast for the girls, Lu said, "Daddy, I forgot to give you a message last night. A man called 'coo misser' called and said for you to call him at this number in the morning. He wouldn't tell me his name, but here's the number." She had written it on what looked like the back of her homework. Blackie recognized the prefix 643 as Slidell and wondered what the Commissioner was doing in Slidell instead of Baton Rouge. It was about 6:45 a.m. when Blackie dialed the number. A sweet thing answered the phone and Blackie said, "I may have the wrong number. One of my children took a message last night from a friend of mine who was supposed to be at this number."

"Are you David Steece?" the person on the other end responded.

"10-4."

"Hold on, I'll get the Commissioner."

After a couple of minutes, the Commissioner came on the line and said, "This is the Commissioner. You know where Eden Isles is?"

"Yeah," Blackie said, as his mind wandered.

Eden Isles was a privately developed island consisting of about a twenty-five acre lake, plus 2200 lots, all backed up to the waterway, which included a beautiful 200-boat private marina. This gave you access to the Rigolets waterway which, with a fast boat, put you into the Gulf of Mexico in minutes. Eden Isles had been developed by Blackie's Godfather, Rolland Pfister and E. Bee, of Richard Nixon donation fame, by draining a swamp, dredging a maze of canals, and using the canal bottoms as land fill. They conned T.L. James, one of the biggest contractors in the south, through a foreign corporation, to pour miles of concrete bulkheads, then screwed them out of the money. The only access to the island, except by water, was a two-lane bridge off US Hwy 11 and was manned twenty-four hours a day by an armed guard. Blackie figured someday he'd retire and build him a big house there, sit on the back porch, and watch the bikinis go by on the bows of boats.

The Commissioner's voice boomed and brought him back to reality. "I'm at the Isle Apartments on Hwy 11, just before the bridge. I had to spend the night here," he snickered. "Obviously my car is not here, so I need you to come pick me up. I'm in number 9."

"Yeah, I know where it's at," Blackie answered. "It'll take me about an hour to get there." Thinking to himself, *that pompous ass surely didn't wear that young thing out so she can't drive. She probably has to go to work in the city, and don't have time to drive his arrogant ass around.*

He finished stirring the grits as Lu and Alley fought over the last piece of toast, Blackie thinking, *God, I need to get a woman to take some of this stress off of me.*

Blackie slowed down on I-12 as he approached the Hwy 11 exit that would take him to downtown Slidell and rolled through the quiet little sleepy town. He picked up speed again as he drove southwest, passing the guard gate to the infamous Eden Isles. He pulled up in front of the Isle Apartments and knocked on Apartment 9, thinking to himself, he and Woody had told Ronnie Harrell and Archie Seals to meet them in Baton Rouge this morning. He guessed they would think he was just like all the other asshole politicians: stupid, undependable, and never where he said he was going to be. The door opened, the Commissioner thrust his garment bag out the door to Blackie, and said, "I'll be out in a minute." Blackie walked back to the car and hung the garment bag in the back, wondering where the Commissioner's car was. As he stood by the front passenger door to open it for the Commissioner, a pretty brunette came from the direction of Apartment 9. She got into a Ford Pinto and smiled as she pulled away. Blackie wondered if that was her. Hope so. She wasn't a red head. He didn't want the Commissioner messing with any red heads. A couple of minutes later, the Commissioner came out. Blackie opened the door for him and asked, "Where to?"

The Commissioner said, "Get on I-10 toward Mississippi. You been around long enough for me to trust you. I'm in business with former Mayor Danny Guice of Biloxi. We're gonna go over there and meet with him. How well do you know the coast?"

"Good enough."

"Okay, we're meetin' him at the Broadwater."

"How fast you wanna get there?"

"Don't waste any time."

When Blackie hit the interstate, he clocked 110. Forty minutes later, he turned south on Hwy 49 heading down to the coast. At the coast highway, he turned left again, and, shortly after, pulled into the Broadwater Marina and Restaurant.

Blackie followed the Commissioner over to a table where he was introduced to Danny Guice. Lunch was small talk. As they left the restaurant, the Commissioner told the Mayor to come ride with them. Then he directed Blackie through several back roads arriving at a location called Cedar Lake Mobile Home Village. Blackie stood around and picked his nose, while the Commissioner and the Mayor went over some books and talked to a lady whom Blackie guessed to be the Manager. After about twenty minutes, the Commissioner called Blackie over and introduced him by saying, "This is my H.N.I.C., and I'll be sending him over here from time to time to pick up the books and money from you." The lady acknowledged the Commissioner and they left. Blackie drove Mayor Guice back to his vehicle at the Broadwater Marina, then headed back to I-10 West.

Because it was late in the day, he was in a hurry to get the Commissioner back so he could get home to his girls. As they crossed the high rise span over the Pearl River, re-entering Louisiana, the speedometer passed the 130 mark on the police package Plymouth. The Commissioner looked over and asked, "Are you in a hurry or just like to drive fast?"

"Well, I like to drive fast, but I figured you wanted to get back to Baton Rouge as soon as you could to check on your office; we've been gone all day."

"I don't give a shit about that office. I need to start makin' some money. I want you to pick me up in the morning and me and you and Jim Knotts will go see some people in New Orleans who need to give me some campaign money."

As the Plymouth crossed I-55, the north exit to Jackson Mississippi, Blackie remembered a long ago encounter in Jackson.

He was on the way back to Camp LeJeune, a young United States Marine Corps Private. When the bus pulled into Jackson, Blackie looked out the window and saw three red heads standing there waiting for the bus. One especially caught his eye. She was wearing a lavender dress. Damn, she looked like one of those pictures you get when you buy a new wallet. Another one, not much older must have been her sister. The oldest one obviously was the mother, or aunt, or something, but way too old for Blackie. He remembered saying under his breath, "Shit, this broad ain't gonna look at me anyhow. Her dress probably cost more than I make in a month." Ironically, a few minutes later, the sharpest Mississippi twang he'd ever heard said, "Hon, is anybody sittin' here?" He thought, shit am I lucky! "I hope you are." And Patsy

Jean Hollingsworth, a gorgeous red headed Irish Mississippi beauty queen with emerald green eyes, entered Blackie's life. Patsy wasn't too modest and was busy telling Blackie all the way to Tuscaloosa how she'd first won Miss Jackson High, then Miss City of Jackson, then Miss Ole Miss, and had plans to run for Miss Mississippi. Blackie thought," Shit, I'll vote for ya." Patsy didn't shut her mouth for two minutes all the way to Tuscaloosa. He thought about pulling her over and giving her a big kiss to shut her up, but figured that would just chase her away. So he just listened and gawked from the red hair on down. As the bus was parking at the Greyhound depot in Tuscaloosa, Patsy was giving Blackie her address. He thought, shit, I'll never hear from her again. *Amazingly, months later, going back to New Orleans on leave, when the bus pulled into Tuscaloosa, guess who got on? Although Blackie had someone in the seat next to him this time, he knew there was going to have to be some re-seating immediately. He remembered her name, and yelled, "Patsy, I'm over here," and then asked the guy next to him if he would mind moving to another seat so his wife could sit down. Patsy twanged, "Darlin'," as soon as the seat was clear, gave him a big hug as she sat down. Blackie thought,* "shit, stay away six more months and maybe I'll get head when she gets on the bus". *Motor mouth started and didn't slow down until the bus pulled into Jackson, when she begged Blackie to get off and spend a few days with her family. Blackie figured it was bullshit and the parents would lose their minds when they saw him, but thought what the hell; he'd try anything once, and sometimes twice. He was on leave anyway, not on any schedule.*

As they got off the bus, Patsy squealed, grabbed his hand, and dragged him toward a chubby doughboy about fifty, the same red headed trim woman, must be momma, and the third member of the crowd, the same girl he had seen the first time, with the killer body, but this time he saw her face. Though she had all the equipment, she looked like, when they were installing it they stood on her face. It would definitely be one of those "approach from the rear" deals. Patsy explained to mom and dad that they had met several months before, and that she hadn't mentioned him because she wasn't sure when he'd get his leave. But she knew it would be just dang all right for him to come on. She could sleep with Jewel, the sister, and he could sleep in her room. Blackie thought to himself, and sleepwalk regularly. The doughboy daddy had hardly anything to say, and Blackie wondered how he'd made those two girls. But hell, they had milkmen in Jackson.

Blackie didn't give a shit; he was interested in the red hair, the green eyes, and that dynamite body. He thought about how much time he'd get in the brig if he ever got her in the bed, because he knew he'd never get out until the S.P.s came to get him.

They all got in doughboy's car, a '57 Plymouth push button, snot green, and full of boxes, which Blackie learned was doughboy's job, selling Price pots and pans, door to door, all over the state. They got to their house at 3644 North Haven Drive in North Jackson, a quaint little three bedroom, with the bedrooms not located too conveniently. Mom and Pop were on one side of the bathroom, Patsy was on the other, and Jewel was down the hall and around the corner, making sleepwalking difficult, if possible at all. They all sat around and told war stories while doughboy smoked his pipe and drank a beer. Mom made a killer meal of mashed taters, pork chops, corn on the cob, more mashed taters, and gravy and more corn on the cob, and a big ole apple pie with ice cream on top. He was gonna have to go AWOL or get in the Navy to get a pair of those baggy stretch pants those swabbies wore.

Patsy's war stories were all about how beautiful she was and how many beauty contests she had won. Poor Jewel; although she had a killer body like her sister, she mostly sat there intimidated. Sleeping arrangements came, and Blackie figured since he had been accepted so well, he'd behave himself.

About 7:00 a.m., there was a knock on the door, and he heard Patsy's twangy voice calling through the door. "What do you want for breakfast darlin'?" He jumped up, opened the door a couple of inches and said, "you." Patsy was standing there in a green satin gown that made that red hair and those emerald eyes stand out even more than they normally did; she giggled and said, "You're bad, I'm a virgin."

"I won't hold that against you."

She giggled again and said, "For real, what do you want for breakfast?"

"Well, what I'd like is some American fries, buckwheat pancakes, basted eggs, and ham or bacon, and about a gallon of milk, but any part of that will be okay."

"Can you really eat all that? If you can, momma will make it."

"Well, if you add biscuits and gravy I know I can."

With that, Pasty sashayed down the hall toward the kitchen, while Blackie bent over in pain, pushing the door shut. Oh shit! For the next three days, Blackie was escorted all over Jackson and surrounding areas, meeting girl friends, grandparents, extended family members,

*teachers, and the preacher, as Patsy showed off what Blackie was sure
she thought of as her latest trophy. And all the while, Blackie foolishly
stumbled behind her, drooling like a dog in heat.*

As they reached the State Capitol, the Commissioner brought his
thoughts back to the day. "I'm just gonna get in my car and go home.
Meet me here about eight in the morning and we'll go raise some
money." Blackie acknowledged him, turned the Plymouth East on I-12,
and buried the speedometer again. Damn, he was going be late for
dinner with his girls. He needed to get this schedule worked out.

Chapter 11

Blackie heard a far away explosion.

"Damn, they're shellin' us again."

Opening his eyes, he realized that he was home with the girls, not in Viet Nam, and there was a serious thunderstorm. He saw the red digital number, which showed 5:26 a.m. and realized that it wasn't quite time for the alarm. He knew it was morning but, when he looked outside, it was black as night and pouring rain. Another clap of thunder shook the house, and he wondered if the storm was going to let up or if it he would pour all day. As he walked into the kitchen, after showering and shaving, to think about breakfast for the girls, he faced a new problem. School started at 8:30, and he was supposed to meet the Commissioner at 8:00 which was an hour away. He wasn't about to let anybody drive his girls on wet roads. As the girls opened their eyes, Lu wanted cheesy grits, Alley wanted scrambled eggs, and Rae wanted cereal, which was out of the question.

"No way!" Blackie replied. "You have to have something hot."

"Hot chocolate," Rae replied.

"Okay, but hot food too…what?"

Rae tossed her beautiful long hair and replied, "Oh, whatever, Daddy."

"You want your whatever scrambled or over easy, and do you want grits with whatever, or taters?"

Rae grinned and said, "Do I have to have whatever, or can I just have grits?"

Blackie thought, *shit, besides being more beautiful when she grows up and driving some guy nuts, she's practicing being a wife, too, and she isn't even six yet.* Blackie longed for the help that he had gotten from his oldest daughter, Teri, before she went to college. She could have made breakfast while he was reading the paper. As the girls argued over who had the most jelly on which piece of toast and whose orange juice had the most pulp, Blackie worked mentally on the lie that he would have to tell the Commissioner to justify him being an hour and a half late. He was sure Mr. self-centered-ego-maniac would not be able to understand why Blackie was driving the girls to school just because it was raining, instead of letting them ride the school bus. *Shit,* Blackie thought, the Commissioner might not even know his own kids were in school, or he might not even know he had kids. He probably thought those were just little neighbor kids running around his house. As Blackie put the raincoats on the girls, he thought, *damn, this looks like Disney World. One pink, one blue, and one yellow—why couldn't they all be one color?* Shouldn't be complicated since they were all different sizes. Raincoats secure, he parked the girls at the front door under the protection of the drive-through. He then went back through the house and out the den door, ran the twenty something feet to the garage and pulled the car around to the front. By the time this was accomplished it was twenty minutes to eight. He pulled over at the first gas station that had a phone booth. He told the girls to be quiet and hoped some extra-loyal employee was in the Capitol before 8:00. Blackie dialed the Commissioner's private number collect, hoping for maybe a recorder, or a switchboard throw-over, or anything. When a whiney little squeaky voice answered before the operator could say collect, Blackie thought, *oh shit, this little wimp Gerald ain't gonna take my call,* and was shocked when he did. Blackie told the wimp that he had gotten a flat tire, was having it repaired and that he was going to be forty-five minutes to an hour late, and please tell the Commissioner. Then he listened to the wimp lecture him about how he should have called the closest highway department garage for repairs.

As he pulled out of the third and final school drop and headed West on Hwy 22, he wondered if the Commissioner was really going to go out and put the arm on people in this kind of weather. As he crossed Hwy 51, the radio crackled and dispatch told him to stop and use the telephone to call his office. Blackie pulled into a pay phone at Pumpkin Center and placed another collect call to the Commissioner. This time he got Peter Pan's husband, David Martin, who said the Commissioner was going to be tied up today, and Blackie should go to New Orleans and make some contacts for him. Blackie said, "Yeah," and hung up the phone. He thought, *if bullshit was money, we'd all be millionaires.* Blackie figured pretty boy was afraid to come out in the rain in case lightning struck him. Plus, he was pissed off for having to rush the girls off this morning for no reason. Guess he'd haul ass to New Orleans and have a second breakfast with Uncle Rolland at the famous A & G at Broad and Canal. He got back into the car, made a U-turn, and headed back to I-55. He skinned the Plymouth back. He was in a hurry to get to Uncle Rolland's. As Blackie pulled up in front of CRS (Cash Register Sales, at 124 North Broad in Mid Town, New Orleans), he dashed through the raindrops.

He thought of the day when he had made this same entrance and saw Shari (Beverly Pattison), a gorgeous red head, at the reception desk. Blackie thought he was in love. Right then, Uncle Rolland walked out of his office and said, "Oh my God, we're in trouble. The only red head this animal doesn't chase is my wife Beverly, and I'm not sure about that." With that, he introduced Blackie to the new receptionist as Blackie, faking total shock, stood petrified with his mouth hanging open. Blackie told Uncle Rolland, "We need to go have breakfast, but not eat with men alone, 'cause it can cause me some homosexual anxiety, and I know you don't want to be responsible for any gender adjustments, so we need to take Shari with us to breakfast." With that Uncle Rolland stuck a cigar in his mouth, "Come on, you'll have to deal with me and the cigar. You ain't getting the red head." As Blackie grinned at Shari he told Uncle Rolland, "don't bet the farm on it. She's only seen me for thirty-five seconds and already she's smiling." Blackie smiled to himself, as he remembered how he had made her a bigger campaign than the battle of Iwo Jima. And how, after a torrid affair for several weeks, she had quit Uncle Rolland's when Blackie had been in New York. They had just drifted apart by the time he returned.

Blackie had been moved up to driving Mr. Pete and one of their bi-weekly stops (along with cigarette companies, music companies, night clubs, bookies, and other people who paid what they called "insurance," and "The Man" called shake down protection money), was Ms. Kay's, a white clapboard house, three stories high, which stood between 2nd and 3rd Street on Baronne Street. One end of the first floor was a neighborhood grocery store; the other end was a bakery. Where the two shops went back to back was a stairway that went up to the second floor. At the top of the stairs to the right was a room that almost looked like a hotel lobby, plush as downtown, "CHER." Directly in front was a small office. To the left was a hallway with rooms on both sides, and in a U-turn effect was the stairway going to the third floor, housing Ms. Kay's living quarters. It was laid out just like a house, bedrooms, bathrooms, living, dining, and kitchen with a big balcony outside facing Carondelet Street. At the other end of the lobby was another hall with eight or more rooms on each side. Sitting in the lobby on loveseats and sofas and maybe one at the little bar, was a bevy of blondes, red heads, and brunettes, all dressed for beddy-bye in various styles of lingerie.

To Blackie's shock, right in the middle of all these gorgeous dolls, was Shari. For the first time in his life, he was speechless and maybe a little hurt. He wasn't sure what...shocked for sure. He didn't know whether to acknowledge her, ignore her, or ask how much. But Ms. Kay broke his train of thought when she walked up and Mr. Pete introduced Blackie as his driver and associate. She said, "by that lump under his coat on his right hip, I'm sure he could associate a lot." Smiling, she turned to Mr. Pete and asked, "do you need me, or do you just want to go over the books with Doc?" who Blackie learned was like a live-in CPA, manager, part-time bartender, and stand-by bouncer, until a john would get too rowdy; then they'd call in someone like Blackie to handle it. Pete said, "I'll work with Doc. Maybe you can show Blackie around. He's gonna be with me all the time from now on, so you don't have to hide anything from him." Blackie looked at the lingerie and said, "Shit, can't hide much with what they got on!" Thinking at the same time he'd better level with Ms. Kay about Shari, sure as hell she'd tell somebody, and it would get back that he was hiding something. So as she turned to introduce him to some of the girls, Blackie said quietly in her ear, " Shari used to be my girlfriend, if that's her name here." Kay turned and nodded toward Shari and asked, "That Shari?"

"Yeah."

"Well, she can be again. But this time it won't cost you anything; it's on the house."

Blackie said, "It didn't cost me nothing last time."

Ms. Kay said, "Really? No candy, no flowers, no dinners, no nothing? You're terrible."

"Yeah, I bought her presents and dinner and shit."

"How much did you pay for the shit?" she asked, laughing.

Blackie just rolled his eyes and grinned, to which Ms. Kay turned to Shari and said, "Since you're old friends with Blackie, maybe you want to introduce him to some of your friends. He looks big enough to handle two or three of them."

Shari just grinned and said, "I'll never tell." She got up and, taking Blackie by the hand, she led him over to the bar. "I know you didn't used to drink, do you yet?"

Blackie said, "Yeah, I'll take a virgin," and with a long pause added "screwdriver."

To which Shari popped right back with, "Might as well, sugar, if the car won't start." By now everyone was laughing.

Blackie thought, "Shit, I wonder if this is paradise."

Shari introduced him to four or five of the girls and all the rest said hi. About that time, some over-done dude in a big white hat came in and all the girls got serious except Shari, who was sitting on a stool next to Blackie, obviously not available at the moment. She looked at Blackie and asked, "Well, aren't you gonna ask me why?"

He said, "Nah, I asked somebody last night, and they said it was for the money."

"Are you disappointed in me?"

"I don't guess, mostly surprised. I thought we really had something."

"So did I but you just disappeared."

"Hey, man, I didn't disappear. I had to go out of town on business. By now, I guess you figured out that the people I work for wouldn't be overly understanding if I said, 'Hold on, ya'll, I gotta stop and call my chick and tell her where I'm goin.' That might get me more than a funny look. And if something went haywire like the last trip we were on, and I was the only person who made a call before we left, they'd be thinkin' I was the one who called 'The Man' and put 'em on 'em. Hell, you could a called Uncle Rolland and found out I was outta town."

"Well, I thought he was mad at me for quittin'. Anyhow, let's not fight about it. This is no different than answering telephone and typin'. That doesn't mean anything to me personally, and neither does this. If you can understand that, we'll be just fine."

Blackie muddled that around in his head for a couple of minutes thinking that he hadn't been the fairy godmother, or the Virgin Mary himself, who the hell he to criticize anybody was. He'd just have to see how it worked out. By this time, Pete walked up to the bar and asked, "finished chasin' all these pretty girls?" Blackie grinned and answered, "Hell, I ain't even started."

"Well, you'll have to start next time. We're goin' now."

Blackie turned to Shari and said, "See ya," and down the stairs they went. He started to think of Ms. Kay and her training when...

Uncle Rolland shocked him back to reality. "You want biscuits and gravy?"

"Yeah, and about three basted eggs and some grits."

"What's a matter, you sick, you're not hungry?"

"Yeah, but I had breakfast with the girls a couple of hours ago."

Grinning, Uncle Rolland asked, "How are them dirty little brats anyway? Have they stabbed any more piano tuners lately?" which caused Blackie to laugh, *reminding him of the time that he had dropped the girls off at the house on the island and gone on to run some errands, and hadn't told Uncle Rolland they were there. In the mean time, Uncle Rolland had sent a piano tuner out, because the piano was acting up. He had given the black man a key to get in. Lu had been drying her hair in front of a soap opera, Alley was in the kitchen making a sandwich, and Rae was buried in a dozen huge pillows also watching a soap opera. The piano guy hadn't seen them, and he didn't pay attention to the T.V. being on, and they hadn't seen him, cause when he let the lid down on the big baby grand and it went bang...all four of them freaked out. Lu, with her dramatic self, spun around with her hair dryer, screaming "ROBBER," Rae went screaming to the telephone to dial "O" for operator to get the police, and the piano man stood there in shock. Lu attacked him with the hair dryer like a bolo, and Alley ran out of the kitchen with knife in hand and started stabbing him in the back. The black man, though over 6'2", 230 pounds, fled the house, jumped in his truck and drove to the hospital where he called Uncle Rolland. Blackie remembered the phone ringing at his sister's where he was having lunch and her telling him Uncle Rolland was on the phone. When he answered, Uncle Rolland asked, "where are the girls today?"*

"Oh they're over at the summer house on the island."

"Have any of 'em been in the Marine Corps yet?"

"Come on, they're babies."

"Well, let's hope they never grow up."

"What do you mean?"

"I didn't know they were there, and I sent a piano tuner over to work on the piano. He had a key. He was attacked by a wild kid with a hair dryer, lost his hearing to a shrieking little girl on the phone to the police saying they were being robbed, and received multiple stab wounds to the back from the other kid, and isn't expected to live."

Blackie said, "Shit, are you kiddin?"

"Hell no! I was only kiddin' about him not being expected to live. Either the kid was too weak, or the knife blade was too short, so the wounds are only superficial."

Blackie said, "Hell, I guess he should have knocked."

Rolland asked, "are you gonna eat or sit there and daydream all morning?"

To which Blackie replied by wolfing down his food.

Chapter 12

As Blackie and Rolland walked back to the office, Rolland asked him if he was really working for the Department of Agriculture or playing cops and robbers again, which got the response, "I gotta do this shit once in a while to keep the man thinking I'm really on his side."

Rolland asked, "Any way we can make any money?"

"I'm sure we can, but not with this asshole. I gotta take him down too."

"Hmmm," was the response Blackie got. He told Rolland, "See ya later," and jumped into the Plymouth and headed across to the West Bank. He figured Dr. James Dudley Day, a renowned plastic surgeon and a political whore in his own right, who loved to give money to politicians, would be a good place to start.

Blackie knew that the people the Commissioner wanted him to contact were those people they regulated. He also knew that, if he did this their way, at some point down the road, they'd try to say it was entrapment. Hell, he'd just play dumb and call on regular political hacks. Blackie turned off the West Bank Expressway on Stump Boulevard and into the parking lot for Dudley's office. Sticking his head in the waiting room, getting the receptionist's attention, he motioned so she would know to let him into the back office so he could visit between patients. As Blackie walked around to the rear of the building, he wondered why Dudley didn't hire young foxes like most of the doctors, but he figured Dudley's wife was such an uptown snob, she probably wouldn't let him hire anything under sixty, for fear she'd lose the money. As the receptionist let Blackie into Dudley's office, and asked him if he wanted a cup of coffee, Blackie thought, *my mama's old and she's beautiful, and she works for a Doctor. So, if Dudley wanted to, he could find an old woman who was good looking.* Saying no to the coffee, knowing he needed cream to drink it, he figured that, if the cream saw her, it would curdle. As Blackie thumbed through *Time* magazine, Dudley came in and shook hands with him. Dudley asked, "How ya been doing? I haven't seen you in awhile, since the last Senate race to be exact."

"Yeah, I'm working with that new Commissioner now. I need to get you interested in taters and corn, cows, pigs, and eggs, so you support our agriculture department."

Laughing, Dudley asked, "Do ya'll regulate beef too?"

"Yeah. Why?"

"I been thinking about building a bar-be-cue pit."

"Hell, you can buy one at Sears."

"No, I mean a bar-be-cue pit. Tandem wheels, forty feet long, enough to cook for several thousand people."

"Shit! That'll cost a lot of bread, man. Gimme the money. I'll buy 'em some bologna and use the excess to buy my girls new bikes."

Dudley laughed again. "Think about it. It would be great for political rallies, especially in North Louisiana, but it would even be good in the metro area. Blackie and Dudley visited for a few more minutes.

Blackie ended the visit with, "I know you got patients to see, so when you hear from us, we need you to come support us. Ya hear?"

Dudley agreed. They shook hands and Blackie left.

His next stop would be at Bon Marche Mall, owned by Doug and his son Dirk Schonacher, who had always been strong political supporters of his candidates. Doug was married to Judy LaBiche, daughter of Albert, who owned LaBiche's Department store on Canal Street, one of the big five department stores, the others being D.H. Holmes, Maison Blanche, Gus Mayer, and Godchaux—old money. Albert also sat on the Greater New Orleans Expressway Board. Never hurts to have a friend there. Blackie pulled into the Bon Marche parking lot, thinking, *God loves me*—there was a parking space right in front of the office. He walked into the reception area and was greeted by Doug who was just coming out of his private office. As they shook hands, Doug asked if he would like some coffee. Blackie declined and asked where he was going.

"Down to the warehouse. We're supposed to be getting a shipment of appliances. I want to make sure they all get unloaded and none get stuck on the truck."

"That sounds like fun. I'll walk with you."

As they walked through the store toward the warehouse, Blackie told Doug that he was now working for the new Commissioner and, even though washing machines, dryers, refrigerators, furniture, and carpet were not necessarily agriculture products, it still wouldn't hurt him to be friends with the new Commissioner. Doug laughed. "Let us know how we can help you."

When they reached the warehouse, Blackie said, "Damn." The rolls of carpet were being lifted by a long rod down the middle with a fork lift. *Boy they look heavy. Who the hell would want to steal them and what would they haul them in if they stole 'em, and what would they do with them after they stole them?* Blackie asked Doug, "Do they really steal this shit when it's being unloaded?"

"No, not the carpet, but we have lost a T.V. and a refrigerator now and then. There's no way to know if it was when it was being unloaded, out of the warehouse, or off the delivery truck. With this much inventory, it's not too hard to lose one item before the monthly head count." Doug added, "Stay in touch, and if we can help, let us know."

With that, Blackie shook Doug's hand and left.

As Blackie pulled onto the West Bank Expressway and headed toward the Huey P. Long Bridge, he passed a turnoff to Churchill Farms, the name of "the little man's" hundreds of acres in Southwestern Jefferson Parrish. He wondered why they'd named it after the famous Churchill Downs, or if they had.

His mind floated back to the early sixties, when the Feds had been trying to get "the little man" deported to either Sicily or Italy, and neither Country would take him. Supposedly, "the little man" had been born in Tunisia in North Africa, while his Sicilian parents had been on a holiday. Blackie guessed, even though they were Sicilian, the kid was whatever Country he was born in, according to the laws back then. Hell, it used to be like that in this Country once. Anyhow, everybody got their panties in a wad, and Feds packed him up and deported him to Guatemala. The next night, this was back when Blackie used to drive Mr. Pete, about the time the Feds were getting back from Guatemala themselves, Blackie, Pete, and Pas, a younger brother, went out to Churchill Farms about ten at night, and guess who was sitting there. Carlos had beaten the Feds back from Guatemala. The Feds probably needed to rethink that program, because all they did was piss the taxpayers' money away.

As Blackie crossed the Huey P. Long, he tried to decide where he was going to eat, thinking if he didn't eat soon he would die of malnutrition. As he turned onto Jefferson Highway, he pulled into a Toddle House.

He remembered not only the delicious icebox pies, but the time he and Mike Dearmann were sitting at one end of the U-shaped counter with three or four seats on each end and about fifteen seats in the middle. Louisiana State Police Officer Dickey Horner, a.k.a "Trooper Richard" and one of his buddies were at the other end of the counter off duty and in plain clothes. A few other regular customers were in the restaurant. It was about 2:00 a.m., and Blackie and Mike were wisecracking with Trooper Richard and his buddy, when some nut came charging into the front door waving a gun around screaming, "Stick up." With everybody in plain-clothes, there was no way for the guy to know that he'd really stepped into a shithouse of trouble. Blackie, trying to figure out a way to get to his weapon, must have moved a little bit, cause the bad guy turned and looked at him. There was a hellacious explosion. First, Blackie thought the building had collapsed, then he realized that Trooper Richard had put a .357 round right through the bad guy's head. Now, his fucking brains were in the icebox pie. The poor chick behind the counter, gasping for air, looked like she was gonna die any second. The customers between the bad guy and Trooper Richard were petrified, absolutely concrete pieces of shit. The ones between the bad guy and Mike and Blackie were splattered with little pieces of bone and brain, like they were. Somebody must have kicked in a 64G. The chick must have tripped a silent alarm or maybe Dickey's partner, because everyone could hear the sirens coming. Blackie and Mike were screaming for a rag to wipe all the shit off them, and Mr. Tact, aka Trooper Richard, said, "Ms., my coffee's cold." Only Dickey Horner could do something that crazy and want a hot cup of coffee.

As Blackie walked in the door he decided he'd better sit on the left side of the left end of the counter, leaving his gun hand free in case there was a replay, where he could shoot down the counter sending the blood and brains flying the other direction. *Shit, they got an old Buffalo in here today instead of some chick*, he thought. *I don't know why I picked this place to eat.* Blackie ordered a banana cream pie, and the famous Toddle House potatoes.

The Buffalo asked, "you want a whole pie?"

"Yeah, if I'd wanted a half a pie I'd ordered a half a pie." Blackie ate in silence, finished, paid the bill, and left. No damn robbers today.

As Blackie got in the car, he checked his watch; it was almost 2:00 p.m. If he hauled ass, he'd be able to pick his girls up from school. They'd be able to fight with each other longer than if they had to wait to come home on the bus. Plus, they'd have more time to drive him crazy. He pulled up in the toll plaza for the Lake Pontchartrain causeway, started to flash his ID and go around the gate, but realized that wasn't too smart, reaching in his pocket and handing the toll tender a dollar, waving off the receipt, since it would have the time stamped on it and it was too early to turn in to get his money back. A dollar was a small price to pay for a day with such a new and better schedule—not going to be late for dinner this night.

Blackie picked up Lu a few minutes before school ended, so he would have time to get to Alley's school before the bus left. The day care where the baby was didn't care when you picked children up as long as it was before 6:00 p.m. Lu was in the middle of "The Little Princess," and Alley jumped into the back seat. As they swished under the I-55 overpass, Alley asked, "Where's Button Roe, Daddy?"

"I don't know. Why?"

"'Cause I just saw a sign that said Button Roe."

"I never heard of it; must be a new sign."

With Rae in the car, heading back under the same Interstate, Alley screamed, "Look! There's the sign again, Button Roe."

Blackie laughed and said, "I hope I ain't payin that teacher a big salary out of my taxes if she's teachin' you how to sound out words, cause that sign says Baton Rouge." Alley, oblivious to the remark asked, "What's a Baton Rouge?"

Blackie thought, *hell, I might as well totally confuse her*, and replied, "It's a stick red." At which everybody looked confused. Blackie explained that there had been an island in the middle of the Mississippi River and many, many years ago, the American Indians had strung deer up on the big tree to clean them. In the process of cleaning them, they bled. Blackie guessed after a few hundred deer, the stick got pretty red and when the French came along, not known for their imagination or fortitude, they just named the town Baton Rouge, which means stick red in French. To which he was immediately questioned by Lu, "wouldn't it be red stick, instead of stick red?"

"Yeah, but the French do everything backwards, and Baton means stick and Rouge means red; therefore, it really is stick red, even though it should be red stick." The response from the girls was, "We want Pizza. We want Pizza."

Blackie said, "I don't know how to say that in French."

To which Lu said, with her grown up voice, "Daddy, that's Italian, not French."

Five minutes later, they all paraded into a pizza place, ordered two pepperoni and a third, half sausage, half cheese. As they left the restaurant, everybody wanted ice cream to go with the pizza, which required a stop at the grocery store and then home to Rommel and Gretchen. They'd be happy dogs tonight, because they could have the pizza crust.

Blackie flopped onto the bed totally exhausted. Pizza, homework, baths; hell, he bet it was easier to invade a Pacific Island held by a battalion of Japanese than handle these little angels. Blackie lay in bed gazing at the ceiling, running names and faces though his head. Of all the chicks he thought liked him, he wondered how he could get one who all the girls would agree on. It was harder for them to pick a mother than for him to pick a wife. Hell, all you needed to be his wife was be red-headed, gorgeous, rich, sexy, and never talk back. Mothers, on the other hand, needed all kinds of talents, like cooking, washing, sewing, cleaning, keeping the little sweethearts from killing each other, and making Daddy happy. Must be why the divorce rate was so high. Oh well, he figured he'd run an ad in the paper. He read one time where a guy put a billboard on the side of a highway, and got over 400 phone calls. He wondered if he had any kids! Just one of the many problems for Blackie to address…tomorrow.

Chapter 13

As Blackie opened his eyes to that damn buzzing clock, he was glad to see no raindrops were falling. He knew he'd have to get his behind to Baton Rouge to pick up the Commissioner, since yesterday's morning rain had dampened the Commissioner's plans for that day. When he got out of the shower and went to the kitchen, he saw pizza boxes everywhere but no little girls. Down the hall and around the corner, he found three tousled haired little girls asleep. Blackie began singing, "Lazy Susan will you get up, will you get up, will you get up? Lazy Susan will you get up, you gotta get up in the morning." To which he got slow stretches and blinking big brown eyes, then cute little grins. Thinking to himself, *now you started something*, and sure enough, the "can I's" started, followed by the "no, you gotta have breakfast," followed by a little bit of pouting, then all smiles again by the time they reached the table. Sunshine and shadows, the sunshine of his life for sure, despite uneven distribution of the jelly on their toast.

Blackie, drawn away from these pleasant thoughts by a ringing telephone, said, "screw it. I ain't gonna answer it." But as he turned around to butter more toast, Lu, ever ready to help, answered it and yelled, "it's for you, Daddy, it's the Coo miser." Of course, Blackie made a face at her causing her to say, "Should I tell him you're not here?" Blackie grabbed the phone from her and told her to shut up and eat.

"Yeah?"

"This is the Commissioner. How soon can you get here to pick me up?"

Blackie, not giving him a chance to choose the time said, "I'll pick you up as soon as I drop the girls off at school. Your house or the office?"

"The office."

"Right," he said and hung up before the Commissioner could add anything else.

Blackie left the elevator on the 8th floor at the State Capitol Building grinning at Vicki as he headed for Jeannie's office, hoping he'd see Jan.

"Hi gorgeous."

Jeannie looked up smiling. "You can go in. He's waiting for you, and he's been trying to find out how to reach you on the radio for the last thirty minutes."

"Thanks, baby," Blackie said and went into the Commissioner's office.

"I been trying to get you on the radio for the last hour," the Commissioner said.

Blackie thought, *lie number one...Jeannie said thirty minutes.* "Maybe one of the girls turned the volume down. You know how girls are."

"Let's go. We need to get to New Orleans."

As they left through Jeannie's office, the Commissioner told her they would be out of pocket all day. As they entered the reception area, Jim Knotts joined them from an office Blackie had not seen before, and he wondered if that was his office, because he knew he was domiciled in Shreveport, thinking, surely as important as he was, he probably had an office here and in New Orleans. As they waited for the elevator, Blackie asked, "Jim, how the hell did you walk by Vicki without looking at her?"

Jim smiled and the Commissioner rolled his eyes. Then the elevator came. As they walked towards the Commissioner's parking space, Blackie noticed CRII pulling into his parking space, thinking, *if I go speak to him right now it would really piss the Commissioner off and ruin his day.* Blackie turned the Buick onto I-110 and the Commissioner said, "somebody told me you were friends with Gus Weill."

Blackie didn't respond.

After a few blocks, the Commissioner asked, "Are you?"

"Are I what?"

"Are you friends with Gus Weill?"

"I would think so. We worked together with Governor McKeithen. I think he's one of the most honest men in the State."

The Commissioner thought about this for a while. As they turned at the I-12, I-10 split towards New Orleans, Jim said, "Besides Dorignac's, who else do you plan to see today?"

"That Italian guy. Blackie, do you know his name? It's that other big supermarket right there on Veterans Memorial Boulevard."

Wanting to be a smart ass, Blackie said, "Schwegmann's is on Veterans, but he ain't Italian. There's Canal Villere, but its owned by some Jewish people I think."

"No, it's not as far toward Kenner as Canal Villere."

"Oh, do you mean Economical Supermarket? The Zuppardo brothers own that," he said, glancing in the mirror at Jim, who was grinning from ear to ear, and thinking *he knows I'm fucking with him.*

"Yeah, that's the one," The Commissioner said. "That Economical Store."

Blackie thought, *you better be careful there, Mr. Commissioner. Those Italian fellows all stick together, and if "the little man" has an interest in that supermarket, you'd be in more shit than a Christmas turkey.* As they approached the first Kenner exit, Blackie asked, "Are we going to Dorignac's first?"

"Yeah."

Blackie exited on Bonnabel Boulevard up to Veterans and turned right. They parked the car in front of Dorignac's and got out. Jim asked the Commissioner, "does he know you're coming?"

"Who?"

Blackie said, "Joe."

"Joe who?" the Commissioner asked.

"Joe Dorignac. Don't you know him?"

"No, I never met him," the Commissioner stated.

Blackie said, "We're gonna put the arm on Joe Dorignac, and you don't even know 'em?" Blackie look at Jim, who shrugged. "This ought to be interesting."

As they walked inside and over to the private office in the front of the store, there was a young lady sitting behind the glass reception window with a speaker hole.

"Is Mr. Dorignac in?" Blackie asked.

"Who should I tell him is calling?"

"The State Commissioner."

The girl picked up the telephone and dialed an intercom number. After a few words, she asked, "What is this in reference to?"

Blackie glared at her and said, "We want a little meeting with him." She looked a little intimidated, but the look didn't transfer over the phone to her boss.

After a few more words into the telephone, she said, "Leave your name and phone number, and someone will call you to set up an appointment when he has time to see you." Blackie turned around to the

Commissioner and asked, "Do you want me to kick the door in now or later?"

The Commissioner, completely confused, looked at Jim, who said, "Come on, let's go. I know how to get his attention." Out in the parking lot Jim asked Blackie, "Aren't you in the weights and measures division?"

"Yeah, why?" Blackie asked, as the Commissioner stood there apparently still in shock.

"Friday, about three or four in the afternoon, come in here with a crew of inspectors. They got twenty or thirty scales in this place, plus hundreds of boxes to weigh of pre-purchased products. Some of the scales will be out of calibration. Some of the boxes will be wrong. The percentage is with you. You have the authority to condemn everything put through that scale that day. Get a huge red condemned stamp and a big roll of that brown paper. Everything that you find out of calibration, cover with brown paper, stamp it with *condemned* while the customer is standing there. Have an officer standing by, and when the customer asks what's going on, tell them the store was cheating on the weights. By Monday, Mr. Dorignac will be begging to see us. Friday and Saturday are his big days, but they won't be this week."

The Commissioner, nodding like it was his idea, said, "Yeah, Yeah, do that."

Blackie said, "No problem," as they got into the car. "Where to now?"

Jim said, "Let's go on to Economical," and turned to the Commissioner. "Do you mind if I talk to Zuppardo when we get there?" The Commissioner just looked out the window of the car.

In less than five minutes, Blackie wheeled the car into the parking lot of Economical at Transcontinental and Veterans Boulevard. As the three walked into the front of the store, Blackie recognized a security guard named Steve and said, "Hey, bro, where's your boss?"

"He's in the back, Blackie. What's goin' on?"

"No problem, just personal. The Commissioner wants to talk to him."

"Okay, go through those doors that say, 'Don't Enter. Employees Only,' right back in the back of the store there."

"Okay, man. Thank you," Blackie said, as they walked toward the back of the store. As they walked through the rear door, Blackie saw a man in a white shirt and tie, obviously the boss talking to several employees.

Blackie strolled up to him and said, "Hey, Mr. Zuppardo, this is our new Commissioner. And I know you remember Jim Knotts." Zuppardo nodded, and Blackie thought, *he don't remember anybody.* Joe Zuppardo, was black headed, 5'6", of stocky build. He carried himself like somebody who had either been a wrestler or boxer in his younger days and had the confidence to go with it. Blackie could pick up bad vibes as thick as syrup and knew whatever damage was done here today, he would have to correct later. The Commissioner was just so God-damned vain, he wanted to think they knew him. *Zuppardo don't know the Commissioner. If he knows me, it's only by name from muscle, and probably the only way he ever heard Jim Knotts' name was when it was in the paper with all that Board of Education shit.* The Commissioner, Zuppardo, and Jim shook hands, and Jim told him that he just wanted to make him aware that word on the street was the old Commissioner wasn't very astute and that the new Commissioner and his staff would be checking scales, age on meat, processing areas, and just doing the best for everyone involved: citizens, retailers, and the State. They just wanted to stop by and meet him, and tell him if he had any problems to give them a call.

Zuppardo looked somewhere between shocked and confused, and Blackie wondered if Jim already knew that Dave Pierson's crew had never checked these scales, or for that matter none of his people had ever been in this store. Zuppardo offered coffee, which everyone declined. But then, Jim followed him around the store on a tour, and Blackie and the Commissioner trotted behind like two puppies.

As they got back into the parking lot, Jim said, "After you knock Dorignac off Friday and Saturday he'll get the message." The Commissioner said, "I think I'll get a room at the Monteleone Hotel and spend the night. Blackie can drive you back to Baton Rouge and pick me up tomorrow. Let's go down there. I'll check in and we can all have lunch."

As they got back on the Interstate at Clearview and I-10, the Commissioner said to Blackie, "You're supposed to know everybody in New Orleans. You shouldn't have any trouble finding some young lady to have dinner with me."

Blackie thought, *now he wants me to be a pimp.* "The only women I know are connected one way or the other to 'the little man' and they work by the hour and cash up front. You want me to send you one of them?" The Commissioner just looked out the window like his feelings were hurt. *He thinks he's such a lover*, Blackie thought. *He's playing with the big boys now. If he wants to dance he has to pay the band.*

They drove in silence, until Blackie turned off Royal Street into the Monteleone garage. Blackie scanned the attendants, not recognizing anyone and, not being a regular patron of this garage, he figured he'd have to throw his weight around a little to keep the Buick from being parked three hours away on the top floor. He stopped the car, jumped out, ran around and opened the passenger door, and made sure his .44 flashed two or three times for the attendant coming up to get the car. Turning to the Commissioner, he said, "Yes sir, boss. It'll be right here on this floor." Then, turning to the attendant, Blackie stuck a fin in the attendant's hand, and said, "keep it close, bro." The attendant nodded. "I'll have the keys. I'm Number 11." Then the attendant whispered to Blackie, "Who is this guy?"

"You don't wanna know," Blackie said.

"Must be somebody if he's got two bodyguards with him."

They strode into the hotel lobby, and Blackie went to the registration desk. "The Commissioner wants Governor McKeithen's old suite on the 9th floor. Is that a problem?" The clerk, looking like he had just pissed his pants said, "No, sir!" and pushed the registration card forward. Blackie scribbled a post office box on the card under the Department's name. "If you gotta bill us, just bill the State," he said, adding, "when I was McKeithen's bodyguard, they would always comp a room. I can't believe you all changed. I don't ever remember signing a registration form for him." Turning to Jim, Blackie said, "I guess I should have listened to you and went to the Roosevelt."

Jim said, "Maybe they'll want our business here; let's give 'em a chance."

"I'll speak to the manager," the clerk said. "I'm sure he'll work something out."

In the meantime, Jim said, "We're starving. Send us a bunch of everything, club sandwiches, po'boys, French fries, couple of pitchers of milk, some iced tea—"

"Some red heads and a blonde or two," Blackie cut in, to which the nerd blushed, and the Commissioner was back in his shocked mode. Jim picked up the key and they headed for the elevator. As soon as they got on the elevator, the Commissioner regained his self-important posture. Blackie thought, *shit, if it wasn't for himself and Jim, the Commissioner would still be trying to find his way out of the dumpster at Dorignac's where Joe would have dumped him.* After the

Commissioner settled in and they ate lunch over small talk, Blackie and Jim headed back to Baton Rouge. Jim did most of the talking. Blackie learned a lot about Jim's personal stuff, like being a basketball star in college, where his main home was in Ringgold. Blackie was surprised to find that he had a runway for his plane behind his house, and that he just missed being indicted when his previous boss, the head of education, went down. Blackie talked about his girls and how rough it had been raising them alone since he and their mother had gotten on different highways.

At over 100 mph, they were in Baton Rouge in less than an hour. After Blackie dropped Jim off at his car, he turned west on I-12, burying the needle again, trying to get home in time to have a little quality time with his girls. Twenty-three minutes later, he turned into his winding driveway and saw Jamie's car parked ahead. He thought, *oh boy, home cooked meals, clean babies, and a straightened up house.* As Blackie pulled the car up beside the garage, he hoped that by now Rommel recognized the Buick. He parked the car, then trotted up to the back door, in a tie with jumping Gretchen, friendly Rommel, and a bunch of big brown eyes, and a smiling redhead. *Shit, is was like a war hero coming home. Wonder if she'll pin a medal on my chest after the girls go to sleep.*

Jamie put the girls to bed while Blackie showered. When he came into the bedroom, Jamie was perched up on those black silk sheets again. Three and a half hours later, his day was complete. He had his wish and drifted into heaven.

Chapter 14

Blackie heard the alarm ringing in the distance and reached across the bed before he realized Jamie was gone. He knew she had a husband and had to leave, but he could always hope, couldn't he? He dragged himself out of bed and, when he walked into the kitchen, he found a note on the coffee pot. "It's ready, just push the button. Last night was great!" After waking the girls, he opened the refrigerator for their juice and found a sheet of paper taped to the shelf that said, "Thanks." *Shit,* he wondered, *does this mean I'm cold, because it's in the refrigerator, or that I was a good enough lover to melt it?* He smiled to himself as he poured the girls' juice. With Malt O Meal on one burner and grits on another, he was trying to balance a piece of toast, while scrambling eggs, when the damn phone started to ring. Shit, he damn sure wasn't lucky if they were calling this early.

"Yeah?"

"This is the Commissioner."

No shit, Blackie thought to himself. "Yes, sir."

"Something's come up, and I'll need you to be in town with me tonight. I wanna give you plenty of warning, so you can make arrangements."

Blackie thought, *Yeah, plenty warning, like friggin' Pearl Harbor.* "How late will I be?" he asked, adding, "do I need to bring a change of clothes?"

The Commissioner said, "Yeah, that's a good idea."

Blackie wanted to kick himself in the ass. *The dummy hadn't thought of it until I opened my big mouth.* "Do I have time to get a babysitter lined up this morning?"

"Yeah, I'll be in my room most of the day making phone calls, just come here as soon as you get everything taken care of."

"Ok, check ya later," Blackie said, hanging up to the morning chorus of, "Lu took my piece of toast." "Rae took a bite of my Malt O Meal."

"I did not, she took some of my grits."

Jesus, maybe he was safer with the Commissioner.

As they started out the door to the car, Blackie realized he hadn't fed the dog, as Gretchen started bounding around in a circle like a hamster in a cage. He had to fend her off or he'd end up changing all the kid's clothes again. Why the hell did his brother Victor's dog mind so good and this Doberman pup was an idiot? Oh well, he'd been a little wild when he was a kid, and look how well he grew up. There was still hope for the dog.

As he turned the Commissioner's Buick south on Hwy 51, he tried to figure out who he was going to get to watch the kid's all day, and if he was lucky, all night. Maybe Margaret; she hadn't been out there in a while. Or maybe his sis. Well, hell, maybe mom. *Shit, I'll just drop them off at school and then figure it out.* As he pulled up at his mom's place on David Drive, he wondered how much longer till his brother Lynn came home from the Marine Corps. Blackie knew that he was close to finishing his second tour in Viet Nam, and he sure missed him a lot.

As Blackie walked in the door, Poppa Joe stuck one of those Quail eggs into his mouth. "Sit down, son, have some coffee."

"I can't, Daddy, I'm really jammed for time. I wondered if you and Momma could watch the girls today. I might have to work all night."

Momma came in from the kitchen. "Sure, heart, that's not a problem."

But Daddy was grinning. "Are you working or chasin' some skirt?"

"You know, Dad, I don't chase them, they chase me, so I'm really working."

He said, "I guess I'll get someone, Zap or Big John, to pick them up after school and bring them here."

"We can get them," Mom said.

"Nah, I don't want ya'll to have to drive way up there."

When that visit was over, Blackie turned toward New Orleans on West Metairie and headed for Clearview Parkway, to the restaurant that Zap and his brother Emile owned. Pulling into a parking lot in the back of the building, he recognized the black Cadillac with the red interior from last year. Zap had bought this one when Blackie's new one came. Several of his men were driving his used Caddies. Blackie walked into the office to Zap's greeting. "What's up, boss?" Zap had been a loyal soldier for years and though a little short at 5'11", he spent plenty of time keeping his muscles built up by working out. He was as mean as a cornered hyena but he and his wife Patsy both had a gentle streak with kids and, therefore, were always the first choice when Blackie needed help with his girls.

"I got a little personal shit to take care of. Can you pick the girls up and drop them off at mothers?"

"No problem, regular time?"

"Yeah, and stop by to get a change of clothes in case they have to spend the night, and call Momma early, say 6:30 in the morning in case they need a ride to school. Got it?"

"Yeah, man, you're covered."

"Thanks, man," Blackie said. They shook hands and he left.

Blackie turned off Clearview Parkway onto I-10, headed toward Canal Street. Exiting on St. Charles Avenue, he made the U-Turn back toward Canal in front of the trolley to the blaring bell-ringing of the motor men. Blackie loved to cut in front of those trolleys.

He parked in the Monteleone garage, found number 11, gave the attendant the car keys, and headed up to the Commissioner's suite. The door was open and there were a few people he had never seen before. The Commissioner introduced Blackie as the H.N.I.C. to Sam Genaro and Gene Tallo, from Hammond, and Gayle Riggs from Cameron, Louisiana, and some short, fat attorney, whose name Blackie couldn't remember. He probably couldn't remember the attorney's name because he was so busy looking over the eighteen-year-old beauty from Cameron, who had stuffed a 125-pound body into a sweater and jeans designed to hold 120 lbs. She had huge eyes that appeared to change color from blue to hazel to brown and just a tiny freckle or two, which was unusual, since she was not a redhead. As he poured himself a cup of coffee, he could tell by the conversation that both Genaro and Tallo had something to do with the milk business, and the Riggs broad was a daughter of some big financial supporter from Cameron. Blackie wondered if the guy would want his money back or just want to kill him when he found out the Commissioner was trying to fuck his eighteen-year-old daughter Gayle. After listening to about thirty minutes of bullshit, a new face appeared. This guy's name was Tucker Bertrand, and he was some kind of labor leader from Lake Charles over in Calcasieu Parish. Bertrand had been a strike breaker, who looked like a longshoreman, who had lifted one too many heavy crates. A little over 200 pounds, it was hard to tell if he was 5'11" or 6', with his hunched-over stance. His hands looked as though he'd picked cotton as a boy and just let the cuts heal and leave big ugly scars. Blackie wondered if he'd been involved with that shootout when the scabs tried to cross the picket lines a few weeks ago.

The discussion turned to food. Blackie thought, *thank God, I'm about to die of malnutrition.*

The Commissioner said, "Can you get us into the Trade Mart?"

"Yeah, but you usually have to give the Maitre d' a double sawbuck if you aren't a member." Blackie looked at the two country boys from Hammond. "You know, the restaurant goes around and around, so if you sit on the wrong side of the table, you can't catch up with your food." That earned him a couple of confused looks. And he figured, *Hell, I might as well play this some more.* "See, I always sit on the other side of the table, across from a pretty woman, so when the restaurant turns around it throws her right into my lap," he said, figuring he might as well piss the Commissioner off, and winking at Gayle, he added, "make sure you sit right in front of me darlin'."

They walked to the parking garage and headed out. They took a right at Charters over to Canal.

Waiting for the red light to change, *Blackie remembered a few years back when Billy Bosworth, had hired them to wire Security Homestead. Blackie took Stu, D.D., and Frankie, along. Stu picked the lock, then he and Blackie went in. While D.D. worked the outside from a car and Frank loitered right by the door pretending he was drunk, Stu and Blackie got into the Chairman's private office. While they were screwing the Mark 6 transmitter to the bottom of the desk, a pair of security guards entered the office from a separate door from the one Stu and Blackie had come through. Blackie and Stu huddled up in the leg well while the guards loitered around in the outer office, drinking coffee and talking. Suddenly, they heard the guards say, "It's midnight; turn on the alarms." Blackie whispered to Stu, "Is that door going to set off the alarm, because it's not locked?"*

"No, but it sure as hell will when we open it to go out."

They huddled together trying to figure out why the alarm was turned on at midnight, and whether or not it would be turned off early enough in the morning to give them time to get out before the employees came. Their experienced guess determined the odds that it was an eight-hour alarm and would be off at eight a.m., just before the Homestead employees arrived. They walkie-talkie communicated to D.D., who could answer, but Frank could only hear, on his ear receiver. D.D., an off duty N.O.P.D Lieutenant, said the last watch only had two cars in the Central Business District, and knew they weren't going to break their ass to get to an alarm, knowing there were two armed guards in the building. They would figure it was just some drunk who shook the door and would take their time. "That's great!" said Blackie. "We have our own drunk. Frank, walk around on O'Keefe Street where the other lobby door is, and as soon as we finish, we'll let you know. You shake the door when D.D. says the patrol units are tied up and, when the guards are telling you to get the hell off their door, we'll go out the unlocked door."

Stu said, "There is one problem with that. We can't stop to pick the lock back to lock the door, and the guards are only going to be sixty or seventy feet away and could turn around at any minute.

Blackie laughed. "Shit, we'll just leave it open, and some poor asshole will get fired for leaving it open."

As Frank started to leave the door, D.D. said "man, don't leave now, if some real drunk comes down and leans on the door it will just open up, you have to be there to fend them off.

Within thirty minutes, Blackie and Stu had the phone and room transmitters working fine. They advised D.D. that he was now in control.

He said, "The two guards are sitting right there on the bench by the elevator, and one First District Unit went on a 10-40 at Tasty Donuts on Claiborne, and the other one is down by the River Walk. There's nobody on Gravier either way. Go on Frankie, go around to O'Keefe."

As Frankie made the corner on O'Keefe and Gravier, he banged on the windows, waving at the two guards sitting by the elevator. They both looked up and one made a motion like, don't lean on the door dummy.

Frankie stumbled another thirty feet to the doors, and then acted like he was trying to open them.

Blackie asked D.D., "What's happenin''?"

D.D. said, "Only one guard got up and went to the door, I can't hear what him and Frankie are saying, but Frankie definitely has him engaged."

All of at sudden, Blackie heard the alarm go off as Frankie banged on the door, and the other guard got up and went to the door. D.D. said, "I guess, come now." Blackie and Stu started crawling along the counter from the President's office to the side door. When they were almost to the door, they barely heard over the alarm and the guard's shouting, D.D. say, "hold on. There's a unit responding to the alarm, it's right on the corner."

Blackie and Stu crouched against the counter and could see the blue lights flashing through the windows as they pulled up. Blackie said, "Shit, they're at the wrong door. They're at our door!" Then they could hear D.D.'s voice and realized he'd gotten out of the car to confront the officer, probably as their friend.

The voices faded away, and suddenly, the alarm went off, but the blue light was still lighting the whole room up every time it rotated. Blackie peeked around the counter and could see D.D., Frankie, both patrolmen, and both guards by the other door. He grabbed Stu's arm and said, "Let's go!"

They sprinted the eight or ten feet from the door and were at D.D.'s car in seconds. Crouched down behind his car they were afraid to open the door and hoped no one walked down the street and saw two men in black clothes, their black leather bag, and black gloves. In a couple minutes they could hear voices approaching and didn't know what to do, until they realized D.D. and the two patrol officers were joking and Frankie was tagging along.

They heard the patrol car doors close and then saw the blue lights go off. A second later, they heard D.D. open the door to his unit, and then Frankie came around and almost stepped on them. They opened the back door and crawled in on the floor, while Frankie opened the front door and got in the passenger seat. As they pulled away from the curb, Blackie said, "Shit, that was luck." D.D. said, "Yeah, I knew both of them and told them that Frankie's old lady had sent me down here to find him cuz he'd been drinking again. And I told the two security guards, shit man, everyone has a drink every once in a while, and it all happened at the other door, so I don't think we'll get any heat for the other door being unlocked. They'll really think someone left it unlocked, I'm sure someone has forgotten to lock it sometime."

As they headed out Canal Street, the red light caught them right in front of the Brass Rail, and before you could say, "Aww damn" there were screeching brakes, what sounded like an explosion, and they were thrown around on the inside of the car.

D.D. said, "Son-of-a bitch, some asshole just ran into us."

Even though Blackie and Stu had taken off their black sweaters and were in white T-Shirts D.D. said, "If the same unit comes to handle this wreck, they'll want to know where you two came from." While unbuckling his seatbelt and getting out, and it seemed almost simultaneous, he screamed, "Halt, police!"

As Blackie, Stu, and Frank all got out to see what was going on, they could see D.D. chasing some tall skinny white kid down Canal and toward the river, and the relatively new Pontiac buried into the back of D.D.'s unit. Blackie said, "C'mon Stu" and he and Stu ran into the Brass Rail shouting, "Frankie, let us know what's going on."

It was 6:00 a.m. and three gallons of orange juice later, when Frankie came in.

"You ain't gonna believe this shit. The god damned Pontiac was stolen, the same unit that responded to my drunk act caught the guy over at Basin, and D.D. rode to the motor pool to get another unit to come back and get us.

"All the fuckin' buggin' equipment's in the back seat, did he get it out?"

Frankie said, "That's why he went over with them to the motor pool, so he could get it over there."

"Whatever Billy B. wanted in this Homestead it better be worth all this hassle."

Blackie came back to reality as the entourage crossed Camp Street with some fool leaning on his horn. As the elevator stopped at the top of the Trade Mart, Blackie stepped off and headed for the maître d' with a double sawbuck in his hand, greeting the guy like they were old friends. While shoving the bill in his hand, he said, "Put us in the corner with a few extra chairs, The Man will be here after a while." The maître d' led them across the restaurant to a secluded table, where Blackie pulled the Commissioner's chair out for him and then stepped back to the wall. As he glanced down at the Commissioner, he could see he was puffed up like a banty rooster. As the waitress arrived to take their order, Blackie wondered if the Commissioner was going to invite him to come sit down, or did he really want people to think he was important enough to have a bodyguard standing behind him as he ate. The Commissioner looked torn between trying to flirt with the waitress and not offending Gayle. *Like she gives a shit*, Blackie thought. Finally, he ordered one of those big seafood platters that will feed half a dozen people. Blackie thought Genaro and Tallo were relieved, since they obviously couldn't read some of the appetizers, or the entrees. By the time the food came, Blackie was sure that this was just another ego meeting for the Commissioner, since nothing of substance had been discussed. As they left the Trade Mart and headed back to the

Monteleone, Blackie was looking for an excuse to get out of staying the night away from his girls. When he pulled into the Monteleone garage, Tallo and Genaro got their car and left. Blackie, the Commissioner, Gayle, and Tucker went back up to the room. Blackie sat around the hotel room till nearly midnight when Gayle said she was leaving to go to her room at the Royal Sonesta. All this time, the Commissioner had been in his bedroom, supposedly making important phone calls. Shortly after Gayle left, he came out of his room and nearly had a heart attack when he found out she'd left. When Blackie saw how upset the Commissioner was at the loss of his attempted conquest, he figured it would be a long night for all of them. Ironically, Tucker had a few comments about fund raising in Calcasieu Parish and the Commissioner seemed to forget all about Gayle. What an ego!

Chapter 15

The hotel phone started ringing at six o'clock. Blackie realized he'd slept in the chair all night, as he reached for the phone and got the wake-up recording. Why in the Hell had he needed to be here all night when he should have been home with his girls? He looked around, since there was only one bedroom and he assumed Tucker must be gone.

He heard the Commissioner stirring around in his bedroom and he called out to him, "I'm going to run down to the car and get my change of clothes," adding sarcastically, "it's been a long time since I've slept in my clothes in a chair." To which the Commissioner grunted some unintelligible response.

When Blackie got back upstairs with his bag, the Commissioner had a pot of coffee delivered and was on the phone motioning for Blackie to get a cup. Blackie shook his head and pointed at the bathroom. *As Blackie stood in the shower for a prolonged length of time, he wondered, what in the hell did the Commissioner think was so important that I should be there all night?* When Blackie reentered the living area of the suite, feeling somewhat alive again, the Commissioner met him with, "don't you know those people at Louisiana Computer Company that do a lot of the payrolls for state and parish agencies?"

"Yeah, you talkin' about Bob Westerlund and his partner John Somethin' or Other? We call the business LCC. I know John when I see 'em and I know Bob real well, why?"

"I heard that he's generous to people who give him the contracts."

"You mean Bob?"

"Whichever one is the main guy."

"That's Bob. John runs the employees that run the key punch and stuff like that in the building."

"Can you get an appointment with him?"

"I'm sure if I tell him I'm Monty Hall, he'll trot right up here."

"Who's Monty Hall?"

"He's the Game Show host on *Let's Make A Deal,* you don't know that?"

"Oh yeah, I know who you mean."

Bullshit, Blackie thought, *you ain't got a clue what I'm talkin' 'bout.*

"Well, call 'em."

"Okay, that's one call, what else do you want me to do? By the way, why isn't Jim Knotts here?"

"He's supposed to be here later today."

Blackie called the Louisiana Computer Company (LCC) and talked to Kathy Genaro, Bob's personal secretary, opening the conversation by saying, "I bet you didn't know I just traded two blondes and a brunette for you and that flaming mop on your head."

"Get outta here. Bob couldn't get out of the parking lot without me; he'll never get rid of me."

"Right darlin', but not because you're so smart, but because you know where all the bones are buried, or should I say checks?"

"Don't be a smartass. You're on a telephone you know. Nothing's sacred on the phone."

"Tell Bob to call me at the Monteleone. I'm in the governor's suite."

"Ho ho, moving up in the world."

"Actually, I'm working for the new Commissioner, so I'm still in the same world."

"Hmmm, bet I can guess what you want."

"Hmmm, I bet I know people in Hell want ice water, and I bet if I was in Hell and had ice water, I'd trade it for you."

"You're just a big flirt; you'd get tired of me in ten minutes."

"That's really an insult. It takes me two hours just to get through the preliminaries."

"Okay, Lover Boy, I'll tell my boss to call you."

Blackie hung up the phone and got up to answer the door. "He's not in; he'll be calling me back."

When Blackie opened the door, he greeted Jim Knotts. "What a fun night you missed," he said and then rolled his eyes.

Jim winked back. "What's happenin'?"

Blackie shrugged. "Just trying to set up some meetings."

As Jim and the Commissioner started a conversation, Blackie interrupted them. "If we're going to put the arm on Dorignac's, I need to line up some inspectors I can trust and get ready to do it this weekend. You won't need me with Jim here, will ya?"

Jim answered for the Commissioner. "No, we'll be fine, and that's a good idea, go get that started."

Blackie grinned at Jim as their eye contact acknowledged that he had just usurped the Commissioner's authority.

Blackie cut through the lobby to the parking garage, got his unit, and, as he turned on St. Charles Avenue toward the interstate, he realized he was going to have to hook it up if he was going to get to Baton Rouge, set up an inspection, and get home in time to see his angels before they went beddy-bye. And he wasn't about to give them up for two nights in a row.

An hour and fifteen minutes later, as he exited the interstate, he radioed LAD14 to meet him at the office on Florida Boulevard. NOW. By the time Blackie pulled into the parking lot, Woody was already standing there leaning on his car. Blackie asked him, "Have you got a hold of Ronnie Harrell, and do you think we can trust/use him?" Woody answered in the affirmative. As they reached the top step to enter the building, Blackie stopped him. "How many do we need to work one supermarket?"

"If you're going to be there to handle the management, I could do it alone. But if we have Ronnie, it'll go twice as fast."

"When are we going to do this? How long will it take to do the average supermarket?"

"Depends on how many scales, usually three or four hours."

"How do they run? Are they usually pretty accurate?"

"Yeah, pretty much; usually one or two are off a little bit."

"What do you do then?"

"Usually give them a warning, sometimes a written warning, come back in a few days, and see if they had the Fairbanks-Morris people out to calibrate the scales that were off."

"But the law says we can confiscate the product that's not weighed properly and everything that might have come through that scale since it was last calibrated. Isn't that correct?"

"Well, I guess you've checked the law, so, yeah, but that's pretty heavy. However you want to do it is fine with me; you're the boss."

"We'll hit this store about nine a.m. Friday. I want you to get a big roll of brown paper, one of those three-foot wide rolls that will cover a counter. And what do we put, *contaminated* or *Condemned* on the paper?"

"Condemned."

"Okay, get some eight- or ten-inch rubber stamps with the word CONDEMNED and two or three rolls of masking tape. I don't want anyone to know what store we're going to hit until right before we get there. I've had a tip that this store is really short-weighing customers and someone tips them off right before we get there."

Woody grinned at that, and said, "no problem boss; plus, we have condemned tape. Do you want it or masking?"

"Okay, condemned, and line up Ronnie Harrell to go with us, and meet me Friday morning at eight in the Howard Johnson's restaurant at I-10 and Veterans Boulevard. If you need me before, then get me on the radio."

"Okay."

As they walked into Pat's office, Blackie stepped in front of Woody and told Pat, "Tell the boss we're going to be in North Louisiana checking scales—me, Woody, and Ronnie Harrell. We're following a direct order from the Commissioner and just wanted to let you know in case you were looking for us. Got it?"

Pat nodded and looked a little stunned.

Blackie turned and ushered Woody back out into the parking lot.

"You pick up Ronnie and, between now and Friday, go check some scales between Alexandria, Monroe, wherever. Don't kill yourself; just make sure someone sees you up there. And don't tell Ronnie you're going to end up in New Orleans Friday morning. Do you need expense money?"

"No, I'm okay."

"Just keep your receipts. I'll get you reimbursed."

"Okay, what if we find some scales that are out in any of those towns?"

"Give them a written warning and make sure you both sign it. I'll see you Friday morning."

"Okay, boss, see you Friday."

Blackie turned his unit east of Florida Boulevard and stayed on Florida all the way to Sherwood Forest Boulevard, before getting back on I-12. As he looked at his watch, he realized he wouldn't be late for dinner after all, and he took the Plymouth roaring home.

As he turned into the estate, the sun was still high in the sky. He wondered if he had time to take the girls swimming. Hell, he was going to play hooky tomorrow, anyway, so he could take them then. Shit, they had school tomorrow; damn, how come he couldn't have been born rich instead of good lookin' he thought as he pulled up in front of the garage. Rommel met him the minute he opened the door, and he could hear voices and splashing water coming from the river out behind the house.

As he rounded the back of the house, all three girls were splashing around like they were swimming in ten inches of water as Zap and his lady Patsy watched over them from the dock. Lu spotted him first and screamed, "DADDY!" which caused a chorus of "daddies" from the girls and a thorough mocking of the girls' "Daddy" from Zap. Blackie threw his coat over the dock rail and dropped into one of the lounge chairs responding to Zap's, "What's happenin'?" with "Same old Bullshit."

Patsy said, "I'll watch the girls if ya'll need ta go talk."

"Nahh, we ain't got nothin' to hide," Blackie said, while grinning at Zap. "She already knows about the blonde don't she?"

After another forty-five minutes or an hour of splashing, Blackie suggested Pizza, which got a chorus of "yays" from the girls. "Me and Patsy'll go pick 'em up," Zap said.

Three hours later, Patsy and Zap picked up Pizza boxes and Coke cans, said their goodbyes, and headed back to the city.

Blackie tucked in the girls, kissed them goodnight, scratched Rommel's head as he went to his bedroom, and flopped down. Damn he was tired, thinking he needed a good woman, as he felt himself drifting away almost instantly.

Chapter 16

Blackie awoke to the buzzing alarm Friday morning. He needed to get his motor running; this was a big day. He rolled the girls out, shuffled them toward their showers, and went back into the kitchen to make breakfast. He loved the girls, and he loved taking care of them, but he was going to have to get someone in the house, the more complicated this job got. Like today; hell, he didn't know what time he would finish.

"Daddy, there's a roller skating party tonight," Lu said, breaking his train of thought. "Can I go?"

"Of course, my heart, what time is it?" Blackie said, thinking, *this will sure put a crimp on what time I have to finish.* Before he digested that, Ally romped in and said, "Daddy, there's a birthday party tomorrow for one of my friends and Rae wants to go, but she can't 'cause she's little." *Now all I need is the goddamn dog to get the shits and have to go to the vet, my Saturday will be complete.*

Rae tugged on his pant leg. "Tell Al, I'm not little. I'm just short. Isn't that what you tell me?"

"Yeah, my love, but sometimes you gotta be taller to go to certain birthday parties."

Blackie called Zap. "Man, can you come meet me at seven at Hwy 51 and 22? I gotta be some place and I can't be late this morning."

"Yeah, man, I'll just drive 'em around until it's time to drop them off."

"Okay, man, I really appreciate it."

Blackie made one more phone call to The Man and told him, "I'm gonna hit one, maybe two stores hard today. I'm sure before it's over the press will be out there. Anything special you think I should say?"

"If you can't duck 'em, you'll just have to wing it."

"Okay, I just wanted to let you know."

Blackie put the .44 on his hip, the Chief on his ankle, and left the Derringer at home. He loaded the girls in the car and started toward the rendezvous with Zap. As Blackie pulled under the overpass on Hwy 22,

Zap wheeled in behind him. Blackie thought, *man, he musta flew to get here so fast.*

As he switched the girls to Zap's caddy, Zap was met with a chorus of, "Mr. Zap, are we gonna get McDonalds cookies?" "I wanna orange juice." "I want cookies too."

Blackie thought, *shit, he's more than a loyal soldier, he's gotta be a saint.* As he turned the Plymouth south on I-55 he picked up the radio mike.

"LAD 4 to LAD 14"

Blackie was both surprised and pleased to hear Woody's voice crackle, "LAD14, go ahead."

"10-20?"

"We're on I-10, passing the Sorrento exit."

"10-4. I'll be there a couple of minutes ahead of you. You had breakfast?"

"Negative, we thought you were buying."

"We?"

"10-4. I've got LAD 18 with me."

"10-4. I wonder if I can put it on my expense account."

"I'm sure you can. I'm domiciled in Ringgold, and 18 is domiciled in Greensburg."

"10-4. Then it sounds like biscuits and gravy for everyone."

"10-4."

When I-55 merged with I-10 Blackie again asked LAD 14 for another 10-20.

"Look in your mirror," LAD 14 responded. Blackie looked in the mirror, then at his speedometer which was registering just a little over a hundred and ten and smiled to himself, thinking, *I knew I was going to like this Woody.*

Ten minutes later they exited I-10 onto Veterans Boulevard, made an illegal U-turn, and pulled into the Howard Johnson's parking lot.

Blackie got out of the car and waited while Woody parked, and he and Ronnie walked over to him. Woody said, "This is Ronnie Harrell, Boss. He's the inspector I chose to help us do whatever we're gonna do today." Ronnie Harrell was kind of an average everything: mousey brown hair, sad liquid eyes, about 5'10", 170. Just kind of average all the way around. Blackie smiled to himself again. Woody hadn't told him shit, so there wasn't any chance there was a leak.

The three men shook hands and walked into the restaurant. The waitress recognized Blackie at once and gave him a big smile.

Blackie's men followed him back to his usual table as the waitress walked up with his orange juice. "I'm sorry, Sir, I didn't know what these men wanted to drink."

Blackie said, "Not a problem. Tell the lady, and she'll never forget; she's got a memory like an elephant. He'd probably like diet Jack Daniels," Blackie said, pointing at Woody. "You better give them a menu too. They wanna eat."

"Would you like one too, Sir?"

"Nahhh, I've been eatin' more than thirty years. I want biscuits and gravy, two basted eggs, some hash browns, and a big piece of Mrs. Piggy."

Ronnie, though Blackie was sure was curious, ate without saying a word as Blackie and Woody exchanged small talk about everything from women to hunting to politics.

In the parking lot, before they left, Blackie said, "Ronnie, you ride with me, and, Woody, follow."

Five minutes later, Blackie had not read anything in Ronnie's expression as he pulled into the Dorignac's parking lot. Blackie retrieved several copies of the state law for weights and measures from over the sun visor as they exited the vehicle. He hollered to Woody, "BRING BOTH TEST KITS, WOODY." And the three men entered Dorignac's supermarket.

As they walked down the aisle to go to the meat department, Blackie said, "Clip your IDs on your shirt pockets so they know who we are, refer all questions to me, answer nothing. Anything you find short weighted, just bring it to me; make no comment to anyone. If anyone tries to stand over your shoulder while you're testing, politely ask them to move."

As they entered the Employees Only door in the back of the meat department, Blackie held up his ID and asked, "Where's the manager?"

One of the females packaging meat pointed toward a middle-aged man with his back towards them, at a cutting board. Blackie walked over and said, "I'm David Steece, in charge of the Weights and Measures team, here to check your scales and products."

He practically had to yell to be heard over all the machinery, adding, "I'd appreciate you turning off these machines and giving your people a coffee break. We'll work as fast as we can."

Woody was at a big Fairbanks/Morris prepackaging machine and Ronnie was setting up on one of the few steel tables that was clean.

The manager looked a little perplexed and said, "I never heard of this. Who are you?"

Blackie thought, *shit, nobody has been doing their job*, as he handed the man a copy of the state law enacted in 1952, stating, "It's the law, man, and if nobody's been doin'' it, makes you wonder why, huh? Interfering with us doing our job is a crime. So I'm trying to be nice, but the final choice is up to you. We're going to check these products and scales one way or the other." With that, the man bustled out of the meat department and toward the office in the front of the store, with the law clutched in his fat little hand.

As the various machine motors, grinders, and cutters slowed down to a stop, you could finally hear yourself think. Woody raised his eyebrows and started to repeat something he had just done. Blackie had no clue what he was doing as he grabbed a basket and went out on the customer side of the meat counter and randomly picked up packages of meat for Ronnie to test.

As Blackie came back with a basket full of meat, Woody motioned him over and said, "this one's off between two and three-hundredths of an ounce."

"Hell is that enough to even worry about?" Blackie asked.

Woody said, "Yeah, that means they're paying the per pound price, some of which is as much as six dollars a pound for air. On a big volume store it could be a lot of money I'm sure."

Blackie said, "It sure don't sound like much. Tell me again."

"Two or three-hundredths per ounce. It's varying between two point eight to two point nine to three point zero to three point one."

Blackie jotted them down, picked up the phone, and dialed the number for an old friend and C.P.A., L.T. "Sam" Montalbano, an absolute genius with numbers.

The phone was ringing in Blackie's ear when Joe Dorignac, yelling and accompanied by two of his flunkies and the meat manager came in.

"What the hell's goin' on?" Joe Dorignac asked. He was in his mid-fifties, with dark curly hair and carrying a little more weight than he needed. You could tell by his clothes and his jewelry that he had more money than average. You could tell by his attitude and arrogance that he thought he had more clout than he really did. Blackie ignored him as he asked the girl answering the phone for Sam. She asked who was calling and then told him to hold on.

"I want you all the hell outta my store," Dorignac screamed. This caused Ronnie to stop in mid-motion, with a prepackaged piece of meat on his test scale. Woody had totally ignored him. Blackie put his hand partially over the mouthpiece of the phone, put on his nastiest look, and looked into Dorignac's eyes. "Looks like you been fuckin' the public Dorignac. It's your right to stand here and watch us test, but your fuckin' stooges gotta go, and the next time you raise your voice, I'll have the State Police here so goddamn fast you won't know what happened, and you'll be tied up and gagged during the test. You got that big shot? I don't give a fuck how much money you got, or how many political friends you got. Right now, your scales show that you've been cheating the public. We're rechecking right now and if we're right, I'm condemning *all* your product, and if you're nice, I'll write you a citation and you can appear in court. If you wanna be an asshole, I'll take you to jail, then write you a citation, then you can bond yourself out, and still go to court. Now the score is forty-love my favor, the ball's in your court, and your racket's broke, whaddaya wanna do?"

Dorignac looked down at the bill his manager had obviously given to him, mumbled something unintelligible, and stormed back to his office with a parade of flunkies behind him.

Blackie turned toward his men, Ronnie still looking like he was in shock and Woody grinning like the cat who'd eaten the canary.

Blackie said, "Goddamn fucking assholes, get a little money, know some politician's first name, think they own the whole fucking world."

Woody said, "Well you 'splain'd' to him he didn't."

"Whatcha got?" Blackie asked.

"Four tests, same thing," was Woody's answer.

"Wrap that pretty son of a bitch in that orange condemn tape, and make it high enough so customer's looking in the window can see it," Blackie said, while turning towards Ronnie.

Ronnie looked back at Blackie and said, "These are all off too."

Blackie said, "Woody, you check the rest of these scales; every one that's off, condemn. Ronnie, grab your shit and come with me."

As he exited the cutting room and went out to the meat counter, he first noticed that a crowd of customers and a couple of employees had gathered right outside the meat department's window, he guessed because of all the screaming and yelling between him and Dorignac.

Each package that Ronnie tested was off. Blackie first tried stamping with his large red condemned stamp, and when it was too large for the package he took a large black marker and put a big X across the price label.

In a few minutes, Woody was out and said that he had all the machines wrapped in tape. Blackie sent him out to the car to get the brown paper.

As Ronnie kept testing, one of the customers finally got enough nerve to ask what was going on.

Blackie said, "We're from the state and we're checking the scales, and if you're a customer that's been buying meat from here, you've been buying air."

Just then, Dorignac burst into the crowd with a Jefferson Parish Sheriff's Office deputy and some gray suit who Blackie assumed was his attorney.

Before the deputy could open his mouth, Blackie handed him a copy of the law and said, "The state police are on the way," sarcastically adding, "you do know this is part of the state of Louisiana. And whatever you had in mind, our jurisdiction supersedes yours."

Just then, Woody arrived with the paper. Blackie said, "roll it across the meat counter, and stamp it condemned, and mark it with tape."

"DO SOMETHING!" Dorignac sputtered to the gray suit.

Gray suit, reading the law in his hand, kind of shrugged and mumbled something. Dorignac then turned to the deputy, who also shrugged. *Hell*, Blackie thought, *maybe we can make a new dance. Two shruggers, the fat man sputtering, and the customer's murmuring for a background. Maybe I'll get a gold record.* Blackie laughed at the thought, as Dorignac, gray suit, and deputy headed back toward the front of the store. Blackie thought, *shit I'm on a roll. I might as well get rid of all his business.* Speaking loud enough for everyone to hear, he said, "Start cutting open those soap boxes, like Tide and all that other soap, check the Corn Flakes and the cereal; he's probably cheating on everything in here. They're probably paying for five bananas and only getting three."

By now, half-filled shopping carts were being abandoned all over the store as customers filed out.

Woody whispered in Blackie's ear, "You really wanna cut the soap boxes open? We can, but that would be the product supplier that was guilty, not Dorignac; they come sealed."

"Nahhh, I was just trying to scare everybody off."

"Hell, you did that."

"Get Ronnie and your shit. Let's go to lunch."

As they exited the store, some ditzy blonde in a low-cut top with a decent looking rack was getting out of a Channel 4 T.V. car, trying to figure out who to talk to. Finally, seeing Blackie strolling along like John Wayne, she figured he must know something.

"You wanna tell me what's going on here, Sir?"

"Yes, ma'am, the Commissioner had a tip that Dorignac's that's D-O-R-I-G-N-A-C-'-S Super Market had been selling their customers air. In another words, when you paid $4.89 for a pound of steak, you weren't getting a full pound, and Dorignac, 'cause he's got a little money, and he knows a couple politicians by their first name, thought he could bully me into turning my head the other way."

She said, "I bet it's hard to get your head turned the other way."

"Not for you, darlin'. I'd turn all the way around for you."

She smiled and added, "Can you tell us how much money is involved?"

"I spoke to a C.P.A. this morning, and I'm sure when the Commissioner gets the report, he'll be holding a press conference. In the meantime, let me say this to the customers of Louisiana. I'll paraphrase the greatest President to ever serve the United States, John F. Kennedy, 'The torch has been passed to a new administration, tempered by crooked politicians, disciplined by smoke-filled back room deals,' and the new Commissioner will not let us shrink from our responsibility or allow the people of Louisiana to be cheated or taken advantage of any longer. Any other comments will have to come from the Commissioner himself. Thank you, ma'am." As Blackie and his men walked away from the reporters, he thought to himself, *Jesus, will the public shit when they find out this asshole's a bigger crook than Dorignac. Oh well, I'm hungry.*

"C'mon ya'll, let's go eat."

Woody asked, "Should we take both cars?"

"No, man, ya'll ride with me."

As they turned onto Veterans Boulevard, Blackie decided to go to Bud's Broiler in Kenner. They'd have a better chance to be left alone to enjoy their lunch there.

Woody said, "Wow, this new guy must really be straight if he'd let you jump on someone as big as Dorignac."

Blackie just looked out to the driver's window and rolled his eyes. Ronnie, still looking in shock, didn't say anything.

As they crossed David Drive just a few blocks from Bud's Broiler, the radio crackled and the dispatch said, "LAD 4 please give your office a 10-21."

"10-4," Blackie answered.

When they pulled into the Bud's Broiler parking lot, Blackie dialed the payphone as Woody and Ronnie went inside. Paula was on the switchboard. Blackie guessed that everybody else was at lunch.

She said, "The Commissioner is looking for you."

"Here I am."

"Hold on, I'll ring him."

The phone rang twice and the Commissioner boomed, "This is the Commissioner."

"Yeah, you lookin' for me?"

"Who is this?"

Jesus, you know he knows my voice. "Dave Steece."

"Oh, yeah, what happened in New Orleans? I've had about ten phone calls from Legislators, the Sheriff, the District Attorney, reporters, everybody."

"You told me to rattle Dorignac's cage. I rattled it."

The Commissioner hung on the phone for a few seconds not saying anything, but Blackie thought to himself, *I guess he's trying to figure out what rattle means.*

Blackie broke the silence. "I'm about to have lunch with the men. Jim said he wanted a report when I was finished, and I'm sure you'll want to sit in on that, so I'll give you all the details in a few hours."

"Oh yeah, right, that's a good idea."

"Can you run Jim down for me, tell him I'll be there around three or three-thirty. I don't think I'd talk to the press if I were you, until you have all the facts in front of you."

"Good idea, I'll see you then."

Blackie went into Bud's, ordered two #5's (that's a half pound patty, a ton of chili and cheese, on a bun that takes two hands to hold) and the biggest shake they had.

As he headed for the bathroom to wash his hands, he called out to Woody, "Don't pay these people, it's on me."

During lunch, Blackie asked Woody, "Is there any way to just look at a scale from a distance and have an idea of what it's doing?"

Woody laughed. "Maybe, if you're Superman and have X-ray vision; otherwise, you have to check it to find out."

"How long does it take for them to change it from good to bad?"

"Just a minute or two. You just have to make a couple of adjustments."

"So, if they had a spotter by the front door, before we got to the meat department, they'd have it set back."

"Yeah, but it wouldn't calibrate. They could take it from calibration to short-weighing with a wrench in just a minute or two. And they could turn it back close to calibration, but not calibrated. That would take ten minutes or so, and we'd be at the scale before then."

"But it'd be close?"

"Yeah, but you'd know it'd been screwed with."

As they left the restaurant, Blackie told Woody, "You and Ronnie go back over to Dorignac's and mark out all the prices on the meat in the front counter. Fairbanks/Morris is probably there right now, fixing the scales. As soon as they're certified again and you've picked up all the meat that was out there short weighed, you can let 'em start putting newly weighed meat back out on the counters. I'm going to go turn my report in; try to handle it without me having to come back."

"We'll handle it," Woody said. "Don't worry, boss."

Chapter 17

Blackie took the split off I-10 to I-110. He hoped Jim would be there when he arrived.

As Blackie entered the elevator in the capital, he thought, *man, musta been a fire, no one's left on a Friday afternoon.* Instead of the usual bustling lobby, Vicki was reading a book, and the switchboard was silent.

"Whaddaya readin' about darlin'? Marilyn Chambers?"

Vicki smiled and looked up. "Who's that?" she asked.

"You know, the world famous porno star. 'Cause I do training free; you won't have to buy the book."

"You're bad. They're waiting for you in the conference room."

"There you go again. You shouldn't say things like that. I might be great; I might be a dud. As soon as your curiosity's piqued, you'll find out, huh?" he said as he walked into the conference room without knocking.

The Commissioner sat at the head of the table Jim at his right, with lots of empty chairs.

Blackie thought about sitting at the other end of table and decided that would be like a second head, and he'd want to be first, so he walked up and sat down across from Jim.

"Man, I'm dyin' of thirst. Can somebody get me a Tab?"

Jim dialed the phone without comment, looked at the Commissioner and asked, "You want something?"

"I'll take a Coke."

Jim spoke into the receiver and made the order. Then he looked up. "Anything else?"

"Yeah," Blackie said, "a couple bags of peanuts and a glass of ice."

When Jim hung up he asked, "How'd it go?"

"I shook his cage real hard. I know it'll be on Channel Four's evenin' news; maybe it'll be on the other stations too."

"Tell us about it."

"The first prepackaging scale was off three-hundredths and the other five were off one-hundredth. All the meat on the counters was short.

The men have boxed it up and marked it *condemned* and stored it in the freezers there. If I read the law right, we don't have to let them repackage it. We can confiscate it, can't we?"

"We need a written opinion from the Attorney General's office," Jim said, "but that's the way I interpret the law also."

"If that is the law," Blackie said, "I want to send this stuff to Angola or St. Gabriel, which will make us friends with the taxpayers by cutting down the taxpayers' cost of prison food."

"Good idea," Jim said, while the Commissioner looked out the window, probably trying to figure out how to get it for his own use.

"We had quite a scene with Dorignac and some of his stooges. I did a short interview outside. I told about fifty to a hundred customers he was selling them air. I personally saw five or six half-filled shopping carts that people left and walked out. Dorignac acted like he had never heard of the law I gave him, and I'm sure there's never been an inspection there for the many years he's been there. I bet one thing, the next time you call on him, he'll have time to see you. In fact, I'll bet anything, he'll be calling you; you won't have to call him."

Jim said, "Sounds like you did a good job. What's your next plan?"

"Well, we need to get rid of the director and move me up to that job, because I gotta get control of all the inspectors; you know they're out there picking their noses and not doing their jobs."

"Yeah," Jim said, "but the Commissioner will probably have a better plan for you as soon as you can prove this wasn't just a one-night stand."

"Not a problem. I'm going home to feed my girls, have a fun weekend. I suggest ya'll take your phones off the hook. 'Cause startin' Monday, I'm gonna kick some ass, and I'm gonna kick it hard enough to get out of that two-by-four office out on Florida Boulevard and get me a big fancy office with some foxes up here on the eighth floor like you big shots."

The Commissioner finally spoke. "You do a good job, I won't forget you."

Blackie thought to himself, *you're right, I'll do a good job, but you'll wish you could forget me when I'm finished.* He picked up his last bag of peanuts and Tab and headed for the door.

Blackie looked at his watch as he turned on I-12 East and slammed the accelerator to the floor, wondering if he could set a record for getting home to his girls. Twenty-nine minutes later, he turned down the rolling driveway, and watched his little angels coming out of the playhouse, jumping for joy at their father's return. Dinner, baths, and much needed sleep came none too soon; as Blackie drifted away, the numbers on his clock read 11:10 p.m. He hoped he'd dream about the most beautiful redhead in the world, Susan Hayward...

Sunday night after a lazy day of playing in the yard, realizing he'd had his police radio and answer phone turned off all weekend, he decided to call Jim Knotts to see if there were any surprises waiting for him tomorrow. Jim answered the phone.

Blackie said "What's going on, dude?"

"You lit them up alright" Jim said. "Commissioner's been calling me all weekend."

"I hope you're cool," Blackie responded, "but is this sonofabitch as dumb as he acts?"

Jim laughed. "Don't worry about nothing. You just keep doin' what you're doin', and you'll be fine. We don't give a fuck about him."

Blackie said, "Aren't you still hangin' in the breeze about that Michot thing?"

"Naw, don't worry about that. I'll be ok."

"Ok," Blackie said, "but I don't look good in stripes, and I'm too old to make little rocks out of big rocks. As far as I'm concerned, this guy couldn't pour piss out of a boot without help."

He said, "Yeah, but I can handle him...We went to college together and actually played basketball together."

"Ok, man, I'm dependin' on you."

"Think of a plan you can present Monday," Jim said. "We'll meet for breakfast before we go to the Capitol. Tell me what you're going to do. Since he's so paranoid, I'll make him think it's my idea."

"Ok, where?"

"How about Rick's on Airline Highway?"

"Ok, that's cool." Blackie hung up the phone, thinking, *I hope Jim ain't too dirty, 'cause I like him and it would make a hell of a splash if they went down together.*

Blackie went and tucked his girls in, flopped down on the bed, thinking, *oh, what a week.*

CHAPTER 18

Blackie's alarm went off at 5:30 a.m.; he rolled out of bed thinking, *damn, Monday morning,* feeling more tired after the weekend of being momma and daddy to the girls. *I need another weekend off just to catch up, but by then these angels would wear me out anyhow.*

As he started breakfast, he thought, *how the hell can I accomplish all this shit and I can't find a decent woman to help me with these babies?* His train of thought was broken immediately by Alley running, screaming through the house.

"Lu squirted toothpaste on me!"

This blended with Rae's, "I don't want nuttin' to eat, Daddy."

"Lu, stop it, Al, quit running. You gotta eat, baby. If you don't start eating without me yelling at you, I'm going to start feeding you ten eggs every morning." Blackie said this as he calmed Alley down and sent Lu to clean up the toothpaste.

After the girls were distributed at school, he turned the Plymouth west onto I-12, and after negotiating some heavy traffic on I-110 in Baton Rouge, he turned into Rick's Pancake House on Airline Highway. He saw Jim's Pontiac already there. Walking inside, he realized he'd be at the table in about thirty seconds and would have to put the plan together before he got there.

Jim stood up and shook Blackie's hand. "You doin' ok?"

"Yeah, but I have to take enough time off to get these girls situated."

"That's ok," Jim said. "Give me the plan and I'll cover for you."

Blackie said, "Ok, this is what I want to do. I want to get four or five inspectors we can trust and go out in, say, Terrebonne Parrish and hit a couple of stores, and then jump to Rapides and Ouachita, Calcasieu; just jump around so nobody will know where I'll be next."

"That sounds like a good idea—when will you have it ready?"

"Oh, I should have it together by the end of the week," Blackie said, thinking to himself, *shit I have no idea how long it'll take.*

Jim said, "I got a new title. I'm the Executive Assistant now. When the press wants a comment, just refer them to me. That way, he can't fuck it up."

"Oh, are you sure? I bet he can," Blackie said, and they both laughed.

Jim picked up the ticket for breakfast. "I'll meet you at the Capitol and see if we can calm him down."

Blackie called Woody on the radio and told him to meet him in the parking lot at the Capitol.

He had to decide how he was going to get this done with the Commissioner initiating the shakedowns; otherwise, it would just be a form of entrapment.

When the elevator opened on the eighth floor, Blackie grabbed his chest, feigning pain, and staggered toward Vicki's switchboard.

"Chest pains, chest pains, Vicki. I need mouth-to-mouth, quick."

Vicki looked up smiling. "You're just being silly."

Blackie pretended to be in total shock. "Me? Being silly? You're embarrassing me. How can you say such a thing, when you know it's just because I'm in love with you?"

Vicki said, "Go on; I'll send Jan in with a cup of coffee. She'll calm you down."

"I'm going, but I'm heartbroken."

"Yeah, right, a heartbreaker would be more like it."

"Oh, you've wounded me again," he said, as he walked into Jeannie's office.

Jeannie looked up and mouthed the words, "He's in."

"So?" Blackie said, arrogantly.

She whispered something unintelligible, so Blackie leaned down close to her and she said, "The press has been calling him all weekend. What did you do in New Orleans?"

"Just enforced the law. Why? Is there a problem with that?"

"No, but why is the press calling?"

"'Cause Dorignac's been cheating the public, and I told the reporters, and I guess his feelings got hurt."

"Who's Dorignac?"

"JEANNIE, a supermarket that was short weighing the customers, okay?"

"I guess I don't understand."

"You don't have to darlin', you can type."

Jeannie smiled, just as the Commissioner opened his door and said, "Bring me some coffee." Seeing Blackie he said, "Oh you're here? C'mere."

Blackie strolled into the Commissioner's office and sat down in front of his desk. The Commissioner said, "Jim's on his way from Ringgold, and should be here soon."

Blackie just shrugged nonchalantly, as Jeannie came in with the Commissioner's coffee. She asked Blackie if he wanted a cup.

Blackie's usual cocky response was, "What's my choices?"

The Commissioner looked at Blackie with disbelief, as she said, "Water."

Grinning, Blackie said, "Guess I'll take coffee, then, but it's your loss."

The Commissioner waved her off, and as she closed the door, he said, "Boy, *we* got their attention in New Orleans."

Blackie thought, *what do you mean,* we? *Ya gotta turd in your pocket? You couldn't get their attention if you hung yourself from a Canal Street red light.*

The Commissioner asked, "Think I should go ask him for a campaign contribution now?"

Blackie thought, *shit, this guy's gonna hang himself without any effort from me,* but he said, "I don't know much about the money thing. I'll just enforce the law. You'll have to do the money thing." Then he thought to himself, *I can't tell him to break the law, or how to break the law, and then charge him with the crimes.*

The Commissioner looked back at him with that stupid stare. Just then, Jim Knotts walked in and Blackie thought, *damn, saved by the bell,* while standing up. "Boy, am I glad to see you?" he said, thinking, *if you really knew how much.*

Shaking hands with Blackie, Jim said, "You did good and made the Sunday paper in Shreveport. Do you have a plan B ready?"

Blackie said, "Yeah, I need more control of that division, but I think Ronnie will be okay, Woody's definitely okay, and I know enough about it now so that I can take a couple inspectors that know how to calibrate scales and put one man with Woody and one man with Ronnie and hit three stores at one time. That way, if they're communicating, they won't have time to call each other. I'm sure most of 'em are doing this on purpose and some by accident, but the bottom line is, nobody from this office has enforced the law; the stores have had nobody from

Fairbanks/Morris calibrate the scales in a long time, so none of the supermarkets have paid that much attention if they were wrong. And if they wanted to cheat, there was no threat of getting caught. I think we hit a few more stores in New Orleans on Tuesday, say Monroe Wednesday, Lake Charles Thursday, and Baton Rouge Friday. If we hit three stores in the morning and three in the afternoon in each of these towns this week, the press will eat it up, the public will love it, and everybody with a scale in his store, who hasn't had it checked in a couple of years, will be pissing his pants."

Blackie had been looking at the Commissioner and, when he looked back to Jim, he was grinning from ear to ear.

"Go get 'em, tiger," Jim said.

"I need some stroke," Blackie said. "I don't need to be messing with this Holmes Johnson every day. You need to send a memo over there today. Tell him he's the director, he's in charge of the division, and he runs things from his office. I'm the honcho out there in the hot sun doing things on the street, where he don't wanna be anyhow. That way, he won't think we're trying to usurp his authority."

Jim said, "That's a good idea. I'll have Jeannie type a memo over the Commissioner's signature, and I'll deliver it in person, and I'll bullshit him and tell him how you're gonna take a lot of the workload off of him and crap like that."

The Commissioner, with zero input to match his I.Q., nodded his agreement and pushed the buzzer for Jeannie to come in.

As soon as she walked through the door, Blackie said, "It's a good thing you're beautiful. You forgot my coffee."

"Oh, I'm sorry. The phone's been ringing," she said, as she passed a handful of messages to the Commissioner. "These are mostly newspaper and T.V. reporters. There's a couple from radio. They all wanna talk to you about the Channel 4 story that came out of New Orleans Friday."

Before the Commissioner could speak, Jim said, "Take this memo from the Commissioner to Holmes Johnson."

"Excuse me. I'm goin' to the head and to get a cup of coffee," Blackie said, not wanting to hear the exact wording of the memo.

When Blackie came back from the head, he stopped at the coffee machine in the lobby, and after getting his coffee, propped his arm on the console and leered at Vicki.

Vicki smiled. "Boy, the phone hasn't stopped ringing this morning. You must have stirred up a hornet's nest down there Friday."

Before he could answer, Jeannie's door opened, and she said, "They're looking for you."

Blackie asked, *"They're?"* hoping to himself that it was Susan Hayward and Kim Novak, as he walked through Jeannie's office to the Commissioner. Jim was standing with his briefcase in his hand. "I'm getting ready to go over to Johnson's right now. Gimme about thirty minutes before you go over there and blow his mind for about the fiftieth time."

Blackie grinned. "Uh uh, only the fourth time, not the fiftieth." He looked at the Commissioner whose eyes were still on blank.

"I'm gonna meet Woody and Ronnie for lunch to ask them about which inspectors I should use. That should give you plenty of time to calm Johnson down, shouldn't it? I should be there around one o'clock."

"Yeah, that should be perfect," Jim said, as they both walked into Jeannie's office. Blackie plopped down into a chair, and Jim continued into the lobby and toward the elevator.

Blackie told Jeannie, "Call State Police Troop A and tell them to raise LAD 14 and LAD 18, and tell them to give me a 10-21 at this office.

"More action, huh?" Jeannie asked, as she reached for the phone.

"You bet," Blackie said, as he picked up the *Morning Advocate* and started to read it.

After about ten minutes, the phone rang. When Jeannie answered, she said, "You wanna pick up line three? It's Woody."

Blackie picked up the phone. "Yeah?"

A couple minutes later he said, "Jeannie, when Ronnie calls, if he can, make it to the Capitol House Hotel before one. If not, tell him to call me on the radio after one, and I'll set up a different place to meet him. I'm going to the Capitol House Hotel dining room to meet Woody. You can call me there if you need me. If anybody else calls, tell them I died."

"Ronnie's got to meet you some place today, right?" Jeannie asked.

"Right."

"You don't want me to really tell people you died, do you?"

"I don't care what you tell them, darlin'. I just don't wanna talk to anybody but you, my girls, and Ronnie. Okay?"

"Okay, big boy. See you later."

"See ya," Blackie said, as he strode to the elevator; he blew a kiss to Vicki as he walked by.

As Blackie got off of the elevator on the ground floor, he saw Eddie D. coming toward him. He stopped and waited as Eddie D. walked up to him. "Goddamn, Blackie, you got Dorignac really pissed off. He called me up in the middle of the night."

"Hey, man, this is about business. Me and Jim and the Commissioner went in to see him, and he had one of his flunkies basically tell us to go fuck ourselves and threw us out. He's been selling about, according to Sam Montalbano's figures on how he was weighing, 52,000 pounds of air a year, at a cost to the public of about $4.00 to $6.00 a pound. I'm sure everybody would like to make $300,000.00 a year sellin' air."

Eddie sighed and said, "He's a big supporter of mine."

"Good, then you yank his chain and tell him to get it right."

"I guess. I'll see."

"Don't *see*, get it done."

As they parted, Blackie hollered over his shoulder, "You ain't thinking' about takin' away my office key are you?"

Eddie just waved back at him.

Chapter 19

As Blackie pulled into the Capitol House parking garage he saw Lewis Johnson's blue Cadillac, meaning that he must be up from New Orleans checking on his hotel. Blackie thought maybe he could hustle a comp lunch.

As Blackie walked into the dining room, he saw the group sitting at the table: Lewis, Ed McGraw, AKA, Mr. Magoo, and Billy Bosworth. Magoo was a big builder, who was involved in everything slightly bent. Billy owned the Governor House, the Bourbon Orleans, Dauphine Orleans Hotels, and The Manhattan Properties, which consisted of over a thousand apartments on the West Bank Expressway and Manhattan Boulevard. His first thought was to wonder what was going on.

Blackie walked his most arrogant walk toward them until one of them noticed and motioned him over.

Acting like he'd just noticed them, he said, "Wow, what's this, a meeting of the Boss of Bosses?" knowing that all three had egos that would float the Titanic.

Lewie said, "Sit down. We need to talk to you."

"Hey, man, I'm an important crop cop now, I can't be stoppin' and talkin' to ya'll. I'm meeting one of my inspectors."

Magoo said, "Come on, Blackie, sit down."

"Well," Blackie said, "maybe you can buy my lunch if this is a bullshit session, if my employee can sit wit us, because if he can't, I'll have to buy his lunch, which will cost you twice as much."

"We need to talk to you about some business. He can't sit with us," Billy said.

"I'm serious, I'm really workin'," Blackie said. "Look, I'll be in New Orleans in a day or two. Can we talk then?" He thought to himself, *I gotta be down there with the Commissioner and Jim to meet the 'Little Man' on Thursday night.*

Lewie said, "When?"

"How about Thursday afternoon about one at the Governor House?

Magoo said, "That'll work. Here's a double sawbuck. Buy your man lunch."

"Whatta we supposed to eat, hamburgers?"

"Aw shit, Blackie," Magoo said and gave him another double.

Blackie took the second double and walked away from the table. He saw Woody coming in the door and headed for a table by the window. As the two men shook hands, Blackie asked Woody if he'd heard from Ronnie.   Woody said, "Yeah, I just heard him go 10-97 in the parking garage as I was getting out of my unit." The two men exchanged small talk until Ronnie entered the dining room and came over to their table.

The three men exchanged greetings. After ordering, Blackie said to Ronnie, "I don't want ya to take this wrong. I'm not saying you're not the most loyal dude on earth, but in my world, loyalty is earned, not anointed from heaven. We did Ok with Dorignac's, but next week, we're gonna kick ass and take names all over the State. Woody's gonna be my In-Field Supervisor, in charge of everybody. Anybody got a problem with my delegation of authority, or not responding to it, will be lookin' for a new job. I'm thinking you can earn your bones and move up. Are you interested in that or just passin' your time away?"

"I don't have a problem with that," Ronnie said. "I'm just trying to feel my way with all these changes. There's no question you're the boss. You obviously know what you're doin' and, hey, I need a job; plus, I got this one, I might as well keep it."

"Ok, here's what we're gonna' do., I'm gonna devise a plan and hop scotch all over the state and bust everybody who's been cheatin' the public. Some days I'll be with ya and some days I won't. When I'm not, I'll call Woody right before it's time to go and tell 'em where to go, and he'll tell ya'll."

Right then, the food arrived. Blackie said, "This afternoon, after we're through eatin', ya'll go out to the Weights and Measures office, and go over our inspector list to decide who you're gonna use. I would say you need between maybe ten and twelve, maybe fourteen. Enough you can hit eight or nine major stores in a city like Shreveport, which means you're gonna have to have eight or nine good people that won't be intimidated by owners, so, when you're figurin' this out, put a weaker one with a strong one. A real big store, ya'll might want to both be there. You two know exactly how to handle yourselves from what I've showed ya, plus you'll have copies of the law with ya. I'll notify the State Police in every area where I send you. Anybody gives you any shit, call them. They'll be expectin' your call."

With that, the three ate, talking about women, politics, and football. When they finished, they shook hands.

As they walked to the parking garage, he told them, "Don't diddle around. Get your ass to the office 'cause I'll be in Baton Rouge for another hour. If Holmes Johnson or grandma gives you any problem, I want to be available to come out there and straighten the shit out. You know why you're goin' to the office? Because you have access to the Centrex line to call all over the State."

With that, the three men parted company. As Blackie drove out of the garage, he noticed Johnson's caddy was gone, but he didn't remember seeing him leave the dining room. Hmmm…Guess he was gettin' old. He'd have to pay better attention.

Blackie piddled around Baton Rouge for a while, making sure the men didn't have any trouble, then headed East toward his girls.

As he turned off I-12 onto Highway 51, his radio crackled with LAD 14. Woody said, "We pretty much have a list of who we want to use. Do you want us to start calling 'em now?"

"Naw, it's after three o'clock. Take the rest of the day off." He added, "ya'll stay there in town and start callin' in the mornin'. Kinda section the State off. Do about a third Tuesday, a third Wednesday, and a third Thursday, rest up Friday. I'll talk to ya over the weekend to tell ya where to have everybody meet Monday morning. "When I talk to ya, and get the list of names, give me an approximate driving time from their residence to Baton Rouge."

With Woody's 10-4, Blackie hung up his radio mike and turned into his driveway, excited about the fact that he'd get to see what his girls looked like in daylight today, thinking, more balancing angels and assholes. He was going to have to do something about a woman or a caretaker for his girls, and he was going to have to do it soon. *Well, shit. It's too bad Rommel can't speak English and drive a car. Hey man!* Thinking to himself, Sandy Zanca was still Sandy Steece wasn't she? Hmmm.

He had made a deal with her on a sort of a marriage thing. She'd been his nurse and probably saved his life when he had been in a coma at Southern Baptist in New Orleans years ago. Because his brainwave was flat, dumb-ass Dr. Ferris, the Neurologist, wanted to unplug him. Sandy, the only licensed EEG tech at the time, argued "if there's sweat there's life." There was sweat showing at the bottom of the graph. Sure enough, a few days later, he woke up. It scared the shit out of her when he woke up, paid her back by having her share several dinners with him in the hospital catered by Masson's Restaurant Francais, one of the then top five-star restaurants in the city of New Orleans. Then, after he got out of the hospital, had a couple dates with her and took her to Masson's in person. Months later, he got in a pissing contest with Liz, which ended up in divorce court in a custody battle. After months of fighting in court, Harry R. Cabral, Jr., Blackie's attorney, informed him one Friday about 3:00 p.m., that because of the age of the children, Rae-Rae, nine months, Alisha, two and a half, Lu, six and a half, and Theresa only twelve, the court didn't care how many maids or governesses were in the house, they wanted a wife in the house. Harry wanted Blackie to have one by Monday when they went to court.

He had got his little black book out and started calling some of his regulars—Carol, Elaine Rita—who were either out of town or didn't answer. The next one, because they were alphabetized by first names, was Sandy and the first one he got on the phone. Blackie asked, "how would you like to marry me?"

She said, "That's not nice to play with people's feelings. You know anyone would love to have you."

He said, "Yeah, if I'm so great, how come Liz and I got divorced?"

Sandy came back with, "In my opinion it would be Liz's loss."

"Well, that proves that I'm serious if that's how you think, doesn't it?"

She said, "Well then, why me?"

He said, "A lot of reasons You know I really got to know ya when you came back to the hospital every night after you got off duty an sat an' talked all those weeks. I know you worry about your kid's education, your mother and father's financial position, and Grandma Dixon, your mom's mother, who's up in age, plus I need a mother in my house for my girls, and you get along with them good. You're good lookin', got a nice body, you can cook, and you act like you like me sexually."

She said, "Slow down. Yes, to most of that, or all of that, I guess, but is that a good reason to get married?"

"Let me be very honest with you, Sandy. I believe if two people are physically attracted, like some of the same things, and actually work toward the rest, it will turn into love. That "I love you" bullshit that gets you into bed on the second date, gets you pregnant, and causes a

wedding, has much less of a chance of succeeding than we do. That's what happened to your first marriage, wasn't it? You got pregnant and had to get married?"

She said, "Yeah, it makes sense. When would you want to do this?"

"Hell, as soon as we can. I'll come pick you up and we'll go to Billy Zeller's to pick out a ring."

She said, "Oooh, ok...I guess...so..."

Blackie immediately called John Mamoulides, gave him the story, asked him to call Judge Doug Allen to get him ready to perform the ceremony, and have him call Bill Justice, Clerk of Court, because they needed a license in the middle of the night. After John and Doug picked up the license, they needed to meet at his house, aka "The Fort" on Haring Court. Blackie called Harry R. Cabral, Jr., who was out of town. Then called George Scariano, told him to draw up a marriage contract guaranteeing Sandy's children's education, reasonable help for her mother and father, and that he'd pay for the funerals of all three: her mother, her father, and Grandma Dixon. He picked up Sandy, took her to Billy Zeller's. While Billy was sizing her ring, Blackie called Mr. Joe at D'Avanti's Fashions, one of the better suit and dressmakers in the entire South, told him she needed a dress good enough to wear to an informal wedding, and she needed it today, that he was on his way. Mr. Joe had his women ready to measure her, and sew it up as soon as they got there. He called Finnin's Florist, told them to make her a bouquet, told Ken to bring it home with him and he'd pick it up at his house. An hour and a half later, they left with her dress. On the way back to Billy's, Sandy said, "You know, I never have asked you what you do for a living, but I'm a little curious. The best dress store in New Orleans stopped everything to make me a dress. It's about six-thirty on Friday, the jeweler who's been closed for two hours, is waiting for us to pick up a ring, and now the florist is bringing a bouquet home for me. All these places are closed. Don't they close for you too? And what kind of work do you do? I was very curious that Masson's catered your food at the hospital, that you have a private table at the restaurant. Now you tell me that the Court House opened up to issue a license. The District Attorney, John Mamoulides, and Judge Doug Allen are going to be at your house to witness and perform the ceremony."

He grinned at her. "You like gold?"

She said, "Why?"

"Because two black and reds wouldn't go together and I only have one car," he said, thinking to himself, I don't want the girls riding around in another black and red Cadillac that could be mistaken by one of my enemies. *"You're obviously gonna need a car to drive the girls around." He called Marshal Brothers Lincoln dealership from Billy's office, told them he needed a gold four-door Town Car and to bring it to the house as soon as possible. Sandy stood there in total shock. By the time they got to the house with the bouquet, John, Judge Allen, Big Paul and his wife Bonnie, his sister Patsy, and her husband Ed, Zap and his wife, Patsy, were waiting. His sister Patsy took Sandy in the bedroom to help her dress, which is where she was when George Scariano arrived with the marriage contract. Blackie tapped on the bedroom door. When Patsy came to the door, he said, "Soften her up on this marriage contract thing." She nodded, went back inside the bedroom. By the time they finished dressing and came out, the Lincoln had arrived. Thinking it might add a nice touch, they all walked her down that long red carpeted hallway to the gate. He handed her the keys saying, "This will be your transportation as long as we're married."*

She responded "WOW! This is beautiful. But I'm not looking at this as a marriage of convenience. I plan on staying married to you forever. This car is going to wear out before then."

"Then darlin', we'll just get a new one."

"One last thing before we tie the knot. Let's go back into the house and get this marriage contract signed." About that time, her long time friend, Kathy Yenni, Mayor Joe Yenni's niece, arrived. She was going to be the Maid of Honor. When they got to the kitchen he handed her the marriage contract, saying, "I hope this meets your approval. It's pretty standard except that it guarantees your kid's education, reasonable help for your parents, and the family funerals you've been worried about. Those are not standard things. If the marriage lasts forever you can steal enough off your grocery money to live forever. If it doesn't, I guess you'll have to trust I'll be fair in a divorce."

"What exactly does this mean?" Sandy asked.

"Well, it means that in the event we get a divorce, anything you brought with you, stays with you, plus any gifts, personal clothes, etc. But what I had before you came stays with me." She signed it and a few minutes later they were married. Monday, when they went to Court, she had him convinced that she'd been in the girls' lives much longer than she had, but that's what it was all about.

It had worked pretty good for a couple of years, but Blackie got tired of her and had eased her out, going back to the maid thing, which had ended when they moved to this secluded estate in the country.

He no longer needed maids. He was with his girls all the time until this case. He hadn't needed anyone for a long time, but guessed he'd have to call Sandy to get these girls handled until he got through with this case. Hell, he'd call Zap right now, have him find her, and find out what she was doing. After dinner, homework, and playtime, Blackie decided he'd go to his sister Patsy's in the morning.

Chapter 20

After dropping the girls off at school, Blackie headed down I-55 to get his second breakfast with his sister Patsy in LaPlace. While Patsy was cooking his eggs, Blackie called Zap to see if he'd tracked down Sandy. Zap said that she was at Turo Infirmary running the EEG Department, that he'd stopped by to see her and the first thing out of her mouth was "Blackie must need something or he wouldn't be sending you by here."

Blackie said, "Whatcha tell her?"

"I told her, I could bullshit you and lie, but we always liked you, so I'll tell you up front. He told me to find you a couple a days ago but he didn't say why. I just got around to it because he didn't say it was an emergency, but you know that's how it works. He wants somethin', just like when your Grandma Dixon died a few months ago, you called me. I told her I told you and I know you took care of the funeral. She kinda laughed and told me you even sent flowers. I got her current phone number. I already checked it out and got her address. It's an apartment on Lake Avenue, right inside the Parish on the Seventeenth Street Canal.

Blackie thanked Zap and went back to his breakfast with Patsy.

After leaving Rae and begging Patsy to pick up the girls after school, he took the Plymouth flying down I-10 to the Bonnabel exit.

As he pulled up in front of Sandy's apartment, he hoped she was home from work, noticing it was only a little after two. He knocked on the door. With no answer, he got back in the car and drove the six blocks to Harry Cabral's office, where he knew he could easily use up enough time visiting for her to get home from work.

As he thought about Harry and his wife Barbara, it reminded him how she had once been close to Jim Garrison, the then New Orleans District Attorney, who had become world famous for his investigation of the President John F. Kennedy assassination. Blackie's mind always drifted to his long-time friend Max Gonzales, who had been one of Jim Garrison's investigators during that era. Max had lived just a few blocks from Blackie's Haring Court home on Green Acres Road. He thought of the evening that Max came by Blackie's home. In retrospect, Max had acted a little strange. It had been about four in the afternoon, and Blackie had been out in the street refereeing the bicycle races between a dozen or so neighborhood kids, which was pretty standard for Blackie. When Max arrived, Blackie asked him how the Kennedy investigation was going. He said, "Ok I guess," and said to Blackie, "Don't you know David Ferrie?"

Blackie said, "Yeah, he's some kind of fruitcake pilot. He used to fly Joe Nose around. I met him through the Nose, why?"

"Well, nothing really; we're investigating him and that other queer Clay Shaw.

Blackie said, "Isn't Clay Shaw some big wheel with the Trademark?"

Max said, "Yeah, but he might have been paying somebody something with this deal; we don't know."

"What are you doin now?"

"I'm getting ready to go over to Slidell."

Blackie said, "You sure picked a shitty time. There's traffic all over the place this time of day."

Max said, "Yeah, maybe so, but I'm going to fly. I'm going out to the airport right now."

"You're going to fly twenty miles? Jesus, why would you do that?"

After a few more words, Max left. Blackie never got over the fact that Max and the plane disappeared. They never found the plane or the pilot. A couple of days after it had been reported missing, Blackie went over to see Earlene, Max's wife, to see if he could do anything for her. He was surprised to find her working out in the yard, pretty much like nothing had happened, which was really odd because they had been very, very close and had socialized many times with Blackie and his wife. A few weeks after that, Earlene disappeared, just up and moved someplace in South America, which didn't seem to surprise anyone in the DA's office, but it did Blackie. Blackie decided, someday, he'd go to South America and find out where that sonofabitch went and why.

**LAST KNOWN PHOTO OF MAX AND EARLINE GONZALES (ON RIGHT)
AND TWO OF THEIR FRIENDS TAKEN AT A PARTY AT BLACKIE'S HOME AT
5024 HARING COURT, METAIRIE, LA A FEW DAYS BEFORE HE DISAPPEARED**

Blackie strolled into Cabral's office and learned that Harry wasn't back from Court. He went back to the conference room, where there was always plenty of goodies to eat, and watched TV until 4:00.

As Blackie was driving back up to Sandy's apartment, he caught up to this cute little nurse's uniform bouncing along Lake Avenue, pulled up and called, "Taxi!"

Sandy rolled her eyes, grinned, and asked, "Where's the rest of your line? 'Ass, gas, or cash, nobody rides for free?'"

"I'm being charitable today, plus I need to try and be serious with you."

Sandy was grinning as she got in the car. "Ok, what do you need?"

"Oh come on, I'm starving. Let's go eat dinner and talk there."

Sandy rolled her eyes again and said, "Food? Isn't this the way this started, Masson's dinners catered at the hospital?"

"You mean I have to get hurt, go into a coma, and have you revive me to get you to eat? Can't we skip all that? You already know I need ya—why can't we just go eat?"

"Aw, I was only kidding, you know that."

"Hell, you're a woman! Nobody ever knows what they're thinking."

With that, Blackie made a U-turn and headed back to Veterans Memorial Boulevard.

They chatted as they drove along Veterans about family, work, and light general stuff. As they pulled up in front of Sal and Sam's, Sandy grinned and said, "I guess you haven't gotten too far from that angel hair fetish have you?"

Curly Maniscalco greeted them as they entered, asking Blackie, "You want the private back room?"

Blackie grinned mischievously. "Nah, we're gonna eat, not make love," as they were ushered to a quaint little table.

Sandy picked up the menu and, looking through it, exclaimed, "Wow, this must be serious!"

One of regular waitresses walked up. "Ma'am, I already know what Blackie wants. What would you like?"

Sandy said possessively, "We've been together long enough. I eat the same thing he does."

Blackie could read the waitress' mind when she thought, *oh yeah? Where the hell were you last Friday?* as she smiled and turned away.

As Blackie scanned the restaurant again, Sandy asked, "What are you doing in a Plymouth? What happened to the Cadillac?"

"Awww, this is a company car. I'm working for the new Commissioner, and that's one of the problems; I'm traveling all over the state and you know me and din-din with the girls."

"Why are you working for the Commissioner?"

"Awww, ya know, I'm getting old and have to get legit."

Sandy rolled her eyes again and said, "Uh huh."

"No, really," Blackie said. "I really want to settle down and do right."

"Listen, let's not start this out with all lies."

"Well, its not all lies; it's the best I can do. I *am* working for the Commissioner, and it's a regular job. As far as I know, it's supposed to be up front and straight."

"All right, if that's what you're going to tell me."

"Well, it don't take a genius to tell if I travel all over the State. I want someone with the girls who has more of an interest than just feedin' and bathin' them."

"We did this already, remember? It didn't work."

"I know, and it might not now, either, but keep this in mind; I never filed for a divorce did I?" he said, thinking, *she couldn't know I never filed for divorce because I was never gonna get married again.*

Sandy seemed to toy with that thought as her food arrived, remembering how much Blackie hated to talk while he was eating, much like when he watched a movie. After they finished, he asked her if she wanted coffee or a drink.

She declined. "What was it you have in mind?"

"Well, I still got the fort on Haring Court, plus I use an estate of Uncle Rolland's out between Ponchatoula and Hammond, which is pretty nice. Lu and Alley go to school out there. I'm sure you remember the last firefight we had with the Confortos and, even though it's been about a year ago, I just feel more comfortable with them not right here in the City. Maybe later, depending on how this job works out, I may want to move all of us to Baton Rouge, but for now, I believe the estate is the right place for us.

Grinning, she said, "Do I need to run for my life?"

"Nah, I still got all my men around. You know how it works. Anybody fucks with you, they have a problem."

"Yeah, I know, but will you be fucking with me?"

Blackie grinned. "We'll just take it a day at a time."

Tossing her hair, she said, "What about a night at a time, and when do I get my first night?"

Blackie figured he was half-way home, might as well finish the deal. "I really didn't have nothin' to do ta-night, wanna start now?"

She got up and walked around the table and pulled his head to her chest. "You know I've always loved you."

They left Sal and Sam's and headed back to her apartment. As they drove, she asked, "Is this another one of those crash courses, or do I have time to give the hospital notice?"

"Well, I really need ya by Monday, but sooner would be a lot better."

She laughed and said, "Hell, two days won't help my situation about giving notice any better than no notice."

They pulled into her parking place and went upstairs. As they entered her apartment, she turned on her tiptoes. "You need me now for the girls, but I need you now for this, then she kissed him as she took his hand and pulled it between her legs.

Blackie pulled back grinning devilishly. "You know I don't like furry cats—is that thing shaved?"

She smiled and pulled back, lifting her skirt. "I always hoped I'd get another chance, and I knew if I did, you wouldn't wait for me to shave. So I kept this special just for you," she said, as she dropped her skirt to the floor.

Blackie took the edge of her blouse and pulled it over her head. "Oh, you remember I hate bras too, huh?"

"Yeah, but I gotta be honest. At Sal and Sam's I thought I might have a chance to get you in bed tonight so I went into the bathroom and took it off—it's in my purse," she said, as she knelt in front of him and started to undo his pants.

It was after midnight by the time they woke up.

"I'll go in tomorrow morning," Sandy said, "tell the hospital, notify the landlord, and start packing."

"I'll pick you up late the day after tomorrow, Thursday, after some kind of meeting I got that night."

They then drove to the back of Dorignac's Supermarket to get some empty boxes. He thought to himself, *wouldn't Joe Dorignac shit seeing me get these free boxes?* The next stop was K & B Drug Store on Veterans and Martin Berhman. As they pulled into a parking space and Sandy got out of the car to get a roll of box tape, Blackie's *mind wandered back to the 1960s when he had an apartment at J.C. Colletta's right down the street. He had been in the Hallmark Store, a couple of doors down from K&B one evening and saw Little Steve Mariano, not so little anymore. Little Steve had turned into a nice looking 6' 200-pound man, a young soldier in his own right, and Blackie remembered how everyone had such high hopes for his future. Little Steve had been visiting his baby sister, DeLone, a young cashier at K&B who was out in front of the store on her break. DeLone was dating a young white boy named Jimmy Bell, who nobody really liked. While they were standing there, Jimmy Bell rode up on his motorcycle. After some bullshit, Steve got a bug in his ass to ride the motorcycle and, refusing to wear Jimmy's helmet, made a couple of circles around the parking lot showing off. The next time he came around the lot, he cracked down on it, the throttle stuck open and he hit the brick wall at the end of the shopping center at about eighty miles an hour. Blackie was coming out of the Hallmark Store when the motorcycle roared by and, in seconds, hit the wall. He stepped back inside, used the Hallmark phone to call for an ambulance, and then ran down to the scene to see if there was any hope for the rider. By the time he got there, several people were there, including Big Steve's young daughter, screaming, "THAT'S MY BROTHER, THAT'S MY BROTHER." Little Steve, with no helmet, died of massive head injuries.*

When Sandy got back into the car, it brought Blackie back to the moment, and they headed back to her apartment. After depositing her, the boxes, and tape, Blackie turned the Plymouth toward his girls and slammed it to the floor.

He turned into the driveway, trying to figure out what to tell his sister Patsy. He knew she'd be bitching because he was so late. Parked by the house, he rummaged around in the back seat looking for a bag of peanuts or a box of candy, anything for a bribe, but as usual, nothing but empty bags and boxes, wondering while he walked inside why he always ate everything in sight. As he came to the door, he said, now, don't get excited, I could lie and tell you I got a flat tire, ran out of gas, or some other story, but I really was trying to find a permanent way to take care of the girls, and I think I have."

Patsy raised an eyebrow. "I can already figure out your plan, dropping them off with me and running away."

Not a bad plan, Blackie thought, but he said, "I talked to Sandy and she's gonna move back Thursday. We'll see if that's gonna work."

Patsy rolled her eyes again, Blackie kissed her, and she left. Blackie thought, *although this isn't working too bad, the house is clean, no dirty dishes, the girls are sleepin'. All I have to do is warm up the food she left in the refrigerator, feed Rommel and Gretchen, and watch TV.*

BLACKIE'S KIDS

BLACKIE'S FAMILY

BLACKIE'S MANY FACES

MORE FACES OF BLACKIE

BLACKIE THE GANGSTER

MORE GANGSTERS

BLACKIE'S WOMEN

MORE WOMEN

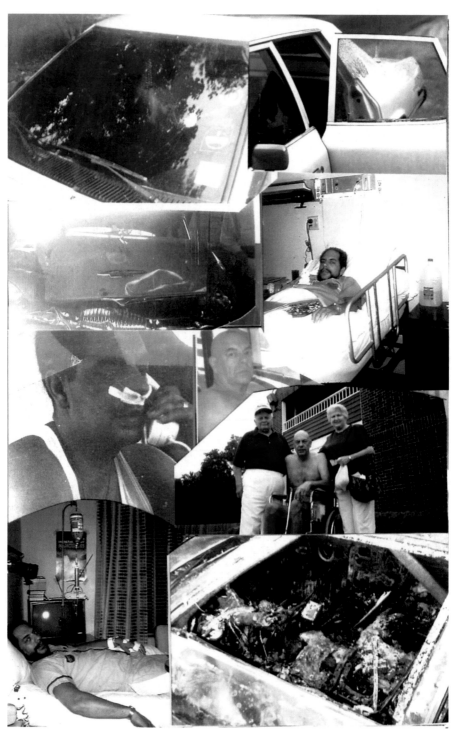

BLACKIE'S NINE LIVES

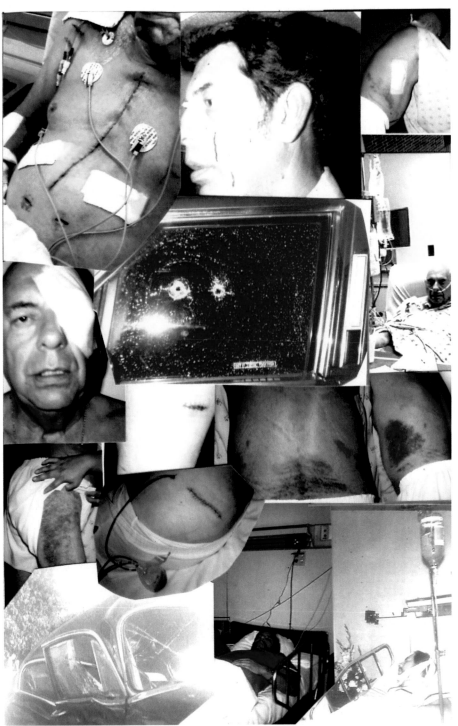

NINE LIVES PLUS

Reproduction of oath of office:

OATH OF OFFICE OF SWORN OFFICES
OF SLIDELL POLICE DEPARTMENT

I, David W. Steece, do solemnly swear that I will uphold the laws and constitution of the United States, the laws and Constitution of this state, all ordinances of the City of Slidell, and obey all lawful orders of my Superiors incumbent upon me as a Police officer, so help me God.

Signature of Person Sworn

Sworn to and subscribed before me this 21st day of April, 1986.

Elaine W. Guillot, /S/
Slidell City Attorney

Sincerely,
Elaine W. Guillot, /S/
Elaine W. Guillot

CITY OF SLIDELL
POLICE DEPARTMENT

Max Rodriguez
Chief of Police

May 17, 1989

To whom it may concern:

This is to introduce Detective David Steece who was commissioned by myself August 9, 1982.

He is presently my driver, confidant, liaison to law enforcement agencies outside of my city, and assists me with our state legislature with police related matters and special investigations.

He additionally served under Lt. Charles Cook, who is in charge of our Training and Disaster Control Division, under Lt. Terry Young in the patrol Division, under Lt. Eugene Swann, Chief of Detectives in our Criminal Investigation Division and also under the command of Lt. D. H. Humphrey in or Fugitive Division.

I have found him to be dedicated, hardworking with no concern to hours, thorough, efficient, flexible and a good friend.

If any further information is required or if you would like to discuss this matter with me personally, please do not hesitate to call.

Sincerely,

Max V. Rodriguez, /S/

Max V. Rodriguez
Chief of Police (Retired)
985-643-5850 (Residence)
Slidell, Louisiana 70458

City of Slidell
Police Department

Max Rodriguez
Chief of Police

March 30, 1987

<u>TO WHOM IT MAY CONCERN:</u>

This letter of recommendation is in support of David Steece, who was assigned to my division at the Slidell Police Department. David was a hard working detective and maintained the highest standards of loyalty and integrity.

While assigned to the detective division he did a very fine job. He was very through in his follow-up work and never minded putting in the extra hours to accomplish the task assigned to him. He showed proficiency in investigating major crimes, undercover operations and narcotics investigations. He was excellent in gathering intelligence Information that helped solve many of our cases.

Slidell Police Department is very fortunate to have David Steece working with them and can wholeheartedly recommend him to you as a dedicated worker.

If you require any further information, or would like to talk to me personally, please feel free to call me.

Sincerely,

Det. Lt. Gene Swann, /S/
Det. Lt. Gene Swann
Chief of Detectives

GS/bh

BLACKIE THE COP

OTHER COMMISSIONS ISSUED DURING CAREER

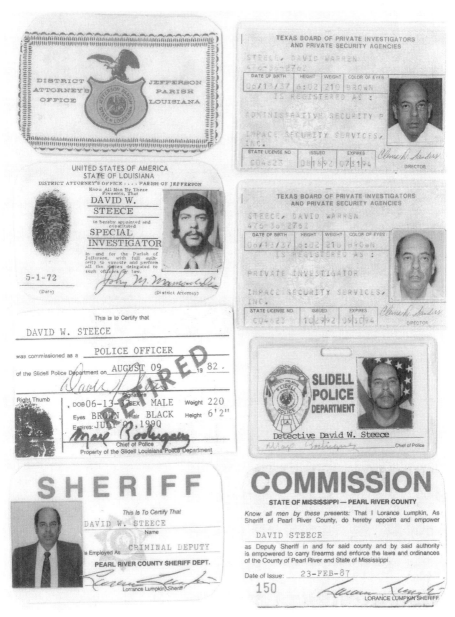

OTHER COMMISSIONS ISSUED DURING CAREER
(2)

OTHER COMMISSIONS ISSUED DURING CAREER
(3)

Chapter 21

Blackie woke up five minutes before the alarm went off and thought, *one more day and I'll have a live-in permanent baby-sitter.* After breakfast and dropping Lu and Alley at school, he decided to take Rae to spend the day with him. As he drove to New Orleans, he decided to go by Big Paul's and get him and his wife Bonnie to watch the girls tomorrow night until he came home with Sandy. He also decided he would go by and pick up the boxes she had packed before he went to pick up the girls from school. Blackie hop-scotched around Jefferson and Orleans, stopping by Jimmy Fitz's, Pas's, and last, back by Harry Cabral's, as he waited for Sandy to get home from work. He thought what fun! Driving his beautiful daughter around hearing raving comments about how cute she was. He was surprised when Sandy got home; she really had more boxes packed than he had room to take with the three girls and said he'd pick up more when he picked her up Thursday night and what was left on the weekend.

As they left Sandy's, she purred in his ear, "Did you bring Rae with you so we wouldn't be alone, or because I wasn't any good last night?"

Blackie said, "Nawww, no babysitter and, besides, I'm savin' up my strength."

As soon as Blackie picked up Alley on the way to get Lu, Rae said, "Guess who's comin' home tomorrow?"

"Who?" Alley said.

"Mom."

Blackie looked out the window thinking, Al and Rae had been so small when the custody fight was over, they really thought Sandy was their mom and Lu didn't seem to care as they had never heard from Liz since court. As soon as Lu got in the car, both Al and Rae chorused, "Mom's comin' home!" Lu grinned. "Great! I won't get in any more trouble cleanin' the bathtub. Huh, Dad?"

As Blackie turned the car home, his mind drifted *back to what Lu was referring to. When they had first moved into the estate, all of the girls had been impressed with the central vacuum system with a hole in the baseboard of every room and a hose you carried around. When you plugged it in the wall outlet, it started to vacuum automatically. That type vacuum cleaner had pipes running up the walls and through the ceiling and, in this case, into a big canister in one corner of the den that also housed the heater. It sucked all the dust and dirt through these lines and, when the canister got full, which was about five feet high and about thirty inches in diameter, it beeped and you dumped this big canister in a garbage can just like you would empty a vacuum cleaner. It had some problems though. One, the girls loved to play with it. Two, it was designed for dust and dirt, only. Three, Lu was an absolute certified "Dennis the Menace." One night, a few weeks after they moved into the house, there had been a big water spill in the garage when the drain hose came off of the washing machine. Blackie, with little kids under his feet, sucked all the water up with a wet-dry vac. The girls said, "Wow, this picks up water, Daddy," and Blackie never thought any more about it. One night, a few days later, after Blackie had dried off Rae and put her pajamas on and was starting to get Alley ready while Lu took her bath, the phone rang. He quickly finished Alley. As he ran down the hall to pick up the phone, he told Lu, "When you're finished, clean the tub." He couldn't remember who it was: Joe Nose, maybe Zap, Big Paul, or some friend, because the conversation lasted way too long. As Blackie lay on his bed talking, a drop of water hit him. He looked up at the ceiling, and there were little droplets of water hanging from the sheetrock all the way back to the den. He got off the phone and started following the water trail through the den, across the foyer into Lu's bedroom, where it disappeared into the wall into the closet. It went into Alley's room where it went across her ceiling towards the bathroom. As he entered the bathroom, lo and behold, Lu was getting the water out of the tub. Not the ole fashioned way, by pulling the plug, but in her explanation, "Just like daddy had used the wet-vac out in the garage." Only the wet-vac was designed to pick up water and this system, just dust and dirt. It would pick up water ok, but it appeared that every joint leaked. The sheetrock eventually fell down in approximately a six-inch trail through the bedrooms, across the house to the canister, which, like the sheetrock, was destroyed. Oh well, Blackie thought, kids all screw up. He remembered his daddy telling him he was the only person on earth who could cut a 22" swath with a 20" lawnmower leaving little 2" hedges of grass all over the front yard.*

"Can we have Pizza?" Lu asked, snapping him back to reality.

"No," Alley said, "I want 'king'" (meaning Burger King) and Rae wanted McDonald cookies.

Blackie thought, *God, I'll be glad to get Sandy back here; wonder if she'll come tonight.* He said, "No, were gonna have hamburger steak, mashed potatoes, and maybe corn on the cob." This was answered by a triple "ugh."

While Lu and Al did their homework and Rae played with her baby doll, Blackie peeled potatoes, grinning to himself about his first mashed potato experience. *Blackie had never learned to cook. He was a tough guy. Tough guys don't cook, mop floors, wash dishes or clothes. They just give orders and eat. Guess what! When you've got five little girls you learn to do a lot of stuff. It took two months to wash clothes without having them all pink, all green or all red. When he was trying to learn to wash clothes, he called his sister Patsy and told her he wanted to learn to wash clothes without having the colors bleed together. Like now, with one of his sweatshirts in his hand, how does he wash it...what water temperature does he use. Patsy asked, "What's it say on the shirt?"*

"Duh, U S Marines."

Laughing, she said, "You'll never learn."

The potato peeling made him remember that, shortly after Liz and he had split, he'd called Mom and said, "I want to make the girls mashed potatoes for dinner. How do I do it?" Mom had told him, "Get a bag of potatoes, fill a big pot with water, peel the potatoes, cut them in quarters, and boil them." That was about 9:00 in the morning, and the Marine Corp had taught Blackie to follow orders. So, he went to the store, got a five pound bag of potatoes, got the biggest pan he could find, almost big enough to bathe the baby in, filled it up with water, peeled the whole bag of potatoes, and started them boiling; now it was around 10:20 a.m. when he started the potatoes boiling. He picked all five girls up from school, about three-thirty and on the way home, told them they were having a surprise for dinner. Mashed potatoes met with a chorus of cheers. When they got home, Blackie fried some hamburger steaks, which he already knew how to do, while Bitsy set the table, and Theresa opened a couple cans of peas to heat. It was the first time the two older girls had tried to help him cook. Blackie dished up the peas and meat, took the cover off the pot of potatoes, assuming all he had to do was scoop them out and put them on the plate. To his shock, he found a cup of potato soup! He called Mom, who laughed hysterically, after asking, "How long did you boil 'em?"

"I guess since about 10:30 Blackie said.

She said, "You're lucky you didn't burn the house down. Twenty or thirty minutes would have been plenty and probably too long if you hadn't peeled the whole bag of potatoes."

Blackie said, "Oh well, we're havin' hamburger steaks and peas for dinner. I'll try again tomorrow." After dinner, when Blackie was washing dishes, he tried to clean the white shit out of the potato pot. After about ten minutes of scraping, rubbing, chiseling, he gave up and threw the pot away along with the evening trash. When he told Mom he had to start over with a whole new bag of potatoes, he told her he'd have to start over with a new pot too. He wasn't about to tell her why. Another big laugh from her was more than he needed.

After dinner, homework, and baths, Blackie called Big Paul to see if they'd watch the girls the next night until he got back from the meeting with the "little man" and brought Sandy home.

"No problem," Paul responded.

Blackie then called Jim. "Don't forget tomorrow night. I'm taking you and the Commissioner to the 'little man.'"

Jim said, "Yeah, where do you want to meet and what time?"

"Between six and six-fifteen at the end of the I-10 Bridge in Kenner."

"Ok," Jim said, "we'll be in my wife's Lincoln, because I don't think we should take State cars there in the event someone's watchin' his place."

"10-4. I'll see ya then."

Thursday morning, Blackie decided to keep Rae with him again until it was time to meet the Commissioner and Jim so that when he went to the meeting with Johnson, Magoo, and Billy, he'd have a built-in excuse for not being able to do whatever it was they wanted.

Blackie pulled into the Governor House parking garage about 12:45 p.m. and carried Rae to the private back door to Billy's office. Magoo opened the door and looked a little surprised to see the baby. Billy was at his desk and Johnson wasn't there yet. They asked, "How come the baby?"

"I really don't have a sitter for her today so it's me."

Lewie Johnson walked in, also showing surprise at the baby. "Hey, we need you to help us out with Murphy's Trucking Company, down in St. Bernard Parish. They're not cooperating."

Blackie said, "Ya know you can't screw around down there. That's not our territory. If I had my way, we'd run the fuckin' Confortos outta the state and take all of St. Bernard over. To do anything down there, we have to have a sit-down with the 'little man' or it'll start another fuckin' war. Have you talked to him?

"Well, we thought we could talk to you."

"I don't think so. One, I'm not going against him; and two, I'm up to my ass with kids with this new job."

Lewie said, "C'mon man, you can't get us an appointment?"

"I'll ask him when I see him, but I can't represent ya. I'm involved with this other man. I'll tell him ya'll want to see him when I see him."

Billy said, "Shit, that ain't gonna help us. We gotta have somebody with clout, like you. Talk to him. You know we need to have you take us there."

"I don't know, man. I'll do what I can."

After a few minutes of bullshit and cracks about how much they'd done for Blackie in the past, trying to make him feel guilty, Blackie got up to split. Magoo shoved an envelope in Blackie's pocket, adding, "I know you'll do what you can, no strings." Blackie smiled, left, and headed for Big Paul and Bonnie's. He'd hang out there until they left to pick up Lu and Al.

At six o'clock, Blackie turned into the median between the East-West lanes of I-10 at the eastern end of the bridge. Ten minutes later, a silver Lincoln pulled to the shoulder across the highway. Blackie put the red light on the dash, crossed the highway, and pulled in front of the Lincoln. Jim let the window down as Blackie walked up to the driver's side. "It looks like I'm getting a ticket," Jim said.

Blackie said, "Nawww, just an escort. There's a lot of traffic this time of day. Put your flashers on and stay on my ass. We're goin' down Veterans to David Drive, to Hickory, to Jefferson Highway, cross the Huey P. Long Bridge. Take the Westbank Expressway to Manhattan Boulevard. We'll turn there and go up to LaPalco Boulevard. When we turn off of LaPalco onto Churchill Farms Road, I'll let ya'll pass me and I'll follow you until about a half mile from the house where I'll park to make sure we don't get any visitors. Now, stay tight on me when we go through the red lights, ya'll don't have a pancake for your dash do ya?"

Jim said, "No. Can you get us one?"

"Yeah, I'll get you one next week. Let's go."

With that, they flew through traffic and still took the better part of an hour to get to the Churchill Farms entrance. It was close to nine-thirty when Blackie saw Jim's Lincoln coming back down the driveway. He pulled out in front and led them back to LaPalco, where he stopped and walked back to the car and told Jim, "I got to finish my plan for the scale raid tomorrow and over the weekend, so I'll see ya some time after that."

Jim winked and said, "Yeah, good job, Blackie."

Blackie flew back across the parish to pick up Sandy, so he could get home to his girls, formulate a plan, bullshit. He needed a break from this. Tomorrow, Saturday, and Sunday would be just that.

As Blackie walked into Sandy's apartment, she looked up from the chair where she was dozing. "I thought you dumped me already."

"No darlin' just runnin late."

Forty-five minutes later, with Sandy's head still in his lap, they turned into his driveway. Sandy said, "Hey, this looks nice," surveying the grounds as well as she could by the car's headlights.

Bonnie had put the girls to bed already and she and Big Paul were watching TV. Sandy figured when they didn't look surprised, Blackie must have already told them about her coming back. After thank yous and good-byes, Big Paul and Bonnie left. It was time for a good night's sleep, not enough energy for anything extra.

Friday was moving day. After dropping Lu and Al at school, they traveled from the apartment to the estate, unloaded and settled in. It was a high-level day and not all the energy was wasted on unpacking. The rest was spent in the black-marble sunken tub.

Chapter 22

Blackie rolled over to the pulsing alarm and said, "Shit, this is Saturday. Why is this damn thing goin' off?" He wished he had one of those fancy alarm clocks that had a reset button. Looking out the window, he realized that, with Sandy here now, he could relax to a breakfast cooked for him. The hectic pace of his mornings had come to an end. Blackie wandered to the kitchen and poured a glass of orange juice. He sat down at the table, looked out at the river behind the house. As Sandy cooked, he thought about his brother Lynn and how much he loved to fish. Hell, why would anyone waste his time sitting on a board or the side of the river with a stick in his hand, with a bent piece of wire to catch some nasty thing that didn't taste good until hours later when you got it cooked. He didn't really have a handle on the more relaxed pace yet. Maybe Lynn was on to something, after all.

His quiet morning reflection ended when he went to wake the girls. He ruffled Alley's hair—his little possum player—and smiled at the peace of Lu's soft snores. They stumbled and romped into the kitchen with a chorus of separate plans. "What are we going to do, Mom?" "I want to go to grandma's." "I want to go to Disney land." "I want to ride horses." After breakfast, they piled the girls in the car and went to La Place to Patsy's. They would play with his nieces, Stacy and Heather, while he and Sandy went to get some more of her stuff.

As they pulled into Patsy's driveway, Stacy and Heather came screaming toward the car with the normal brat request, "Uncle, wadja bring us? Hi, Aunt Sandy!"

Jesus, that's going to start the "we wannas," and of course it did. That's what he came here to get away from—oh well. Brother-in-law Ed came out and said, "I'll take the girls for a boat ride." *Now I know why I wanted Patsy to marry him*, Blackie thought.

After the moving was finished, Blackie relaxed at Patsy's place, subconsciously feeling sorry for Ed with all those kids out there driving him nuts. When Ed got back, they stuffed themselves on Bar-be-cue and all the trimmings. Blackie and Sandy loaded three exhausted little girls into the car and headed home. Blackie deserved this restful day.

Sunday, after playing with Sandy and the girls all day, Blackie heard the phone ring and assumed it would be Woody wanting Blackie to give him the plan for Monday. He realized he hadn't done anything on it yet. Shit, he'd just stall him on it until Tuesday.

Blackie was surprised when he answered the phone to find out it was Jim and not Woody. Jim said, "Are you going to be at the Capitol in the morning?"

"Yeah, why?" Blackie asked.

"Cuz, you need to go over this one more time."

"No problem. How about 8:00 a.m. or do you want to meet first?"

"No, that's cool. I'll see ya at the Capitol at eight."

Blackie took two steps and the phone rang again. It was Woody this time. Blackie said, "Just meet me at the Capitol at 9:00 a.m. Monday and keep everybody on hold till then."

Woody said, "Ok, boss, is there a problem?"

"No, man, I just wanna keep everybody guessin' so they don't know what I'm doin. The only one that is ever gonna know what I'm doin' is you. See ya Monday."

After tucking the girls in and kissing them goodnight, Blackie fell asleep while he and Sandy were watching a movie.

Blackie rolled out of bed at 5:15 Monday morning. Sandy rolled over and said, "Why so early?"

"Hey, darlin', I forgot ya were here ha-ha. No, I forgot to set the alarm back an hour. Now that you're here, I'll do it right now and tomorra I'll be on time. You shouldn't have any trouble finding the schools the way I showed you Saturday, Alley gets out at about three-ten and Lu about three-twenty. Just set your own schedule up. I don't know what time I'll be home. The keys to the Caddie are in the kitchen and the garage opener is over the sun visor. I'll try to call ya. I'll eat breakfast in town this morning. We'll get more organized by tomorrow. There's a piece in my night stand, take it with ya when you're outside or in the car."

Blackie turned the Plymouth west on I-12. As he crossed the overpass of I-55 on I-12 *he thought of the overpass on I-59 at 607 in Pearl River County, Mississippi, and the ironic incident of the famous doper, Barry Seal of Baton Rouge, who had allegedly flown over 700 tons of cocaine into Louisiana. Barry had flown a lesser amount, probably a few hundred kilos into an airport in Miami, Florida, and been caught. Facing a possible life sentence at the time, they were able to flip him and put him to work for the US Government. Barry, who had a strong reputation with the cartels in South America, went back and wore a wire several times. One time, he actually had a hidden camera in one of the planes that was being loaded. He was able to get pictures of Gotcha himself, the head of one of the notorious Cartels. After several of these big undercover operations, Barry went before a Federal Judge in Florida and was given probation. One of the criteria in the Federal System is that you can't be sentenced for more than what the other Federal Court sentenced you to. Barry had been awaiting sentencing in the Federal System in Baton Rouge on a previous charge. When his case came up, he had the Federal judge pissed off, because of the light sentence in Florida. The Judge told Barry in open court, "I can't send you to prison, as you know. I can only give you probation. But I am going to require you to report at six at night to the Salvation Army where you will sleep and not to leave until eight in the morning. Barry, his lawyers, and about everybody else protested, saying it was a death sentence. "Your honor, you know there is a ten million dollar contract out on me."*

The Judge ignored him and said, "that's the order of this court."

At about the same time, IRS had swooped down on Barry's big colonial mansion in Baton Rouge and took everything: cars, beds, mattress, clothes. He had nothing left. After a few nights, his stay at the Salvation Army deal turned bad. When Barry arrived to report at 6:00 p.m., he was met by a hail of gunfire and killed. In the aftermath, the Baton Rouge Police Department got one of the assassins; the other one had commandeered a cab at gunpoint and had torn down the same I-12 that Blackie was on right now, then turned North on I-59 near 607 in Pearl River County, Mississippi; the cab hit a deer, went off the road, and the Columbian assassin was killed in the wreck. Weird huh? His mind drifted to the Dennis Hoper movie made about Barry Seal— Double Crossed. It was the perfect name.

Blackie came back to reality as traffic started to pile up on the outskirts of Baton Rouge. As he sat in traffic, he wondered if his mind had drifted to the Barry Seal incident because subconsciously there was the possibility that he wasn't going straight in the eyes of the law and they were just setting him up. Was he being "double-crossed" as Barry Seal had been? Was this more of the Sheriff back home trying to "get him"? Even his funky captain and lieutenant had tried.

Hell, all he wanted was to get a decent woman to help him raise those angels and do a good job for the state. If he was being "double-crossed," the "Man" would have to know about it. Blackie didn't believe that would be possible. The Sheriff, on the other hand, Blackie thought, was as fucked up as the Commissioner. Hell, he'd just have to take a chance, if he wanted to give his girls an opportunity and a choice that his dad hadn't given him.

Chapter 23

Blackie got off the elevator on the eighth floor, bounded into the waiting room expecting to see Vicki on the switchboard, and was surprised to see Paula. "Where's Vicki, darling? Oh, I bet she's out getting a wedding dress for me."

Paula grinned coyly. "I don't think you'll look good in a dress."

Blackie laughed. "Maybe not, but I look good on black silk sheets. Wanna see? Really, where is Vicki?"

"She's in the back. They're interviewing some new girl and they needed her to answer Jeannie's phone while they interviewed."

"Oh good. Tell me, is this a puppy or an angel and please tell me she's got red hair"

"Of course she's attractive, but she's not a redhead. She's a blonde.

"Shit. that's bad for Jan. She can't type if she's blonde. Well I'm going in Jeannie's office and play with Vicki if they're looking for me."

"No, don't do that! They're waiting in the conference room for you already."

"Shit, this is some plot to keep me away from Vicki, I know." Blackie walked into the conference room expecting to see one idiot and Jim Knotts, but to his amazement he got to see two idiots and Jim Knotts. Redneck Charlie was sitting there with the Commissioner. *Now, you talk about the blind leading the blind if he's involved*, Blackie thought.

The Commissioner said, "Jim's been telling me what a great job you've done on this new plan you worked on all weekend. After you brief me on it, tell me what else you need to start implementing it."

Blackie looked at Jim and winked. "What I'm going to do is hop-scotch all around the State, hit all the big towns like Lafayette, Lake Charles, Shreveport, Alexandria, and then a few little towns in between just to make sure they don't think we're being prejudiced. But I'm not going to use any pattern; even the inspectors won't know where we're going the next day. We'll hit ten or twelve big stores in Lake Charles, spend the night there, head up North like we're going to Shreveport, hit something in Mansfield, spend the night there, then get up early the next morning, drive all the way back to Lafayette, and wipe them out. If we get some bad weights at the local supermarket chain in Lafayette, we won't even check them in Alexandria or Shreveport; we'll do another supermarket there. That way, the supermarket chain won't be able to warn their other stores in the state. No one will know who we'll do next."

Jim said, "That's a great idea. Go ahead and start it and touch base now and then by phone."

As Blackie waited for the elevator, Jim came out to go to the men's room. Blackie said, "Ya know that fuckin' redneck that was in there is as dumb as a bag of rocks and has got a big mouth, so you need to go back in there and feed him something that makes him think we're doin' something else."

Jim laughed. "Blackie, tell me how you really feel about him."

"Go back in there and tell the Commissioner that you're going to call me tonight and tell me to check on the slaughter houses next week and do the scales a couple of weeks from now. Then, so you know just how stupid the redneck is, he's from Natchitoches, ya know, you go up there next week and I guarantee you the Natchitoches slaughter house by him will have been warned, which will prove what a dumb-ass he is and can't be trusted."

"Do you really think he's that disloyal?" Jim asked.

"I don't know, but the Commissioner has him in charge of the Brand Division, and he thinks he's a big cattleman. The only fuckin' thing he knows about cattle is that you get hamburgers from Burger King. You know he's friends with that son of a bitch at the slaughter house where he lives, so he's going to tell the guy to clean up his act."

"Ok, I'll do it. You go on with your plan."

As Blackie punched the elevator button, he noticed Vicki coming out the back office door, with a blonde he presumed to be the new girl. He guessed Vicki would be training her on the switchboard and he'd have to train her to his personality when he got back. As the elevator door opened, Blackie saw a mob of little green uniforms and bobbing hats, Brownies, Campfire Girls, or Girl Scouts, coming down from the observation deck at the top of the capitol. Oh well, that was better than riding down with a bunch of political hacks.

As he got in his unit, he called Woody on the radio and told him to meet him at Rick's Pakcake House out on Airline Highway. Blackie raced down Plank Road wanting to get to Rick's before Woody, who he knew would be tearing down the road. As the two men arrived in the parking lot simultaneously, they got out laughing and talking about who got there a micro-second ahead of the other one.

Woody opened his briefcase when they sat down in the booth and handed Blackie a list of employees who were on standby. Blackie asked him who he thought he could take on one inspection and then be able to take a crew out on his own, like Ronnie was going to do.

"I think Archie Seals would be as good as Ronnie, maybe Herman Lemoine, when he is finished being cross-trained." Thus, this was the beginning of what was later to be called "Blackie's Golden Boys."

"Go ahead, call Archie and Ronnie. Have them meet us at the Capitol House in a couple of hours. Blackie decided to go by the Weights and Measures Office on the way and pick up a hundred or so copies of the law.

When Blackie arrived at the Capitol House Hotel dining room, Woody and Ronnie were already there. After a few minutes of chit-chat, Archie Seals arrived. Archie was the nephew of B. B. Rayburn, a long time senator from Bogalusa, a tall, good-looking, black-haired, thirty-year-old man, who looked more like an attorney than an inspector. Woody introduced him to Blackie. Blackie handed him a copy of the law, and said, "Read this."

After a few minutes, Archie said, "Ok."

Blackie said, "You got a problem enforcing that?"

"No."

"It's not as easy as it sounds. You gonna run into local politicians, sheriffs, attorneys, all kinds of people trying to get you run off long enough to get their scales calibrated before we come back and inspect them."

Archie looked at the other two men questioningly, and Woody said, "Yeah, ya just gotta stand fast, man. The last time we hit a store with the owner connected to politicians, he was there with a Deputy Sheriff and his attorney telling us to get out. The boss just said, "Hey, Asshole, you're in the State of Louisiana. This is the law. Read it, then get the fuck outta here or we'll have the State Police drag you out in handcuffs."

Ronnie chimed in with, "Yeah, that's exactly what happened."

Archie said, "if that's the law and the State Police will back us, I'm ok."

Blackie said, "Where you from?"

"Bogalusa."

"Well, if it'll make it easier on you, I'm gonna send you with three other men, who you'll be in charge of, up in the Caddo Parish area where you won't have to deal with friends. I'm gonna send Ronnie, who's from St. Helena Parish, with three men over in the Calcasieu Parish area. And I'm gonna send you," Blackie said, nodding at Woody, "to the Ouachita Parish area. I'm gonna take some men and sneak around behind and check on ya'll."

With that, they got Woody's list out again and started selecting people to work with. As soon as each man picked three people they liked, Blackie switched them, explaining that they'd have much less trouble asserting their authority with people who weren't their friends—just like training new street soldiers in a crew. By now, Blackie decided they should all eat lunch. They were already in a good restaurant so they might as well eat there. There was always a chance that Lewie, Magoo, or Billy might show up and they'd get another free ride.

After lunch, they drove out to the Weights and Measures Office and, as Woody got each man on the phone that he had put on stand-by, Blackie got on the phone and told them who he was, who they'd be working with and who would be in charge of them, where they would meet the next day, and he was rather pleased that he didn't get too much resistance. Most of the questions, were, "How many days will we be gone?" "Will we get our expense money back?" He fielded lots of general questions. Blackie told each man that the supervisors would be carrying with them a copy of a State law that he wanted them to become familiar with and follow to the letter. With that, the party broke up. Blackie told Woody, Ronnie, and Archie to stay in touch with him hourly by phone or radio, then he turned his unit East on I-12.

As Blackie flew along I-12, he wondered if he'd be able to run this investigation, with so little experience in weights and measures, long distance tomorrow or actually have to go out in the field with the men himself.

As he turned down the rolling driveway, he saw Sandy had just gotten home from picking the girls up from school, and he thought it might be fun to be a family man and not have to cook dinner every night.

As Blackie and Sandy crawled into bed, he thought about the past few hours. It had been a much different evening, sitting around looking at slides without the turmoil of cooking, cleaning, and bathing girls. It had been a welcome relief.

Blackie felt Sandy shaking him as the sun streamed in the bedroom window. "Get up darlin'. Your breakfast is ready."

"What? I didn't even hear the alarm."

"I turned it off before it woke you. By the time you brush your teeth and get to the table, we'll all be ready to eat."

After breakfast, Blackie told Sandy that he'd drop the girls off at school because he was going to New Orleans anyhow. He kissed her and the baby good-bye.

After dropping Al and Lu off at their schools, he stayed on Hwy 22 to the Causeway and turned right to cross it to Jefferson Parish. As Blackie headed South across the Pontchartrain Causeway, his mind drifted *to his brother-in-law Louisiana State Trooper, Wally Gettys, who, at the time had lived in Mandeville and was stationed at Troop B in New Orleans. That required him to drive across the Causeway in the morning to work. One morning he caught up to a pickup truck that was driving erratically, just before the end of the causeway bridge and, by the time he got him stopped, they were on the toll bridge apron on the south side of the Bridge. As he exited his police unit, the guy in the truck jumped out with a shotgun, fired at Wally, missed, and was promptly killed by Wally. Even when a cop kills in self-defense a lot of stuff happens. First, there's a bunch a police cars arriving. In this case, the Louisiana State Police Captain in charge, a couple of Jefferson Parish Sheriff's units, and a coroner's wagon for the dead body. Standard procedure is to take the officer's weapon for ballistics testing, and he gets a couple of days off to make sure he's Ok. Wally, living in Mandeville, turned his unit around, started back across the causeway for a welcome vacation day with pay. Now, all these police units and the coroner's wagon had been on the South end of the Bridge for over an hour and everybody going North on the bridge, of course, had seen all the red lights and the commotion, and Wally, who drives a little fast anyway, caught up to another vehicle on the North end driving erratically. Wally, being the good cop he is, stopped the guy. As he started to get out of his vehicle, he realized that he didn't have a side arm. Intuitively, he grabbed the shotgun mounted on the dash and, as the driver he stopped exited his car, Wally politely said, "Sorry about the shotgun, but I just killed a guy on the other end of the bridge and they took my pistol away. The driver, who had just gotten on the bridge a few minutes before, had seen all the police cars, commotion, and coroner's wagon on the other end, must have thought Wally was a nut. Grabbing his chest he fell out right there on the highway. The incident earned him the nickname, "Baretta."*

Blackie decided he needed more information about Bob Westerlund so that Blackie couldn't get set-up. He knew that Judge Allen had a good friend, Richie Ardnold. Richie got his connections through his now deceased grandfather who was a powerful polititition and judge back when also deceased Clancy was Sheriff and gambling was wide open in Jefferson. Richie was involved, maybe even as a gofer for Bob Westerlund. On second thought, ADA Clarence McMannis (assistant District Attorney for Jefferson Parish) hung out with Richie and went to a lot of the fights that Ray Peacock promoted at the Landmark Hotel. Between that bunch, he ought to be able to get a handle on Richie and thus Bob Westerlund.

Chapter 24

Blackie pulled up in front of First Parish Courthouse on Clearview Parkway and strolled into Judge Allen's office. The judge's secretary wasn't at her desk, and the door to the judge's office was slightly ajar. Blackie knocked loudly, yelling, "Better have your clothes on. I'm coming in." Doug laughed and stood up to greet Blackie. Jackie straightened her skirt and started to button her blouse. Blackie said, "Don't cover them up—I like to look at 'em, too."

"Hadn't seen you in a while. What's on your mind besides my secretary's tits? Jackie, get us some coffee."

Blackie waited until Jackie left the room then asked, "What can you tell me about Bob Westerlund at LCC?"

"What do you want to know?"

"Well, he says he's tight with you and Councilman-at-Large Larry Heaslip, Jr. Rumor has it that if you give him your payroll business he has a kind and generous heart."

"I guess he's ok, but he doesn't do anything directly for the judges that I know of. Why don't you just go talk to him?"

"I'm gonna. I just want to make sure I don't have to worry about his settin' me up."

"Oh no, I know you don't have to worry about that."

"That's what I wanted to hear."

After some small talk about Sandy coming back and the girls, Doug's wife Norma and Doug, Jr., they said their good-byes and Blackie left.

As Blackie turned on Causeway Boulevard southbound, he looked at his watch, and it was nearly 10:30. Thinking he should have heard from somebody by now, he reached for the radio. Just as he picked up the mic, Woody's voice came over it. "I was just getting ready to call you," Blackie responded. "What's goin' on?"

"We hit a couple of little stores on the way to Monroe at Columbia and were just coming out of a big one."

"Any problems?"

"Ahhh, they got a little sassy, but not much."

"You heard from anybody else yet?"

"Ronnie called me a little while ago, and they're doing ok. They hit a couple of stores in Welsh and Iowa and now they're on their way to Lake Charles."

"Ok, check on Archie later and lemme know."

Feeling the pangs of hunger, Blackie decided to cross to the West Bank and eat at La Stella's in Bridge City. Not only would he get some great angel hair, but there was also a good chance he'd see some of the bent noses, and he needed them to see him so they'd know he was back running his crews again. As Blackie pulled out of the La Stella parking lot, he returned a wave from Charlie Trapani, who was pulling in. That sparked a barrage of memories.

First and foremost, Charlie was one of John Tac Elms' super honchos, and the main guy that ran between Tac's elevated ramp to the Landrieu, Calogero Law firm that connected the two buildings. Also, Charlie was Tony Trapani's brother, one of the more widely known bookies. Tony, Charlie, Blackie, and others were regulars at Ronsonette's Barber Shop on South Carrolton Avenue in New Orleans, and in fact, Al had a curious group of customers, from straight cops to some not-so-straight and surely some regular people. Blackie recalled when he and Tony were both getting a shave and Al whispered, "Jesus, that straight New Orleans police Lt. Henry Morris is pullin' up in front! Ya got anything in that sports bag to worry about Tony?"

He said, "Shit, that bag's fulla football cards and a route book."

Blackie, who had just gotten in the chair and knew his shave and facial would take longer than the cop's haircut, said, "put the bag under my apron and he'll see Tony walk out clean. He has no reason to bother me. I'm not a famous bookie like Tony. I can always tell 'im I'm pregnant if he looks at the bulge funny." Everybody laughed as Tony stuffed the bag on Blackie's stomach. Al leaned the chair back, wrapped Blackie's face in a hot towel as everybody laughed about the pregnancy. In any event, it worked because Tony got away and Blackie got another feather in his cap when he took the bag over to Tony's place on Toledano Street. Laughing to himself, he thought about another incident with Al Ronsonette, when he needed some pictures taken and knew his brother was somewhat of a photographer, but when he asked if he could do it, of course, he was tied up. But Al, meaning well, recommended this guy named John Bosh vouching for both his ability to keep his mouth shut and the quality of his work. Al got in touch with the guy, and when Blackie met him back at the shop he was a little surprised at how young he looked but thought nothing of it. They hung the kid off the Claiborne overpass on a rope so he could take pictures of the little restaurant on Claiborne and Perido that was handling the wire service and which they thought was cheating. He did a good job, developed the pictures himself, and it turned out great. They gave the kid 2K for his work and told him if they ever needed him again, they'd give him a call. This was in the summer. That fall, they needed some pictures of a Supreme Court Justice, (no longer sitting) married, and frequenting the Town and Country Motel in Metairie, with a married woman, Marion Slipmann. So, remembering John Bosh, he went by his house. When he knocked on the door, his mother answered it and said he was in school.

Blackie said, "Oh, I didn't know he was in school. He at LSU or Tulane?"

She said, "LSU?" Tulane? He's at Beauregard."

He said, "Beauregard!? That's a Jr. High School. You must be talking about his brother."

She said, "John is in junior high, He's fourteen years old."

After staggering off the steps in shock and leaving, he thought, "Shit! Now what." That evening, before he found another photographer, the phone rang and it was John, very upset and concerned that by Blackie coming to his home in a black Cadillac and the fact that he had so much spending money since the job last summer, his dad had decided he was a dope dealer and was ready to rock everybody's boat. Blackie assured John's father he wasn't and he'd be right over, formulating his story on the way. When he got there, they all met and Blackie convinced Mr. and Mrs. Bosh that he was a private investigator and that John was at no risk taking pictures of businesses so that they could figure out where best to install security systems or place guards there. If he'd known that story would float when he started it, he would have offered them land out in the middle of the Gulf of Mexico. But it worked out. Blackie became friends with the entire family, and he was one of the last non-family members to speak with Mr. Bosh when he was dying in the hospital many years later. John's career as a photographer with his tight lipped attitude and his tenacity with the camera was and would be a fixture in Blackie's life forever. Ironically, one of John's pictures did make the Times Picayune *when a bookie they were watching in case he was raided, Frank Oliveri, was in fact raided. John got the picture of him crawling out the window trying to escape the police.*

As Blackie approached Clearview Parkway and I-10, he decided to take I-10 West and get home to the girls. If Woody needed him, he could talk to him there.

As he approached the exit on I-55 and Highway 22, he called Woody and told him he'd be out of the unit and gave him a pre-arranged code so Woody would know to call him at his residence, so everyone on the state-wide radio would not know where he was.

As Blackie pulled into the driveway, he saw Sandy walking out of the house with Rae to go pick up the girls. He pulled up and said, "Taxi?" After picking up Al and Lu and coming home, Blackie sat on the dock behind the house trying to decide how much time he could expend putting the Commissioner and Bob Westerlund of the LCC together without being accused of entrapment.

The dinner bell rang in the form of "dadee" from Al out the kitchen window and his thoughts went back to kids and food.

About 8:30, after the girls were asleep, the phone rang, and Woody brought Blackie up to date with Ronnie, Archie, and the activities of the day. Blackie told Woody to go the Ruston area the next day with his men, send Archie and Ronnie with their men both into Alexandria, putting Ronnie on the South side of town, with Archie on the North side to really turn that town upside down. He was going to play "hide-out" the next day and to call him on his home phone if he needed him. Blackie spent most of Wednesday organizing his dates and times of the past few days, so they would be ready when it became necessary to prove them.

Wednesday, when Woody checked in, he told him to send Ronnie and Archie to Lafayette with the same attack as Wednesday, and for him to come down to Baton Rouge.

Thursday morning, Blackie drove to New Orleans and went to his office in the Federal Building. He talked to Woody on the way, again, with a pre-arranged code to let him know where to call him later that day. He left a message in Baton Rouge for Jim Knotts to call him, so they would know he was at his New Orleans office. It was afternoon before Woody called, and Blackie told him to round everybody up that night and get their reports and bring them in Friday morning to the Capitol. A couple of hours later, when Jim Knotts called, Blackie said, "I've been going over some of our records, and do you know we have a big empty building on Airline Highway in Baton Rouge?"

"No, but why?"

"How long before you're gonna get my promotion through?"

"I'm sure any day now. Do you have a plan for it?"

"I will by the time you get your act together."

They agreed to meet Monday morning at Rick's Pancake House before reporting to the Commissioner.

Blackie called The Man after his conversation with Knotts and said, "I can't meet ya Monday cause I have to be in Baton Rouge early."

"Is there anything we need to discuss or can it keep another week?" The Man asked.

"Naaa, we're all just really fencing now, but in a week or two we should be gettin' serious." "OK, we'll see you one day next week.

Chapter 25

As Blackie headed down Perdido to Claiborne and out toward Tulane, traffic, for some reason, was backed up under the underpass on Claiborne, so Blackie turned left to go behind the Tulane Student Nursing Building and out the back streets. As he passed the block-long metal building on his right, he laughed quietly remembering *the big metal building, which covered four square blocks and had been the old O.E. Haring, Inc. It was the center of an investigation started by some snitch who called the Bureau and said there were stolen cars in the back half of the building, which was isolated behind a wall by the O.E. Haring parts section, which covered about a block on the East and a Block on the South side, leaving several thousand feet of windowless warehouse with a couple of doors large enough to drive an eighteen-wheeler truck through. Blackie had done several pretense purchases in an effort to investigate the allegations. He was able to establish that the second floor above the parts counter that was used as a storage area had a chain link fence about six or eight feet high. With this in mind, he and Del Hahn, and two other agents, black bagged the side door at O.E. Haring's one Saturday night, to get on the second floor of the Parts Dept. They climbed up on boxes and peered through the fence, and below was an unbelievable number of Cadillacs, Corvettes, Mercedes, and most every other fancy car you could name, parked almost bumper to bumper. There must have been at least a hundred. With egos pumping, convinced they had uncovered a huge hot-car ring, they started to climb over the chain link fence, which did not have a top rail like most chain link, just pointed wires, on the top. It was very wobbly. Del, trying to outdo Blackie, tried to get over the fence first and got his ass hung on the wire and hung there like a Saturday cartoon character, his hands flailing and legs kicking about thirty feet above the roof of a blue Mercedes. Of course, cramped from laughter, it took them a while to come to his aid. The tongue-lashing that ensued was memorable.*

Eventually, this entry effort was abandoned and a discussion among everyone decided, that, since O.E. Haring and his wife, the former

Dorothy Weisfeld, of the Weisfeld family that built most of the dams in the United States, and had immaculate reputations, probably just leased that part of the building out. They decided to approach them, tell them what they suspected, and felt sure that they would allow them access to check the VINS and license plates. With that plan in effect, they went into the office Monday, talked to Mr. and Mrs. Haring, who readily allowed them in to take pictures and copy VINS. This completed and while excitedly running the numbers with NCIC, they were shocked and disappointed. There were no thieves; they learned that the cars belonged to such non car thieves as Billy Kilmer, Jimmy Taylor, Doug Atkins, and many other of the newly formed New Orleans Saints football team who had stored them while away at practice camp. Good thing they had done it that way and not with a search warrant and newspaper and TV reporters, as they would have really ended up with egg on their faces.

Blackie snapped to the here and now with horns blowing as he got on Jeff Davis Parkway and headed home. A weekend of fun with the girls, Sandy, and dogs was well deserved by such a hard working public servant.

Blackie was already waiting for Jim Knotts at Rick's Pancake House on Monday morning when Jim walked in with a smile on his face.

They shook hands as Jim sat down. "I'm getting a few more phone calls. You're getting their attention. Also, I think Holmes Johnson is going to take some leave time. Maybe he won't come back."

"I understand that Gerald Kidder is working on the reorganization of the department to implement this cross-utilization system. I don't know shit about cotton and sugar," Blackie said. "What I really need to be in charge of is all eight regulatory divisions. Are you sittin' in on these meetings?"

Jim nodded in the affirmative, and said, "I'll just stick you in that job and convince the Commissioner that's the only way it's going to work."

"The sooner the better."

After some light bullshit and lots of pancakes and eggs, Blackie asked Jim how he had fared in the Michot indictment, adding, "How did you keep them from figuring out you had one set of Special Ed books and they were paying for fifty or sixty warehouse full?"

"It was kinda like that asshole, Billy Sol Estes, in Texas with the fertilizer tank," Jim responded. "In fact, he was the one that gave me the idea. I just moved the books from warehouse to warehouse and collected my checks. How'd yall get those Sweda Cash Registers everywhere?"

Blackie laughed. "Payback question, huh? It's a better deal to buy our cash register than to try to swim across the Mississippi River with the old one tied to your ankles."

Jim laughed, as well. "Did you have a lot of trouble in the small towns?"

"Not really, once you slap one of those coonasses around, word gets out pretty fast. We really have the majority of registers out in the state and a lot of 'em in Mississippi along the Coast." With that, the two men headed for the Capitol and a meeting with the Commissioner.

Blackie was excited to see Vicki and the new blonde at the switchboard when he got off the elevator on the eighth floor. "Hmmm, just like a double-decker ice cream cone. Now which one should be on top, the vanilla or the chocolate? Hi darlin'," Blackie said to Vicki. "Did ya tell the new girl that I only have ya on Monday, Wednesday, and Friday and if she's real nice ta me, she can have me on Tuesday and Thursday?"

Vicki blushed as the new girl looked shocked. Vicki said, "Joan, this is David Steece, and he's a big flirt, so far it's all bark. He hasn't bitten anybody yet."

"Can you type?" Blackie said, grinning.

Joan said, "Yes, why?"

"I think if ya can type, ya don't have to sleep with the Commissioner," he said, laughing, as he headed toward the conference room.

The conference room held the Commissioner, Jim Knotts, who was just entering from his office door, Redneck Charlie, and Jimmy Meadows, who Blackie later learned was another cousin to the Commissioner. Jimmy Meadows had a hound-dog looking skinny pink face. He had a wimpy stance, and his eyes would flit from one person to another without holding anyone's gaze. His bony hands had fingers so long they actually looked like fingernails.

Blackie pulled Jim to the other end of the room and said, "Look, man, I'm not talking in front a all these assholes. As far as security goes, one is too many, two is ridiculous, and those two don't look like they could keep their mouths shut any better than a colander could hold water. If the Commissioner wants to impress his family with how well he's doin', he can go find another boy. I'm fuckin outa here."

"Wait a minute. Wait a minute. Just wait a minute right here."

Blackie shrugged and leaned on the wall.

Jim went up to the Commissioner, whispered something in his ear, and they both left the room. In a couple of minutes, Jim came back in the room and said, "Blackie, ya want to come in here a minute?" leaving the two idiots pickin' their noses.

When they got in the Commissioner's office, the Commissioner started with, "Now Blackie, these are my family, and I trust 'em."

"I understand where you're comin' from," Blackie said, "but my responsibility is to protect and take care of you. You remember Erlichman and Halderman the Nixon confidants? The only guy that stood fast in the whole crowd and didn't dump on Nixon was Gordon Liddy. Now look at me like I'm your Liddy. And I don't give a fuck if the rest of 'em's feelings get hurt or not. I'm never talkin' to anybody but you and Jim about business."

The Commissioner looked shocked. Jim said, "He's right. People with egos can brag themselves right into jail."

Blackie thought, *the Commissioner probably don't need any help; he'll brag himself into jail on his own.*

The Commissioner agreed. "Jim told me what a good job you did last week, and we've about got this reorganization thing worked out. You'll be able to get a lot more done, soon."

After a few minutes more, Blackie left through Jeannie's office, telling her to call Woody and have him and the men meet him at the Weights and Measures Office.

He spent the rest of the day going over reports with Woody, Ronnie, and Archie and meeting the other men, teaching them all how to write good investigative reports.

That night about seven, the phone rang at home. It was Bob Westerlund. He said, "I understand the Commissioner wants to meet with me about some Monty Hall stuff."

"Let me get back with ya," Blackie said. "Keep your schedule open for the next few days."

"OK," Bob said and hung up.

Blackie called Jim Knotts at the Holiday Inn in Baton Rouge and said, "I think we have a potential meeting for Wednesday. Can you arrange to have the Commissioner down in New Orleans?"

He said, "No problem. You set it up for whatever time you want."

With that, Blackie called The Man at home. "Breakfast in the morning?"

Brief as usual, The Man said, "I'll see you then."

After Blackie hung up, he was pleased to see that Sandy had some of Lu and Al's school papers to go over and a couple of letters from Theresa and Bitsy. He was stunned because neither of the away girls wanted money.

Tuesday morning, as Blackie approached I-10 at the Veterans Exit in Metairie, he glanced left at the Louisiana Computer Company building and wondered just how hard it would come down when the shit hit the fan. Would it implode like the demolition of old buildings, and how many local and state politicians would go down in the dust with it?

As Blackie headed for their regular table at Howard Johnson's, he was a little hurt to see that The Man had already beat him there. *He must have a busy day*, Blackie thought, as they shook hands. After the usual niceties, Blackie said, "We're meetin' with Westerlund tomorrow, and I'm sure he's gonna be after the Agriculture Contract."

"Just make sure you stay far enough back, so you can't get caught in the gears or caught in entrapment, but close enough so you can prove what happened."

"I will," Blackie assured him. "I need a secretary in my New Orleans office, and I think I'm gonna hire Jamie Veverica's daughter, Lisa, who needs a job, plus I can trust her."

"I don't see where that's a problem, as long as she takes the Civil Service test and passes it. Just because she's a friend, if she's qualified, it can't be a problem."

"Alright. I just wanted to run it by you so it wouldn't be a surprise."

With that, the two men left and Blackie decided to go to Gretna and tell Jamie in person.

As he parked in front of Jamie's office on Huey P. Long Avenue, directly across the street from the old Gretna Courthouse, his mind drifted *to a picture that intelligence had shown him. It had been taken of him and Marcello in front of the old Joy Lounge, when Blackie had run it back in the early 1960s. Intelligence thought they really had a bad guy with Marcello, not realizing it was him. Blackie remembered thinking to himself,* God, if only that old Courthouse building, which included the jail, could talk... *That had been Frank Langridge's office when he had been District Attorney for twenty-four years, prior to hand-picking his successor, who Blackie had just met for breakfast. Joe Nose made a very unpleasant visit through there in the early 1960s, during Sheriff Fitzgerald's administration. Judge Floyd Newlin also got his start there as an assistant prosecutor. Blackie thought,* If that old building could talk, we'd be here forever with the stories it could tell.

Blackie walked into Jamie's office and said, "Hi, darlin'. Get ready to be shocked. I'm giving instead'a receiving."

"Wow," Jamie said, laughing, "I'd better record this."

"Nah, it ain't that big'a deal. I need a secretary for my New Orleans office. I knew you're lookin for a job for Lisa, so have her go take the Civil Service Test and, if you make love to me, she's got it."

"Are you serious about Lisa, because I'm always ready to make love to ya?"

"Yeah, I'm serious about Lisa. By the way, I got Sandy back at the house takin' care of the girls with me runnin' all over, thus taking the burden off all my friends. Have ya noticed?"

"Yeah, no panic calls in the middle of the night to get Rae from you off the side of the highway. What about my late night calls? Am I still gonna get that visit?"

"Of course."

After a friendly feel and some tongue trading, Blackie headed back across the East Bank to Jefferson Parish. Exiting at Clearview Parkway, he went to Kawannie, turned left, and headed up to the LCC Building.

As Blackie walked into Bob Westerlund's secretary's office, Kathy Genero, he wondered to himself, *when the house of cards starts to fall, how long will it take for people to find out that Pat Bell's squeeze, known around town as "Frosty," is really Kathy Genero's sister, Sarah Kennedy.* Pat Bell's momma was a Hand, thereby making Pat Bell, Pat Hand's first cousin, connecting all the Irish click's bookies on Jefferson Highway, including the old Sabou Club, Pines Motel, and the Baby Grand Club. That surely would spark somebody's curiosity, newspapers, local cops, or somebody, into just how involved LCC was into prostitution and gambling. Oh well, that'd be somebody else's case. Right now, his job was to look at the prettiest redhead, next to Susan Hayward—ever. "Where's your boss darlin'?" Blackie asked.

"Hey you, I'll tell him you're here," was Kathy's response.

"No, just tell 'im I've come to take you away from all this that we're leavin' for South America."

"You're so silly. I've told you before you change women too fast for me. You'd be tired of me before the plane landed."

"Nah. Give yourself at least a week."

She laughed again as she walked down the hall to her boss's office. *As Blackie waited, his mind drifted back to the old Sabou Club and how Joe Nose had an entire studio on the second floor for the porno business. He remembered the times Gloria had been between shoots and tried to teach Blackie how to splice and edit film. He had always been amazed that the actual porno filming lasted about seven or eight minutes but, because there were five cameras shooting from different angles, when they spliced, edited, and did all the other shit to it, it looked like the guy could fuck forever and cum half a dozen times. Then they took that one film and made hundreds of copies. The poor broad got fifty bucks, the dude got twenty-five, and Joe Nose got twenty grand. That's what you call really gettin' fucked.*

When they put three guys on Gloria, she still only got fifty bucks, and Joe Nose probably made a a hundred grand off of that shoot. People just loved to watch three guys fuck one broad and cum all over her face and tits. Actually, three guys on one broad wasn't a bad deal; Blackie just didn't want his face on film. As Blackie thought about some of the other girls he met while they were filming, like Pat or Barbara, Kathy came back into the office and said, "Hello. Are you daydreaming? Mr. Westerlund will see you now."

"No, I was just trying to think. I bet ya didn't tell him we were runnin' away." As he went into the office, the two men shook hands.

"Tomorrow at ten at the Monteleone. Will that work for ya?"

"Sure, what kind of a deal does he want to make?"

"Oh, no! I don't get inta that part; that's up to ya'll. I'm just a messenger boy."

With that, Blackie left, throwing Kathy a kiss as he walked through her office.

He got on the radio as soon as he got in his unit and called Jim Knotts. "Tomorrow morning at ten, regular place."

Jim answered, "10-4. You be there too."

"10-4. I'll be there."

Then Blackie headed home to his girls and, he hoped, a good TV movie with the girls after a good meal. Later, after the girls had gone to bed, maybe he could find one of Joe Nose's old movies for him and Sandy.

Chapter 26

Wednesday morning as Blackie was leaving, he told Sandy not to expect him for dinner. He had no idea what time he'd be home. As he pulled into the Monteleone parking lot, he scanned the attendants until he found #11, knowing he would keep the unit close by in case he was lucky enough to get away from this nut factory.

When Blackie entered the Commissioner's suite, he was surprised to see Redneck Charlie, the Jimmy Meadows cousin, Gayle Riggs, Sam Genero, the Commissioner on the phone, and no Jim Knotts. But, before he could open his mouth, Jim entered the room from the bathroom. Blackie scanned the room, rolled his eyes at Jim, letting him know he thought this crowd was a bad idea. Jim motioned for him to go into one of the bedrooms with him. When they got in there, he said, "We'll just talk to him in here away from the rest of them."

"I've heard of support groups before, but these are all idiots. They couldn't support a broken chair and that's all the Commissioner has around him, plus I'm not sure Westerlund will even stay when he sees all these people, much less talk about a Monty Hall."

About that time, they heard a loud booming voice say, "I'm the Commissioner!"

They quickly opened the door to see Bob Westerlund standing there with Redneck Charlie trying to look important.

Jim stepped forward and said, "Bob, glad to see you, step in where Blackie and I are. Commissioner, come join us please.

The Commissioner looked puzzled. Jim gave him a look like "come on dumb-fuck; we can't talk in front of all these people." Finally, he got up and walked into the bedroom with them.

Blackie wasn't surprised that Redneck Charlie and Meadows were right on his heels. As he stepped into the doorway he said, "Sorry, this is for the big boys," and slammed the door in their faces.

The Commissioner looked as if he was going to say something in their defense, when Jim cut him off by saying, "Let's get started. Mr. Westerlund's a busy man."

Blackie, not wanting to hear the details, excused himself and went into the bathroom, taking as long as he dared before he returned to the room. When he did, Jim was standing with his hands on his hips and Bob had opened his briefcase, which he'd laid on the dresser. Blackie noticed there were three white envelopes in the briefcase on top of some papers. Bob selected the one closest to the end of the briefcase near Blackie, closed the briefcase, turned, and handed it to the Commissioner. The Commissioner took the envelope, hefted it and turned to Blackie, "You take care of this and bring it to me in Baton Rouge tomorrow."

Blackie, wanting it identified, said, "Ya'll need ta know what's in here, cause I don't want someone to say something came up missing."

Bob said, "10 K. You want to count it?"

The Commissioner looked at Jim Knotts, as Blackie handed the envelope back to the Commissioner, thinking there was probably more in those other two envelopes in Bob's briefcase. He popped the switchblade open and handed the Commissioner the open knife. The Commissioner sliced the envelope open, handed Blackie back his knife, pulled out a bank-banded pack of $10,000 in hundreds. He fanned the ends and started looking for a new envelope.

Blackie said, "here, just put a rubber band around it," thinking to himself *I want all those fingerprints.*

The Commissioner rubber banded the envelope and handed it back to Blackie who placed it carefully in his pocket, touching it just by the edges.

The Commissioner started to ask Bob some operational question, which Blacked did not want to hear. He excused himself, saying, "I'm going to get coffee in the other room."

When he entered the main room of the suite, Sam and Gayle were chatting on the sofa, and the two idiots sat in chairs by the table, obviously pouting. Blackie obnoxiously poured his coffee in between the two. Blackie had treated Redneck Charlie as badly as possible, and he was taken aback when Redneck said, "My wife and I would like you and your family to come spend a weekend with us in Natchitoches."

While Blackie was choking on his coffee, Redneck continued, "We have horses. Do your children like to ride horses? We live right on the river. It's really a beautiful place. We have a lot of room."

Blackie, still too shocked to answer, thought, *maybe I can find where some more bones are buried without even looking.* Finally able to catch his breath, he said, "Yeah, tell me when." He then turned to the newest dummy of the group, Jimmy Meadows, whom he hadn't yet had a chance to treat as badly as he had Charlie, and asked, "Don't you want us to come to your house for the weekend, too?"

Jimmy Meadows looked somewhere between someone who had just been punched in the gut or had just had his breakfast pissed on. He just sat there in total dismay.

When Blackie looked up, he noticed that Sam and Gayle were both looking at him sort of shocked, also. So, true to form, he said, "Hi, darlin', can you type?" which got four more stupid looks. By then, Bob, Jim Knotts, and the Commissioner entered the room. The Commissioner added one more stupid look. Bob and Jim Knotts were both grinning, knowing Blackie, knew that he had just rocked someone's boat.

Redneck Charlie jumped up and said, "Commissioner, I'm gonna have Dave Steece and his family up to my house this weekend. Do you and Jean want to come?"

Which got him even an dumber look, making Blackie realize the Commissioner didn't like these idiots either.

After a few minutes, Redneck Charlie cornered Blackie again and said, "Can you make it this weekend? Do you have to call your wife and see?"

"Yeah, no problem, I'll leave when school's out Friday and be up there in time for dinner. Tell your wife to cook something good."

Redneck said, "Oh, Dave! Natchitoches is North of Alexandria, and it takes three hours just to get to Alexandria from Baton Rouge."

"I know where it's at. We'll be there by six-thirty. You can't wait dinner till then?" Blackie said, thinking to himself, *shit, I could hitch hike to Alexandria in three hours, probably even walk there.*

"Oh, oh, oh, no problem. We'll wait for you even if it takes longer."

"It won't," Blackie said, knowing that he wasn't going to do much the rest of the week.

Blackie took his briefcase into the bathroom, removed a white envelope, took the ten thousand out of his pocket and switched it into another white envelope which he sealed, cut open, put a rubber band around, and put back in his pocket, keeping the original envelope as evidence. He placed the original envelope in a zip-lock to protect it as evidence. He put that one in his briefcase.

As the rest of the crowd stood in the parking lot waiting for their cars, Blackie took the money envelope out of his pocket. "Jim, you want to take this with you or have me waste a trip to Baton Rouge tomorrow?" Blackie asked.

Jim Knotts turned to the Commissioner, said something, then turned back to Blackie. "Yeah, we'll take it with us. You got something to do the rest of the week?"

"Yeah," he said, thinking, *I need to cleanse my brain from being around idiots.* Blackie got into his unit. As he pulled out of the garage, looking in the mirror he saw the attendant bringing up Bob Westerlund's car and said to himself, "If you'd give the attendants a fin when you come in, you wouldn't have to wait forever to get your car back."

Friday morning after breakfast, Blackie took the girls to school so Sandy could start packing for the weekend. He never believed in telling the girls they were going someplace until the last minute, so if his plans changed, they wouldn't be disappointed. When he came back from dropping the girls off, he brought his records up to date while Sandy packed and then loaded the car for the weekend trip.

With Sandy in the front seat and Rae in the car seat, when he picked up Al from school, she started. Once Lu was picked up, they had it in stereo, "I know we're goin' somewhere. I know we're goin' somewhere. Where we going?"

Blackie shot the unit up Airport Road to I-12 and turned west. At a little over a hundred miles an hour, about twenty minutes later, he exited on Hwy 61 in Baton Rouge, to bypass the City and cross the old Huey P. Long Bridge over the Mississippi.

As they passed the Belmont Motor Hotel on the left, Blackie's mind drifted to *Jerry McPeak. He was a soldier visiting from St. Louis while he was cooling off in the early 1960s. Blackie's uncle was now running St. Louis in his dad's name because his dad had gone to prison in the mid-1950s. He was also cooling off running back and forth between Sicily and Mexico with a different name but not as infamous as Jerry McPeak. As far as the press knew, it was still the same organization. One day, Blackie had to go pick up a collection; Jerry was with him. When they pulled up into the yard, Jerry said, "Let me handle it alone."*

Blackie said, "No problem," and gave him the sheet with the name and the amount due and said, that's him sittin' over there on that bench with those other guys Jerry got out, strutted over to the crowd, showing Blackie how tough he was, and after a brief discussion came back to the car and said, "The fucker ain't even there."

Blackie was his usual hot head and jumped out of the car and said "COME ON." As he approached the group, he said "What the hell's goin' on Melancon, why ya telling this guy ya ain't here?"

"Hey, Black, he didn't ask for me. He came over here and asked for some guy named Mel- in-con." Blackie had to laugh because Melancon, pronounced (Mal-law-saw) but does look like Mel-in-con when written and Jerry had asked for some guy named Mel-in-con. Unless you're from Louisiana, all those names are hard to pronounce by Yankees.

They'd been housed at the Belmont and ate breakfast there. It started out bad for Jerry and got worse. They ordered coffee and, of course, got a cup of chicory coffee, which comes in a demitasse cup. Jerry rebuffed the waitress. "I want a cup of coffee, not some eyedropper full." This two hundred pound coon-ass, who still had most of the last two or three meals she'd served on her apron, was obviously insulted. She rushed away and came back with a steaming cup of coffee. She asked him if he wanted cream and sugar. He said, "Of course not. Where I come from we drink our coffee straight down."

To which she said, "I wanna see dat," knowing that if you stuck a spoon in a cup of chicory, you have nothing left but the handle.

Jerry, proud of his heritage, picked up the cup, blew on it a couple a times, took a big gulp and promptly spewed it all over the table and her, screaming "AAAAAHHHHHH!! What the fuck is this?"

Undaunted she asked, "Want another cup?"

Jerry, still sputtering, said, "I'll just order." Tapping her foot, she stood there with her pen in her hand, and he said, "I'll have two basted eggs, a piece of ham, and some American fries."

She said, "What's an American fry?"

He said, "What you eat with your eggs."

"Not here ya don't."

"What do you eat with your eggs HERE?"

"Grits," was her response.

"What's a grits?"

She came back with, "It's what ya eat witcha eggs."

With that he said, "Well, I guess I'll try one."

To which she bellowed loud enough for everyone in the restaurant ta hear, "YOU WANT ONE GRIT?"

They finally got through that breakfast. When they came in that night for dinner, the special was Mulligan Beef Stew, which Blackie ordered and Jerry said, "I'll have one of the same." Back in St. Louis, stew comes on a platter, served with beef, carrots, potatoes, and thick brown gravy. In coon ass land, it comes with rice, vegetables, and a real thin watery gravy. When placed in front of him, Jerry honked, "What's all this white shit?" He was pointing at the rice in his stew. To which the waitress, who, thank God, was a different one from the morning waitress, responded, "Rice."

To which Jerry said, "Rice? Where's the potatoes? I ain't no Chinaman."

"Who ever heard of potatoes in Beef Stew, ya get rice."

Blackie thought he might as well liven it up and said, "Jerry, ya want a cup of coffee with that?"

They finally made it through dinner and the waitress came back and said, "Ya'll want some dessert?"

"Sure, I want apple pie a la mode. Jerry said, "I'm afraid to ask does apple pie a la mode come with raw apples and melted ice cream or does it come like it does back home?

"No, if it came like that, Jerry, it'd be an apple milk float," to which he saw no humor. Jerry was a cool guy, but Blackie hardly ever ate breakfast, lunch, or made a collection the rest of his life without thinking about Jerry.

As Blackie turned on Cane Road, he realized Redneck Charlie lived on the Old Cane River, which was world famous for its Christmas Lights. Knowing it was impossible to get a decent motel room here or to get a good spot on the road to see the lights, he realized he'd have to be nice enough so his girls would get an invite back to see the Lighting of the Cane River.

As Blackie and his family were introduced to Redneck Charlie's wife, he was astounded at how much she looked like Vivian from the Golden Girls TV sit-com series. From that day on, as long as he knew her, he always called and referred to her as "Vivian." He liked naming women after stars, just as he had named Larry Heaslip's wife Marsha, "Farrah" for Farrah Fawcett, Elaine Despenzaro was Susan Pleshette, Sandra Trosclaire became Barbara Eden, and Carol Leger he dubbed Ann Margaret.

Blackie apologized for arriving twenty minutes past his 6:30 designated arrival time and blamed it on the traffic circle rush hour in Alexandria. Vivian laughed and said, "we haven't even made the salads yet. I didn't expect you until about 8 o'clock."

After dinner, the whole family sat out on the back porch. The ladies drank wine, Blackie drank coffee, Redneck Charlie added to his red ruddy look, by drinking bourbon, while the kids romped on the sloping yard down near the river. The next morning after breakfast, Redneck Charlie, Blackie, and the girls went out to his farm, so the girls could go horseback riding. Saturday evening after dinner, Alley did a dive off the back steps and cut her leg bad enough so that they spent most of Saturday night at the Emergency Room in Natchitoches, which pretty well tells how the rest of the weekend went.

Chapter 27

Monday morning Blackie asked Alley how her leg felt, and he asked Sandy whether or not she thought Alley should go to school. Alley said she felt good enough to go to school. Blackie kissed them all and left for Baton Rouge.

When he got to the Capitol, he stopped by Lt. Governor Jimmy Fitzmorris' office (who was also President Pro-Tem of the Senate) to tell him that he knew how unpopular the Commissioner was but that he would be having some legislation introduced by the Jefferson Delegation, led by Eddie D' and Charlie (State Representatives Eddie D'Gerolamo and Charles Grisbaum) in the House, and by Sammy and Hank (State Senators Sammy Nunez of St. Bernard and Francis Lauricella from Jefferson) and could very easily need his help to guide it through the Senate where he expected the most opposition.

Jimmy said, "What exactly are you trying to do?"

"I don't know whether ya know it or not, but Agriculture has eight or more different office buildings rented from Butch (Butch Brum a known political real estate hack) around the city and probably in every other town where he owns buildings. My plan is to move all the small offices, like Lake Charles and Monroe into the state buildings in those towns. Then, here in Baton Rouge, move all eight regulatory divisions into that big state-owned building on Airline Highway, cross utilize all six or seven hundred employees, put them all to work for a change and get outta the 'candy leases' we have all over the State."

"Sounds like a good plan, but you're going to rock some boats."

Blackie laughed as he walked out of the office and called over his shoulder, "We've already rocked a few boats and most of the world is already seasick."

As he waited for the elevator, *he remembered back in 1969 when Jimmy was a candidate for the Mayor of New Orleans and he was Jimmy's body guard and driver. They were in the Up-Town area of New Orleans in the Garden District when a call came that they had to meet William Hellis (the Golden Greek Oil Man) downtown for a campaign contribution at Jimmy's headquarters. Riding with Jimmy and Blackie were Norris Fitzmorris, Jimmy's brother, who tabulated both votes and donations constantly, and Vincent Marinello an alleged organized crime figure. He had rolled over on the Little Man in an insurance scam and actually was instrumental in sending the Little Man to prison for many years. A short time after the Little Man was released from prison, Vincent was found one morning in the Madisonville marina parking lot sitting in his Mercedes with its motor the only thing still running. Someone had put a bullet right behind his ear and, therefore, his heart, and his mouth had stopped running. Of course, the local sheriff had made a statement that the killing was not connected to organized crime. He would know?*

Blackie was jolted back to reality when Eddie D' nudged him in the ribs. "You still trying to piss off all my supporters?"

As they got on the elevator together, Blackie said, "Tell your friends 'if they can't do the time, don't commit the crime.'"

"Yeah, yeah, yeah, wait'll we see how clean your boy is," Eddie D' said, as he got off on the Governor's floor.

Blackie yelled after him, "Go suck up."

When Blackie got off on the eighth floor, he was a little surprised that Vicki was still training the new girl, Joan, wondering, *is she a slow learner or is Vicki a slow teacher*? He walked up to the switchboard. "Ya'll got anything for me?"

Vicki asked, "You mean messages don't you?"

Blackie just laughed as he headed off into Jeannie's office. Jeannie said, "I'm halfway afraid to tell you the message I have for you."

"Why is that?" Blackie asked.

"Because Gerald said when you come in to have you go to the conference room and for me to call him so he could meet you in there. I know how bad you treat him, and I feel sorry for him."

Blackie said, "Naw, tell the dwarf I'm on my way. I'll be good to him just for you." He cut back through the conference room to get one more look at Vicki and Joan before he had to sit across from the little red-faced dwarf. Blackie had been sitting about a minute when Paula walked in with a stack of folders, and he said, "Wow! You really look good today, Gerald."

Paula laughed. "He'll be here in a minute," she said.

Blackie said, "Oh, shit, I thought he had a body transplant and you were the new Gerald."

They both laughed as she sat down, and seconds later, Gerald came in. Gerald sat down nervously beside Paula and took a rubber banded stack of folders off her pile and said, "Mr. Steece, I have organized these by divisions. Each pile consists of the eight divisions you'll be overseeing with your new position as Assistant Commissioner of Agro-Consumer Services. The employees and the positions they currently hold are listed. You, of course, will have the authority to reorganize them any way you see fit. Once the eight divisions, The Milk Division, Meat Inspection, Grading and Certification, Poultry and Egg, Weights and Measures, Fruits and Vegetables, Warehouse Commission, and the Grain Division are reorganized, they will all be under your immediate staff and the overall Agro-Consumer Services."

"Are these the only employees I have," Blackie asked, "or will I have others available to me?"

Gerald said, "You can always call for a Civil Service Register and hire any one of the three top scorers."

"OK, sounds good."

"I've heard a rumor that you're going to put everybody into one building. The one out on Airline Highway."

"Yeah, that's my plan, but I'm sure we won't use the whole building."

"I hope not. The Commissioner wants to have an office there, and I want to move my office there along with my secretary."

"I've only been in the building one time, but I'm sure there's room for everybody."

With that response from Blackie, Gerald seemed to relax a little for the first time since they'd met.

Gerald and Paula left the conference room. Blackie picked up the phone and dialed Jeannie. "Is anyone going need this room or can I spread this crap all over in here?"

"Not that I know of."

"Ok, I'm gonna work in here for a while; don't forget to call me when you go to lunch," Blackie said and hung up.

Blackie took a legal pad and tried to rough draw Airline Highway building from memory. After a few minutes, he decided he'd probably have to go out there to get the private offices right, but he also decided that he would build a row of cubicles for the Directors and Asst. Directors of each division and line them up in the same order as when Gerald had given him the files. After going over some of the personnel folders, he decided to gather them all up and go bug Jeannie to leave early for lunch. After lunch, he would go out to the Airline building to figure the layout of the private offices.

He walked into Jeannie's office and said, "Let's go eat darlin'," and then asked where he could leave the stack of files where they would be safe.

Jeannie said, " I can't leave for ten more minutes."

Blackie said, "Awww, come on. If Joan is going to work for the Commissioner, she's gonna have to learn how to lie. She might as well start practicing about you leaving a few minutes early for lunch."

By the time Jeannie got up and found an empty drawer where Blackie could put his files, covered up her typewriter, got her purse, and got to the door, the ten minutes were almost gone. As they walked by Joan toward the elevator, Blackie said, "If anybody is looking for us, we're both still here, we're just in the bathroom."

Joan, who was starting to fit in, came back with, "Men's or Women's?"

Blackie said, "Women's, of course. I don't want to miss any other dolls that might be in there." So, maybe she wasn't a slow learner, after all.

The elevator descended to a stop on four and CRII got on with a couple of female staffers that Blackie didn't recognize. CRII asked Blackie, "How's things in New Orleans?"

"Lots better than the eighth floor here," Blackie said, trying to elicit some negative response about the Commissioner, but all he got was a casual uncommitted smile. Blackie thought, *I know they don't like each other. I wish I knew why.* By the time they got to the cafeteria, there were already half a dozen people in line. Blackie thought, *what a waste of time. Think how much we could get done if we didn't eat, sleep, and go to the bathroom.* During lunch, Blackie asked Jeannie some general questions about the talent of some of the names he could remember from the files he got from Gerald. He learned that the current director of the Milk Division, Mr. Tag Dykes' brother was a State Senator. That raised the question in Blackie's mind: had the Senator gotten his brother a job from the former Commissioner or did the guy really know what he was doing?

Jeannie didn't know much about a lot of the personnel. She'd had some contact with various directors when they came up to the eighth floor, but mostly she had dealt with phone messages back and forth with their secretaries.

After lunch, Blackie retrieved his files from Jeannie's office and headed out to Airline Highway. After trying to play architect most of the afternoon, Blackie decided to give it up for now and go home to his girls.

As he turned on Sherwood Forest to cut through to I-12, he thought he recognized an old associate, "The Z" (Norm Zigrossi, the blue eyed dago). Laughing *to himself, it brought back memories of years ago during the Black Panthers' heyday, when a snitch had told him that there was a training camp off of Franklin Avenue and Lakeshore Drive in New Orleans East. Blackie had been friends with Norton Glueck, who owned American Moving and Storage/Atlas Van Lines located in an old two-block-long WWII aircraft hanger on Franklin Avenue and Lakeshore Drive. Blackie got permission from him to go on the property that night. Blackie climbed the ladder on the outside of the building that reached the roof fifty or sixty feet above the ground. He sat up on the roof till about midnight when, sure enough, several cars and a van or two pulled up across the street. Twenty or thirty young black men got out and walked over the low levee where he could only see chest high on the men. It was very dark and very hard to tell what they were doing, but they did appear to be going through some sort of training exercise. Blackie watched as well as he could for the next three or four hours until they finally left.*

The next day, when he talked to The Z and told him what he'd seen, Z said, "Are you sure?" They decided to meet that night around 11:00. They'd go back together and watch. About the same time as the night before, here came the young blacks again. This time, they appeared to take what looked to be rifles out of the cars. Both Blackie and Z were excited. Blackie stayed and watched, while The Z got down, got a bunch of New Orleans Police, FBI agents, hell, everybody imaginable, and came back to get this big gang of Black Panthers. There was a big gang of young black men alright, but they were students from nearby Dillard University being rushed by a Fraternity. Talk about a bunch of stupid lookin' people. That was Blackie and the rest. Apologizing really didn't make them look any smarter. Oh well...

Blackie turned into the rolling driveway to see Sandy in a lawn chair watching the three girls playing on their gym set, Rommel lying close by, and Gretchen running around like a nut. It was good to be home.

Chapter 28

As Blackie crossed I-55 westbound on I-12 Tuesday morning, his radio crackled with a message to call his office right away. He pulled into a State Weigh Station, identified himself to the officer on duty, and asked to use the Cen-Trex line to call Baton Rouge. Joan answered the phone

"It's your lover darlin'," Blackie said. "Who's lookin' for me, you?"

"Hold on," she responded. "I'll connect you to Mr. Knotts."

Blackie waited a few minutes and Jim Knotts' voice came on the phone. "Where are you right now?"

"I'm just west of I-55 on I-12 at the State Weigh Station on their phone," emphasizing "their," so Jim would know it was not a secure line.

"Meet us in New Orleans in about an hour and a half."

"Same place?"

"Yeah, go ahead and check us in."

"Am I going to have to spend the night, or are you going get me out of there, so I can be home with my girls?"

Jim laughed. "No, you'll be home in time for dinner. I just want ya there for the meeting."

Blackie said, "10-4," and thanked the officer for the use of his phone.

Blackie turned the unit back East and then South on I-55 trying to figure out who they'd be meeting with and why he would have to be there.

He pulled into the Monteleone garage, laughing to himself, as Number 11 sprinted over to get his unit, his keys, and his fin. Blackie thought, *this guy's really getting used to me.* He was also amused at the registration desk when the clerk recognized him.

"How many keys do you need today, sir? Do you know how many days you'll be here?"

"Give me three keys now, and Mr. Knotts will let you know how long we're going to need the room when he gets here." Blackie liked the idea of everybody getting comfortable with him. It would make it a lot easier for planting a transmitter or a camera in the Commissioner's room if that ever became necessary.

He took the elevator up, turned the air conditioner on, and went back down to the lobby to wait for their arrival. As Blackie waited, leisurely paging through a magazine, he wondered how many of these pretty women coming and going were employees and how many were just hookers. About that time, he saw Jim and the Commissioner coming into the lobby through the door that led to the parking garage.

Jim greeted Blackie and glanced around. "Do you know Marshall Brown?" he asked.

"You mean J. Marshall Brown, the insurance dude?"

"Yeah," Jim said.

"Yeah, I know him," Blackie said. Blackie had known J. Marshall Brown, whose first name was John, all the way back to the early days with the Pecoras, when Brown was a lowly insurance agent. Although he was only about 5'6" and 140, the dark-haired little Irish shit had been able to hold on to some pretty good coattails and, through the years, had worked his way up to where he had a fair amount of political connections and owned his own insurance agency. A few years ago, he had dropped John to J. and started using his middle name. Blackie figured the asshole didn't want to be associated with the John Brown of the Civil War era.

"How well?" Jim asked.

"Well, during Governor McKeithen's U S Senate race," Blackie said, "Gus (Gus Weill, Governor McKeithen's Executive Secretary) told me that his math had gotten bad. We were upstairs in the Jung Hotel on Canal Street talking to him about it and he started to get arrogant about where the dough was, so I shoved his ass out of the window and held him by his ankles while he puked all over everyone on Canal Street. I should have dropped the mother-fucker, but Gus made me pull him back in. It did help his memory though. We went to his office, got a key to a safety box in Algiers, and sure enough, when we opened the box, there was all the dough.

Jim said, "Yeah, I think I remember something about that story, but I thought it might have been a little exaggerated."

"About the only exaggerated thing was the number of people he puked on," Blackie said.

"That's good," Jim said. "It should make him easier to deal with. He's already been through boot camp."

During this entire conversation, the Commissioner had been mesmerized by some attractive blonde sitting there in the lobby. Blackie thought, if this dumb shit isn't careful, some skirt's gonna get him busted and put in the joint before I get a case made on him.

When they reached the suite, Jim told Blackie, "Why don't you watch TV in the bedroom while we make the deal with him? After it's done, I'll ice it up by calling you out of the bedroom and introducing you as my head honcho, like I don't know ya'll know each other."

Blackie laughed. "You better hope he hasn't eaten lately. If he has, he's liable to puke all over you or shit his pants," Blackie said, as he walked into the bedroom, closed the door, and turned on the TV.

Blackie had been lying on the bed watching the *Price is Right* for about twenty minutes, thinking he should have been watching Monty Hall's *Let's Make A Deal*. That's what they were there for. Just then, there was a light knock on the door. Jim opened it, and said, "Come out here a minute. I want you to meet someone." Turning, Jim said over his shoulder, "Marshall, I want you to meet one of my main people. He's gonna be coming by to visit you from time to time to pick up our package." Blackie walked out of the bedroom. He'd left his coat on the chair deliberately, so Marshall could see that big .44 hanging on his hip. Jim said, "David Steece, this is Marshall Brown." J. Marshall's face paled as Blackie stuck his hand out and said, "Good to meet you." Brown not knowing whether to shit or go blind stuck his hand out. When Blackie took it, it was cold as ice with a sweaty palm.

Marshall mumbled something inaudible back to Blackie's comment and turned back to the Commissioner. " I really need to be going."

Blackie thought, *yeah I bet you do, to go clean your drawers.*

As the door closed behind Marshall, Jim and Blackie both roared with laughter; as usual, the Commissioner looked totally confused at what they found so amusing. Now Blackie was sure that he had had his head up his ass watching the blonde during their earlier conversation.

After Jim and Blackie caught their breath, Jim asked, "Can you think of anybody else we should meet with today?" Blackie, faced with the constant problem of avoiding a future accusation of entrapment, once again was forced to fend off the question. Without really responding, he said, "Commissioner, didn't you tell me I had to do something or other at your Cedar Lake Trailer Park?" (By now he had the legal name, Cedar Lake Development Co, Biloxi, MS.)

The Commissioner, gazing out the window, turned, looked at Jim, and said, "I think I'm going to stay in town tonight and let you go back to Baton Rouge. I'll have Blackie take me to see that friend. He'll know how to handle it, so I'll be safe."

Blackie thought, *oh shit, I wonder what this is about.* He looked at Jim with pleading eyes that said *get me out of this.* Jim obviously already knew what the Commissioner was talking about. In an effort to relieve Blackie, he said, "You won't be able to bring her back here. It's too dangerous." Turning to Blackie, he said, "You know a safe house where you can play? If it's a two bedroom, you can bring one of your squeezes and party, too."

Blackie, pretending to be thinking, thought, *I wouldn't go to bed with my wife in front of this idiot, much less some chippy.* He knew he had a key to a couple of playhouses: Uncle Ernie's out near City Park and Uncle Rolland's in Eden Isles. Maybe if he took "dumb shit" there with a broad, he'd be comfortable enough at some later date with some shake-down Blackie would need to both tape and film. Blackie said, "Let me go to a payphone and make a couple a calls. I'll see what I can do." As Blackie rode down the elevator, he knew that Uncle Ernie's was outta the question. There was no way he'd give that location up to anybody, much less this idiot. He wondered who the broad could be that couldn't be seen in public.

Blackie called Uncle Rolland hoping that, because it was Tuesday evening, he'd be staying at the apartment at Saint Louis Street in the French Quarter and not be going all the way out to the Island. When Blackie got Uncle Rolland on the phone, he was happy to find out that Uncle Rolland wasn't going to the Island tonight, but there was a chance that one of their other friends would be using the guest room that night, and, when Uncle Rolland asked, "Do you want him to use your bedroom?" Blackie said, "not in three lifetimes. I'm going to call Hilbert Loeb and see if he's gotta joint we can use."

Hilbert Loeb, owner of Fountainhead Apartments and a fancy apartment building on 1411 St. Charles Avenue, had numerous duplexes and four-plexes in and all around Orleans and Jefferson. He was a well-known builder, a supporter, and friend of Blackie, and of Blackie's ventures.

Blackie was glad to hear Pat Fruchtnicht's voice on the other end of the phone. Pat, a gorgeous redhead with big green eyes and a chest to go with them, had once been Blackie's sister Patsy's secretary. She said, "Hold on, darlin', he can't talk to you right now. He's on the other phone. I'll get back to you as soon as I can. It might be a couple minutes.

Blackie's mind drifted as he waited for Pat or Hilbert to get back on the line. *Pat had been instrumental in solving one of his soldier's problems a while back when the soldier had been arrested and charged with a felony for buying a handgun after being convicted of a felony. Black Jack, a popular criminal defense attorney in New Orleans, was representing the soldier and told Blackie the State's main case was based on a form that had been signed at the time of the purchase, stating that the purchaser had never been convicted of a felony. Blackie had wired Pat with a transmitter. The gorgeous redhead was dressed in a miniskirt and a see-through blouse that was unbuttoned low enough, so her tits almost fell out. Pat went to Gerber's Jewelry Store on Basin Street in New Orleans where the gun had been purchased. There, shamelessly flaunting herself and flirting with Mr. Gerber, she asked all kinds of silly questions: "What was the best gun for a lady's protection," etc., etc. Finally they settled on some useless little .25 cal automatic. When they agreed on the price and Pat was paying Mr. Gerber, he came out with a yellow form, and she said, "Oh my goodness, my lunch hour is almost gone, do I have to answer all these questions, or can I just sign it?" As usual, tits win over brains, and Gerber said, "You just sign it right there honey and I'll fill it in for you." Pat, being well-schooled on the information she needed to obtain on the tape, clearly spoke where the recorder would not miss it, asked, "Mr. Gerber, are you sure it's all right for me to just sign it and not read all those questions?" Mr. Gerber assured her it was fine, that he would fill the form in for her and was nice enough to add, "I do this all the time for customers. Just give me your name and address real quick, and you can go." Pat signed the blank page at the bottom and waltzed out of the store.*

When the case came to trial, the State of course thought they had an iron-clad case, with the testimony of Mr. Gerber and the form signed by the felon. The State was sure they had a conviction, but after Mr. Gerber testified for the prosecution, Black Jack cross-examined him for nearly an hour repeatedly asking, "Have you ever let anyone just sign the bottom of the form blank? Have you ever filled out the form for anyone?" Mr. Gerber's response was emphatically, "No!" After Mr. Gerber was off the stand, Black Jack called Pat to the witness stand. As she walked down the aisle from the witness room, hair pulled back, wearing very little makeup, a business suit, and glasses, she looked like a nice school teacher, not the tit- flashing hussy that had bought the gun without filling out the form. Two things you noticed as she walked down the isle: One, she was carrying a tape recorder and, two, she stopped and said, "Mr. Gerber, it's so nice to see you again." Mr. Gerber looked a little like he didn't remember who she was but then, he probably hadn't looked at her face when she was in his store, just her tits. Mr. Gerber knew his own voice when he heard it, and to say he paled when he heard that tape recording is an understatement.

Black Jack, of course, started to rant and rave that Mr. Gerber should be charged with perjury, and, of course, got his client's charges dismissed immediately.

That night, Blackie, his soldier, the alleged felon, Pat, and Black Jack enjoyed a celebration dinner at Masson's., After dinner, Blackie was nice enough to accompany Pat back to her apartment where they were able to enjoy a special celebration of their own.

He snapped back to reality when Hilbert's voice boomed over the phone, "What can I do for you, Blackie?" After a couple minutes of chit-chatting, Blackie asked, "Ya got one of those furnished apartments that I can use for my boss to get laid in tonight? I don't know what I can have him do for ya. Agriculture doesn't have much to do wit the building business, but I appreciate if ya can handle it."

Hilbert said, "Hold on a minute," and after a few minutes, he came back on the line. "I got a furnished apartment up on Fairfield. I'll get Pat to run up and put a couple of sheets on the bed and leave a couple of towels in the unit. Everything else is up to par; electricity's on, water, TV, it's all furnished, just no bedding or dishes."

"Hey man, I really appreciate it," Blackie said, as he hung up.

Blackie went back up the elevator to the Commissioner's room. He was surprised to see that Jim had already left. He wondered if he'd have time to go home and eat with his girls before this rendezvous was going to take place. As Blackie sat down with the Commissioner, the Commissioner asked, "You ever hear of Kogos Greek Restaurant?"

"Yeah, I know Pete pretty good, why?" Blackie thought, *Kogos Greek Restaurant? Pete Kogos.* Blackie guessed he had inherited or taken over his dad's restaurant on Carrolton Avenue, which was close to Cleanerama Cleaners where everybody who was anybody took their clothes. Pete was a slight man, with gray hair, deep set eyes, and oily like a Greek olive. But as far as a Greek restaurant, Kogos was primarily seafood.

The Commissioner gazed out the window for a couple of minutes like he didn't know what to say next. He finally asked, "Do you know Julie?"

Blackie said, "Yeah, that's Pete's wife. "

Now Blackie got the question. Julie, much younger than her husband Pete, was a tall striking blonde who had a beautiful body, as Blackie knew first hand, didn't mind sharing it. Everyone assumed she had married Pete for security, since before the marriage and after, she got the majority of her sex action someplace else.

The Commissioner said, "That's who wants to see me. Is that a problem for you?"

Blackie said, "No," thinking, *I don't care if you fuck a monkey as long as I don't have to watch or hold the towel.*

Hesitating a few more minutes, the Commissioner finally said, "She told me she usually leaves the restaurant between nine and ten o'clock, when business slows down. Her husband usually stays until twelve or one closing up. She's supposed to call me when she leaves to tell me where to pick her up."

"No problem," Blackie said. "I'll just go home, eat with my girls, come back and get ya around 8:30."

The Commissioner still looking a little spacey said, "Ah, ah, okay."

"See ya about 8:30," Blackie said, and he left the room before the Commissioner could think of something else for him to do.

As Blackie roared along I-55 to get home for dinner, he wondered if the Commissioner realized he was at least number three on her current list. Julie was being poked by United States Senator J. Bennett Johnson, who had been a State Senator from North Louisiana in the Shreveport area. He had been a run-off candidate in the last gubernatorial race that Edwin Edwards had just beaten at the wire. He then qualified against long-time US Senator eighty-plus-year-old US Senator Allen Ellender in his re-election bid for the US Senate seat. No one else qualified in that race, because no one, including Bennett, thought Ellender could be beaten. Bennett had hoped for, Blackie thought, and gotten Ellender to have a heart attack and die shortly before the primary. This had given his him a free pass. It also pissed off a huge portion of the political "King Makers." Tim Ellender, the late Senator's grandson, contacted Blackie and said they were going to ask former Governor John McKiethen to run as an independent. To qualify as an independent in a statewide race required thousands of registered voters' signatures to be certified by the Secretary of State. Blackie knew it was a tremendous undertaking but thought it was possible. One of the reasons was that Bennett had been exposed as somewhat of a racist in the gubernatorial race against Edwin. When he was a State Senator, his voting record had never been one that would help the blacks, plus he had always had his kids in private white schools and was a member of white country clubs. Blackie thought that Governor McKeithen's popularity with the blacks might make it possible to get enough signatures for McKeithen to enter the race. Too bad he hadn't been screwing Julie at the time; that might have been enough to keep him out of the US Senate seat. Her other current lover was a Jefferson Parish Judge, a good friend of Blackie and, after in high school, college, and the Air Force, he was still The Man's best friend. Ironically, they had both busted their ass for McKeithen in the U S Senate race, and now he and Bennett were poking the same squeeze. And they think politics makes strange bed partners. Blackie had this information because he had the outside (guarding the outside from intrusion) on several occasions for both men. Hell, he bet if you shook her inside out, she'd look like a porkypine. Poor Pete. *Speaking of Jefferson Parish Judges, in John Mamoulides first race for District Attorney, one of their mutual neighbors and supporters, Judge Doug Allen, also running for re-election, were at a coffee party together in a Kenner subdivision. The guy who handled the PR for John's campaign called at the party and said some crackpot had said something or other to a Channel 6 TV reporter and wanted John to comment on it before the 10 oclock news, which was about twenty minutes from then. Blackie was John's driver at the time. They ran out and jumped in the car with Doug in the back seat. As Blackie roared out onto I-10, Doug was trying to get the seatbelt hooked. When he couldn't get it connected, he tied it in a knot. When Blackie started braking at over a hundred miles an hour at the Loyola Avenue exit, Doug, a couple of pounds overweight, surged into the knot and pulled it so tight when they pulled up behind Channel 6 T V on Royal Street, he couldn't get it untied. Blackie and John went inside. John handled the interview and when they came back out, Doug, sweating profusely, was still struggling trying to get out of the seatbelt. Blackie flagged down a New Orleans Police car. They used one of them cop-knives to cut the belt off of him. In all the years Blackie knew Doug after that, Doug never rode in the car with him again, but hey remained friends*

Letter from Judge Douglas Allen :

First Parish Court
Parish of Jefferson
3100 Clearview Parkway
Metairie, Louisiana 70002

Douglas A Allen
Judge Division B
Personal

Christmas, 1973

Dear Dave,

My family and I wish you and your family a Merry Christmas and a Happy New Year. We hope that you will enjoy success, prosperity, and all that is best in the Christmas spirit, now and always.

Cordially,
Doug Allen /S/
Doug Allen & Family

Chapter 29

Blackie grumbled as Sandy woke him up, bitching to himself about how late he'd gotten home last night after playing nursemaid to Julie and the Commissioner. They had kept him up. It had been nearly 2:00 o'clock Wednesday morning before he got home. He was still at a loss as to what the purpose was between the two of them. The Commissioner couldn't gain anything except to get laid, and she had no need for Agriculture and probably had more money than he did. Hell, he didn't give a damn. He wasn't about to be an analyst with those two idiots.

Blackie dragged himself to the shower knowing any second the phone would probably ring. Sandy came into the bathroom while he was shaving and asked what he wanted for breakfast, adding, "I hope you were out on business last night," which got her a sarcastic look and no comment.

The phone rang while Blackie was eating, and he was glad to hear Jim Knotts' voice on the other end. "How'd it go last night, cowboy?"

"What the hell's up wit those two, do ya know?"

Which got a slight laugh from Jim. "Honestly, I think he's just pussy crazy."

Blackie laughed. "He better get a shot if he's gonna play with that one much. Everybody I know has been there once and most twice."

"Meet me as soon as you can in Baton Rouge," Jim said.

"Any place special?"

"Hmmm, don't you like the Capitol House?"

"Yeah. I can probably get there before noon."

"That's okay. We can have an early lunch. Call me when you get close."

"Okay man, see ya."

Blackie picked up the radio mic to call Jim as he was crossing Sherwood Forest Boulevard exit. He thought, *I hope Sandy ain't gonna start being a pain in the ass and start thinking she's a real wife, cause that shit ain't gonna work.*

"How far away are you?" Jim asked, responding to Blackie's call.

"I'm coming up on Airline Exit right now."

"So, what…fifteen minutes?"

"At the most."

"10-4. I'll see ya there."

Blackie pulled into the Capitol House Parking Garage surveying all the cars to see if there was anybody he needed to look out for or speak to. When he walked into the dining room, he was surprised that it was almost empty. Then he realized it was only 10:30. Hell, he was surprised anybody was there at all.

He took a seat close to the parking garage entrance and waved the waiter away deciding to wait until Jim got there before even looking at a menu. In about ten minutes, Jim strolled in, but from the hotel entrance, not the parking garage, which raised Blackie's suspicions.

Jim said, "What's up, cowboy?" as the two men shook hands and sat down. "Holmes Johnson has got a zillion leave hours coming and he's going to start taking them now."

"Okay."

"I think the Commissioner's getting more comfortable with you all the time, especially after last night."

"So?"

"Well, I actually want him to let you do some of this stuff."

"Hey, man, I'm not gonna ask anybody for any fuckin' money. If I get sent to pick up a package, I'm bringing it in just like I got it. This mother-fucker's like a loose cannon rolling around on a pirate ship in a storm, and I ain't goin' over the side with him if he goes."

"I understand, but I need you to do certain things to make all this stuff work, cause you're the only one I trust."

Blackie thought, *uh oh, mistake number one.* "I appreciate where you're comin' from," he said, "but I ain't gonna go ask any mother-fucker for any money."

"Well," Jim said, as he looked out the window, "he's probably going to ask you to do some other shit for him, like take some men and go do some work on that trailer park that he owns in Biloxi and maybe some other rental property he owns around town. Is that going to be a problem?"

"Naw, man. He's the boss; if he tells me to go stack BBs on the side of the parkin' lot, that's what I'll do, but askin' people for money that we regulate could be bad. The assholes call the heat and say this gangster came in here and shook me down, because they won't have any way of knowin' if I'm shakin' 'em down for me or for the

Commissioner and ya know that's the rep I'm carryin' around on my back. These fuckin' people been watchin' too many movies and callin' me a gangster forever. You know that."

"Yeah, I see where you're comin' from. Me or him one will get it set up and you can be with us just in case anybody tries to fuck with us."

"That's not a problem."

"Okay, now we got it together."

Business finished, they ordered lunch and steered the conversation to family subjects.

As Blackie headed out to the Airline Highway building, he wondered what benefit it would be to have proof that he took people to Mississippi. He decided that just the fact that they were using Louisiana State cars, gas, and employees being paid by the State to work on private property, would probably put the Commissioner's tit in a pretty tight wringer.

As he approached Essen Lane Exit on I-10, he decided he'd go on to New Orleans and bring The Man up to date.

A little over an hour later, Blackie pulled into the Gretna Courthouse parking lot. As usual, there was nothing that looked like a parking place, so he just made one by pulling up onto the medium, slapping his red light up on the dash and pulling the sun visor down, which, on the back, had the identity tag, "Jefferson Parrish District Attorney's Office Investigator."

Blackie got off on the fourth floor of the Gretna Courthouse Annex, rushing up to Kay Stombo on the switchboard, grabbing a Kleenex off the desk, tucking it under his watchband and saying, "Ya remember Ivanhoe, when he put Rowena's scarf under his wrist armor and became her champion? Well I ain't got no wrist armor and you ain't got no scarf, but I am your champion, and I come to carry ya off into the sunset."

Kay said, "Go over to the door and I'll buzz you in, ya big flirt."

"No, No," Blackie said. "I really came to save you from all this and whisk you away."

"Dave, go harass Marion Edwards or Therese. I really have to work and they won't fire you for screwing around, but they will me."

"See that's what I'm trying to tell ya. I'm tryin' ta take ya away from all this."

"Come on, Dave, please," she said as she pushed the electric door release.

"Alright, alright. The buzzer's drivin' me crazy. I'll go, but my heart's broken."

Blackie walked into Marion Edward's office and dropped into the chair. "What's goin on, bro?" he asked.

"What brings you to this part of the world? You bored?"

"Actually, you're right. I didn't have anything else to do today. Aren't ya lucky?"

"Hard to tell. Lucky or snake bit. It depends on what you want."

"Naw, really just hangin' out brother."

"How's it going up there?"

"I don't know. It's hard to separate the bullshit from the real stuff. They got more slippage in State Government than you could imagine, even if you could imagine."

The intercom buzzed and Marion answered, "Yeah, he's in here." She hung the phone up. "That was Therese. Kay must have told her you were here and The Man wants to see you in his office."

"See what I mean? No rest."

Blackie walked into The Man's office and sat in front of his desk. "Anything important?" he was asked.

"Naw, I just wanted to tell ya it looks like they're gonna send me over to that trailer park in Mississippi and do some work, and I wondered how I should handle it."

"What are you going to do?"

"I don't know. I just heard today. We're probably gonna do some kinda maintenance work. I really don't know."

"Well, if you go in State vehicles, try and get pictures of them at the State line, on his property in Mississippi, pictures of the employees. If they're Civil Service, all that stuff is very illegal. You know that."

"Yeah, I didn't know if ya wanted me to expose myself to the men I take wit me or do it very discrete."

"What's the matter with you? You been hanging around him so long your head's in your ass? You know what breaking the law is, and you know you have to prove what you say happened."

"All right, I guess I just need a pat on the back to get my motor runnin' again. This guy's such an asshole to work for or even be around."

"I understand, but just get your act together. It should start coming together pretty soon. How are the girls doing?"

"They're doin' okay."

"Is Sandy working out?"

"It seemed like it till this mornin'. Ya know how these fuckin' broads are. I was out mosta the night last night and she said somethin' like 'I hope you were workin' last night. Hopefully, it was a temporary memory loss and she'll remember she's just there to take care of the girls and not me."

With that the two men shook hands and Blackie nodded at Therese as he walked through her office to the lobby.

As Blackie walked out past the reception area, he ran into Harry Lee coming in. Harry was a Chinaman over 6'5" and 300 pounds. He was a very well-liked Sheriff of Jefferson Parish. Blackie noticed a limp and said, "What's the matter wit your leg, Harry?" As soon as Blackie opened his mouth, he knew it was a mistake.

Grinning from ear to ear, Harry said, "It's my knee, and you'd limp too if you had a 300 pound Chinaman standing on it." *Always the clown*, Blackie thought.

As Blackie rode down the elevator, he laughed to himself about one of Harry's many notorious acts. *When everybody was young, most of the teenage kids took karate lessons on North Turnbull, in Metairie, and everybody wore those little white costumes with the rope around the waist and the headbands. By now Bing Lee, Harry's daddy had done pretty well with the House of Lee Restaurant, and Harry had brought his dad's big black Lincoln Continental to practice. After practice, as he started home, some jerk was behind him with the bright lights on. So, he flashed his lights a couple of times, waved his hands in the window, everything you normally do to get some jerk to dim his lights, all to no avail. Finally, he slowed down to a crawl so the other car would pass him. Then, of course, being a normal teenager, he sped up and gave the car that was now in front of him, a dose of the big Lincoln's bright lights. After a few blocks of this, the other car had enough and, like Harry had, slowed down to a crawl. Harry, tired of the game, as he passed the car, could see two young men in the front shouting and shaking their fists. According to the way Harry told the story, he was just going to proceed home. Lo and behold, the car accelerated and started flashing the bright lights up and down and blowing the horn. Harry could see when they got close to him, the two men young men in the front seat were still shaking their fists. Harry paid no attention to this but proceeded to the stop sign. When he stopped, he looked up in the mirror and was a little bit surprised to see both front doors fling open on the car behind him and the two angry young men running toward his car. Now, Harry wasn't as big then as he is now, but he was well over six feet and over 250 pounds. Harry put the car in park, opened the door, did a karate stance, and yelled, "HWAAAAAAA!" Now ya have to take into account, that this was about the time the James Bond movies were comin' out and can you imagine a 250 pound Chinaman wrapped in a karate suit, headband, rope and all, standing, projecting his fist in a karate crouch. These two young men stopped dead, turned around and started running, leaving their car, engine running, doors open. Harry said they probably ran all the way to Baton Rouge before they stopped.*

Hell, that was just one of Harry's crazy acts. *Back in his law school days, Harry was more often late to class than not. He was a fan of those James Bond movies and the Goldfinger character, Oddjob, sailing his lethal discus hat particularly appealed to Harry. In an effort to distract his lateness from the professor, Harry stepped into the doorway and hollered "HWAAAAAAA," did the Oddjob stance, sailed the hat across the room, almost hitting the professor. This got lots of laughs from everyone but the professor and a little time off from those dumb enough to laugh, including the infamous Marion Edwards. Harry Lee went on to finish law school, became a pretty good attorney, a United States Federal Magistrate, the Jefferson Parish Attorney and now the Sheriff of Jefferson Parish.*

Blackie came back to reality as the elevator filled up. He was ready to get home to his girls.

As he pulled out of the Gretna Courthouse parking lot and turned onto Huey P. Long Avenue, he decided to stop by Jamie's office.

Blackie walked into the lobby and stopped in the open door of Jamie's private office. "Did Lisa take her Civil Service test?" he asked, causing her to look up.

"Come on in and sit. Yeah, I believe her appointment was this morning."

"Good. I want to get somebody in that New Orleans office I can trust. Okay, darlin', I gotta run. Now I'm goin' home and play with the girls. See ya later."

Jamie said, "Make sure you just play with the girls; don't play with Sandy. Any playing like that, save for me."

"Ok, darlin'." Blackie left and headed home, thinking, *speaking of that kind'a playin, you better get back to work on the Millie project.* All she'd received recently was a bunch of flowers and a few kisses. He'd been so damn busy. He better tie a string around his finger to remember to get the rest of her tomorrow.

Chapter 30

Blackie walked into the kitchen Thursday morning to the aroma of freshly brewed coffee and ham and eggs cooking on the stove, and he was glad to hear a chorus of "Hi Daddy" from the girls and a smiling "Good Morning" from Sandy. She said, "Jim Knotts called you last night and said it wasn't important and to just call when you got up." Blackie kissed the girls and went into his study, calling over his shoulder, "Did he say where he'd be?"

"Yeah, I put the number and the room number on your desk."

"Thanks," Blackie said, as he picked up the paper and dialed.

The Holiday Inn switchboard answered and Blackie asked for the room number. Jim answered on the second ring. "Good Morning."

"Good morning, yourself," said Blackie.

"Hey cowboy, you still at home?"

"10-4."

"What time can you meet me at the Airline Building?"

"Ahhhh, my lady's got a big breakfast on the table for me. Give me twenty minutes to eat, twenty to shower, and thirty to drive."

"How about if I give you forty-five to drive so you get here alive?"

Laughing, Blackie added, "I thought the phrase was 'Alive at 55'"

Jim said, "I think it is but I think it means age doesn't it?"

Blackie laughed. "I'll see ya near about an hour and a half," he said, then both men hung up.

Blackie turned on the Sherwood Forest Boulevard Exit off I-12 exactly one hour after he'd hung the phone up with Jim. Fifteen minutes later, he pulled up in front of the Airline Highway building. As he got out of the car, Jim pulled into the parking lot. The two men shook hands.

"What's goin on, man?" Blackie asked.

"I just want to get an idea of how you plan on laying this out."

Blackie walked him around the building, showing the various offices and his plans for use. Jim said, "That's going to leave you with about half a dozen empty on the other side of that building, huh?"

"Yeah, I'm sure 'numb nuts' will find somebody to put there."
Jim laughed. "You're too hard on him."
"I think that's his problem. Nobody's been hard enough on him."
Jim smiled at that. "I'm gonna tell you a little story that's private. A long time ago, we were both in college together and played basketball on the same team. He was chasin' every pussy in sight, and I was a little more heavy into my sports and my training and probably had neglected my girlfriend a little bit. Anyhow, he got to her. I guess only once, but she felt guilty and told me about it, so after practice one day, we were in the shower. I beat the fuck out of him. I picked the shower to make sure all the blood got washed off him before the coach saw him."
"No shit." Blackie said.
"That's the truth," Jim said. "Anybody that knows us back during those college days knows about it."
Blackie laughed. "So, what are you telling me? That if I beat the fuck outta him, we'll get along better?"
"Naw, I'm just telling you I can handle him."
"Ok," Blackie said, "I'll give you another chance."
"Has he mentioned anything about running for Governor next time?"
"Not directly, but I've heard him say it to other people. Personally, I don't think he can beat Jimmy Fitz."
"Well, it's a ways away. Let's not worry about it now. We need to have a fundraiser, and I know you're good at organizing those. When can you put one together?"
"You mean a legitimate fund raiser and not just some shake down? All we need is Dr. Day's big rolling bar-b-que pit. The meat, chips, and drinks will be easy to get donated. Some kind of small band, hustle somebody to print some tickets, and then comes the tricky part, gettin' his friends to sell 'em. He ain't got any."
Jim laughed. "Then we'll have to get our friends to sell them, won't we? You really don't think we can get anybody to sell them?"
"I don't know, man, everybody thinks he's an asshole, and anybody that has a wife or girlfriend on a scale of one to ten, he's gonna hit on. So between that move and him pissing the legislators off every day and most of the other departments in the State starting with CRII, ya got three big questions: Who's gonna sell the tickets, who's gonna buy 'em, and who's gonna come?"
Jim kinda gazed off and said, "Didn't you raise money for The Man and organize huge parties for Governor McKeithen?"

"Yeah. Five or six thousand at a time for McKeithen and plenty of people for Fitz, and anybody else we wanted to, but they always had people who liked 'em. I'm not shittin' ya, when I tell ya, I don't think even this guy's wife likes him. Probably the only way to get a crowd for this mother-fucker is to have my soldiers go out and wave one week's juice or threaten to throw everybody in the River if they don't come."

"Well, let me think about it for a while. You kick it around too."

"Okay, man, see ya later."

And Blackie headed to the Capitol.

As Blackie got off the elevator on the eighth floor, he blew a kiss to Joan and walked into Jeannie's office.

"Hi, Dave. Lisa just called; she's on the Register. I know you're in a hurry to get somebody hired, so I pulled it and she's number two."

"Okay, what else do I have to do to put her to work?"

Jeannie said, "I'll have Gerald get her paperwork together. All you have to do is get her to sign it and she's working."

"So ya can get the paperwork now, I can take it down and get her to sign it, and she can start work tomorrow?"

"That's right."

"Good. Get him to do it. While you're talking to Gerald, tell him to have prisoners, workers, whoever we need to get that furniture to Airline Highway. I want to get that place up and runnin.'"

"How do you want to do that? You don't want to close all the divisions up while you're moving them do you?"

"Nooo, but they don't do shit anyhow. Just leave one girl and a phone in each division, have whoever the movers are move the stuff out there, and have the employees move their personal stuff and start settin' up while the phone people are hookin' up the new lines."

"It sounds like it'll be mass confusion," she said,

"Can't be any more confusin' than now, when nobody knows what to do or when to do it."

"Okay, I'll tell him."

"Remind Gerald if he don't want to do it for you and do it now, he'll have to deal with me in person. I know he remembers the car incident."

Jeannie grinned. "I'm sure he'll get it done as fast as he can."

"Blackie said, "hurry and get those papers, so I can get them down to Lisa."

Jeannie said, "Okay," and left.

As Blackie sat there waiting for the papers, he thought, *I bet State Government could run on ten percent of the people that are employed, if they'd just work instead of sit around in the fog all day.*

The door opened from the Commissioner's office, and he came in asking where Jeannie was.

Blackie said, "She went to get some papers for me from Gerald. I figured it was better to have her do it than have Gerald piss his pants when he saw me."

The Commissioner rolled his eyes. "Do you know Judge Moreal?"

"Yeah, I know Dutch, why?" Earnest "Dutch" Moriel, was 5'6", a current judge, and the first black State Legislator since Reconstruction, even though he was lighter skinned than Blackie; he had been rumored to be considering a run for the Mayor of New Orleans.

"What do you think of his chances in the election?"

"I think it'll be between him and Nat Kiefer." A current State Senator, Nat was a dark, curly-haired 6', 230-pound animal, who played politics a lot like Dick Butkis played linebacker for the Chicago Bears. Nat had controlled his State Senate District with an iron fist and didn't take any bullshit from anybody. For years, there had been rumors and allegations that he and his brother Zip were being connected to one of Blackie's crews.

"Who would you recommend I support?"

"I'd support 'em both through the primary and, then, dependin' on the vote, go with just the winner in the runoff."

The Commissioner looked out the window at the river and finally said, "When are you going to New Orleans again?"

"As soon as Jeannie gets back with the papers."

Without responding, the Commissioner went back into his office. About the same time Jeannie got back, the Commissioner reentered the room while she explained to Blackie where to have Lisa sign the papers. The Commissioner said, "Deliver these two envelopes for me when you're down there." Blackie took the two envelopes. One was addressed to Nat Kiefer, the other to Earnest Moreal.

As Blackie rode down the elevator with Lisa's papers in one hand and the envelopes in the other, he thought, *hell, I could just keep all the money if I wanted to. Neither one of these guys will ever even speak to this asshole much less believe he sent them money.*

Blackie took the papers by Jamie's house and had Lisa sign them. He gave her a key to the office. When she asked him, "What am I supposed to do tomorrow?" he laughed and said, "Nothin. Just sit at the desk and look stupid. That's what State employees do." He added, "Oh yeah, ya gotta answer the phone when it rings. I forgot that part, but you probably woulda done that anyhow. You're smarter than most."

Lisa, quite capable of being a smartass, added, "Should I write the messages down or should I try to remember them?"

"Naw, write 'em down, I'll try to think of somethin' for you to do in a couple of days; in the meantime, just answer the phone."

Blackie then drove to Barrone Street to Nat Kiefer's office to deliver the first envelope. After a short visit, he left, called Moreal's office and was told he was taping a commercial at Channel 6. As Blackie pulled up to the back door of Channel 6 on Royal street, Dutch and a couple of his aides were just leaving. Blackie hollered to him. Dutch walked over and said, "I heard you were a big shot in Baton Rouge."

"Naaa, I'm just a little shot, but I got an envelope for ya."

"Hey, is it all there?"

"No, I kept half for me."

Dutch laughed and thanked him as he opened the envelope. "Either he's the cheapest fuck in the State or you kept more than half."

Blackie said, "He don't expect too much, only every time he wants something passed he'll want you to take care of it for 'im."

Dutch said, "The only thing I'll pass for him will be on the street without waving."

As Blackie headed out of the Quarter on South Galvez to Elysian Fields, he passed the old building that was years ago known as Gloria's Living Room on Spain and Galvez. Laughing, he remembered, *the incident with the two black bank robbers from Chicago, Levi Washington and Leonard Johnson. Back then, Gloria's had been a known Moslum Den on Spain Street in the 9th Ward in New Orleans and a hangout for Black Panthers and other black radicals. The 'Z' (Norman Zigorssi) had called Blackie and said, "I think these dudes are supposed to be hanging out there. Go check it out." Blackie remembered asking the 'Z', "Hey man, have ya noticed I'm white? I might stick out in there."*

" Ah, man, you must have one of your black soldiers you can go in with. We gotta find these dudes. They're bad people, They killed a nun or priest in a bank robbery in Chicago."

Blackie went by City Wholesale Liquor on Washington Avenue, owned by Joe and Dominic Miceli, both made men. Their manager was a black dude who owed money and had been short a couple a times on the juice. Blackie leaned on him and was a little surprised that this dude, even though he was black and dealt with tough black bar owners all the time, didn't feel comfortable going in that particular bar. Blackie told him that he could say he was checking on a liquor delivery, and all he had to do was go in there at a certain time and that Blackie would come in and discuss some random bullshit with him: (1) that would justify Blackie being in there and (2) give him time to look around for his targets and not raising the patron's curiosity about why Blackie was in the bar. Blackie also felt sure that, as tough as those Blacks were, and as many cops that they liked to screw with, somebody there would tell them who he was and that they wouldn't want to take them on as long as it appeared that Blackie was in there for some other reason than fucking with them personally. After pressure from Joe, Dominic, and Blackie, he finally consented to meet Blackie on an agreed night at 10:30 p.m.

Blackie and the dude met on Elyasian Fields and Blackie said, "You walk in with your liquor list in your hand, and I'll start goin' over it with you."

He said, "I hope this works; they don't like white people."

Blackie said, "I'm not white, I'm Sicilian."

Blackie waited about ten minutes after the dude went inside, pulled right up on the curb, leaving Wonder Animal in the front passenger seat with a shot gun between his legs in case something went wrong. He got out of the car, went in the front door and went to the City Wholesale guy like he knew he'd be there. Everybody looked at Blackie in the black Mohair suit, white on white shirt, and white on white tie, and knew immediately who he was, plus they could see that big .44 on his hip. Right then, he wasn't trying to hide it at all. Blackie went over the list for a couple of seconds, and then called out to the bartender loud enough for everyone to hear, "Where's the head, man? I gotta take a piss." The bartender pointed to the other side of the room and Blackie told the dude, "Wait right here. I'll be right back." He scanned the crowd as he walked to the bathroom. In the bathroom, he was disappointed he hadn't seen anyone that looked like the picture of either one of the targets, but while he was standing in front of the urinal, a dude came out of one of the stalls, who looked like Leonard Johnson. The guy looked a little surprised to see a white guy taking a piss, but Blackie acted like he was finished, zipped up and asked him some random bullshit question that made no sense about something local, to which the guy said, "I don't know. I'm from outta town."

Blackie said, "Yeah, where from?"

The guy, not too suspicious, said, "Chicago."

Blackie reached up, pushed his nose aside, and said, "Yeah? Al Capone territory."

"You one a them, huh? That explains why they allow you in here."

Blackie said, "Yeah, according to the cops, but according to me, I'm a salesman."

The guy laughed and said, "Yeah, how hard is it to get a piece here?"

"What are ya lookin' for?"

The guy pulled his shirt up and showed Blackie what Blackie thought looked like a .38 revolver and said, "Something heavier than this."

Blackie said, "Shit, I can throw rocks harder than that fuckin' thing."

The dude said,"I figure with your connections, you could point me at one."

"What are ya lookin' for?"

"Maybe a couple a clean .45s and a shotgun."

"You got the bread?" Blackie asked.

"Yeah, how much do I need?"

"Ya got the stuff on ya?"the dude asked.

"Why do ya need two .45s?"

"Cause I got a partner."

"He with ya?" Blackie asked.

"No, but I'm gonna pick him up in a little while."

"Let me make a couple calls," Blackie said, "and I'll get back to ya."

As they walked outta the bathroom, Blackie said, "We're gonna have to meet somewhere besides here for this."

"I know," the dude said.

Blackie motioned to the City Wholesale dude and said, "I got some business to do. I'll catch up with ya later." He got a relieved look as he headed for the door. Blackie and the dude, who later became positively identified as Leonard Johnson, walked outside. Blackie said, "I'll make my calls and I guess meet ya back here, what's a good time?"

Leonard Johnson said, "That's my Oldsmobile across the street. I'll be here about thirty minutes. If the car's gone, we're gonna have to do it another time, because I'll be gone across town to pick up my partner.

Looking into the Cadillac sitting on the sidewalk, Leonard added, "looks like you got your partner with ya."

"Just one of many," Blackie said. "Tell ya what, if you're only gonna be here thirty minutes, why don't I just meet you here tomorrow night about ten. I'll have the shit with me and we can go someplace else and take care of business. Leonard Johnson agreed. The two men shook hands. Leonard went back inside the bar as Blackie and Wonder drove away. When Blackie got to a pay phone, he called the 'Z' and said, "I made Leonard Johnson. He's carrying a .38 in the front of his jeans and wearing a green shirt, driving a cream colored Oldsmobile with a black top, license number 386741 Louisiana, current, and he's going to pick up his partner, probably Washington, but I'm not sure that's who he meant, in about thirty minutes if you can get set up. Galvez is a one-way street; he's gonna have to come outta there and you can't miss him if you're ready."

"You don't know which way he's goin? The 'Z' asked.

"No, and I don't know what kinda toothpaste he uses either, but I told ya what he's wearin', what he's driving, and where he's carrying his piece. Gimme my little gold star, and you do the rest of it." Well, the 'Z' got set up in time. Johnson had lied because when he left Gloria's, Washington was with him, but they did head across town and, with no traffic, as they crossed the tracks on Claiborne near Canal, three teams, one on each side and one behind, stopped them. They had the 'Z' poking a shotgun through the windshield, other agents at the side windows, and everything was going fine except the 'Z' forgot to put his car in park and it went across the street, ran over a fire hydrant, and tried to flood New Orleans. Then to top it off, they took both men upstairs in the office, handcuffed, and then and only then did they remember that Johnson had a gun in his waistband. Which probably isn't in the report! Oh well. As Blackie turned into the rolling driveway, he was glad to be home. And glad that long ago incident was well behind him. And now he was home with his little angels.

Chapter 31

Blackie rolled out of bed Friday morning, heading for the shower, and he realized he was going to face another weekend with Sandy and the girls. He knew he wanted to spend time with his girls, and he also knew he didn't want to mislead Sandy with the "wife-family" deal. He guessed he better cool it with her a little while longer, while she got more attached to the children, so he could wean her off of him with the "wife" program. One way would be to get an apartment in Baton Rouge and go back to Baton Rouge after the kids went to bed and not sleep with her. Of course, then, he'd have to find a BFI in Baton Rouge since he'd have to empty his prostate on a regular basis. He could do that with some pretense of having to be on call in Baton Rouge. He decided he'd start instituting that plan over the weekend.

After breakfast, he kissed them goodbye and split for Baton Rouge. Woody could help this work, he thought, as he drove along. He could call him out a few times at night and on the weekends and that would set the stage for his exit. As he approached Baton Rouge, he called Woody on the radio, got his 10-20, and told him to be available in the next couple of hours. He needed to meet with him. As he whizzed by the Brand Division on Florida, he thought about Millie. He realized that he had to put a little more effort in that area, or it would be gone, along with all the other things he'd only been doing half-assed.

As he exited the elevator on the eighth floor, he could tell immediately that it was Friday. Everybody looked as if they had been dressed at the Salvation Army sale. Joan was on the phone when he walked by, so all she had time to do was wave back. As he walked into Jeannie's office, she said, "Oh, our knight in shining armor! Whose day did you ruin yesterday in New Orleans?"

"Hey, darlin', actually I was a bearer of good tidings yesterday. Everybody loved me. Is he looking for me?"

"Yeah, I'll tell him you're here." Jeannie picked up the phone and dialed the intercom. "Mr. Steece's here, Commissioner. Yes, I'll send him right in," she said, nodding to Blackie.

The Commissioner said, "How'd it go yesterday?"

Blackie was in a jabbing mood. "Ok, I guess, they both wanted to know if I stole most of the money after they counted it." Dumb ass first looked puzzled and then insulted, then said, "Don't you have something on your schedule you need to do?"

"Yes, sir, I'm on my way," he said, thinking as he walked away, *I should have told this asshole something insulting earlier so he could have sent me away.*

Back in Jeannie's office, Blackie asked her, "How's the move going?"

She said, "They should be finished today or Monday at the latest."

"Great."

Back in the car, Blackie called Woody on the radio and told him to meet him at the Airline Highway building. Then, with the pretense of finding out if the Brand Division was moving, he decided to stop by Millie's office on Florida Boulevard. He walked into Millie's office and was surprised to see she was boxing stuff up on her desk. "Wow, darlin', I'm just in time to get you?"

"Actually, you just caught me. I'm transferring to Human Resources." "You're kidding!"

"Nope."

"I had to get away from these nuts in AIG."

"Hey! Does that include me?"

"Hell, I never see you. You get me convinced we're going to have a long-lasting affair, and all I've gotten lately is a bunch of flowers."

"Owww, that smarts!"

"Well, that's the truth. When's the last time you called me?"

"Hon, I've been trying to get this thing organized and get away from this nut and get everybody into one building. I was tryin' to get the Brand Division out there, too, so I could see ya every day and eventually transfer you to be my secretary."

"I heard they were going to put everybody in one building. I should have known you were behind it. Were you really going to have me be your secretary? I thought you didn't fool with people who worked for you."

"I wasn't gonna fool with ya. I was gonna be serious, because I can't keep my mind off of you," Blackie said as he closed the door. Turning to her he pulled her to him, gave her a long, warm, soft kiss. Her body responded immediately as she melted against him. He reached down her back and pulled her tight against him. As he kissed her neck and her face, he realized her cheek was wet from crying. "What's wrong darlin'?"

"I'm sorry. Things aren't going so good. My job's a mess. Things aren't going good at home."

"What's the matter?"

"Ever since the new Commissioner got elected, and Bob lost his job, he's been out of town traveling. I don't know what he's doing."

"What time ya have to be at this new office?"

"Why?"

"Because in about fifteen minutes, I'll be finished with Woody, and we can have lunch and talk about everything."

"I don't know if that's a good idea or not."

"Everything's a good idea darlin' if it's with you."

"Hmmm I know."

"Come on, darlin'. Can't be any worse than you feel now."

"I got to take these boxes down there!"

"I know, darlin'. Where's it at?"

"The Human Resources is down in the old State Office Building on North Boulevard."

"Ok, alright, Hmmm, lemme see," he said, looking at his watch, "'bout an hour and a half? Will that give ya time to unload and unpack?"

"Ahhh, ok, alright."

"Let me carry these boxes out there for ya, while you write down your new phone number for me, in case you forget to meet me," he said, picking up the box and heading for the door. "Now listen, Millie, I'm gonna get a room and, after lunch, I'm gonna take you there, make love to you, and hold you until you feel like you look—fantastic." That brightened her up, Blackie noticed, as he walked to his car.

Fifteen minutes later, Blackie pulled into the Airline Highway building where Woody was already waiting. "Hey, boss, what's happening?"

"Hey, this doesn't really have anything to do with work, but you're single, right?"

"Yeah, why?"

"Would it be a lot a trouble for ya to call me a couple a times at night and two or three times during the day on the weekends?"

"No, but what am I supposed to say?"

"Hell, I don't care, the ball game scores. I just need to be called to the phone a bunch, so I can tell my ole lady that I have to get an apartment in Baton Rouge, because I have to be there at night and on weekends."

"Hey, no problem. Who's the lucky girl?"

"I'm sure you could figure it out if you tried, but I wanna break the tie to my ole lady, so she won't think she's there just to be a wife."

"Hey, man, whatever you want."

Blackie and Woody then went inside the building to see how the move was going. After walking around the building for a few minutes, Woody said, "when do you think we'll be moved in here?"

"In the next couple of weeks, hopefully. Ok, I'm gonna hide for the rest of the weekend. Just call me randomly when ya think about it. Even if I'm not there, just leave a message, no number, just a message to call you."

"Ok, man, what else?"

"You're off brother. Go hide, chase a broad, go fishing, and answer the radio when I call ya and nobody else."

"You got it, man, thanks."

Blackie turned the Plymouth into the Greyhound Bus Station parking lot and was a little surprised to see Millie's blue Thunderbird already there and even more surprised when he pulled alongside and there was nobody in it.

After waiting only a couple of minutes, Millie came out of the bus station and got in the car.

"Thought ya were buying a bus ticket and leaving me."

"No," she said a little red faced. "I had to use the bathroom again. I guess I'm a little embarrassed. I've never done anything like this and..."

"Nothing to be embarrassed about," he said, as he wheeled out on Highland Road."

After passing the Louisiana State University Campus, Blackie turned right onto the old River Road. Since it was only around eleven and too early for lunch, he drove leisurely along the Old River Road to Darrow, to one of the old River Mansions that had been used in many movies. Pulling into the driveway, he stopped the car and said, "Come on, let's take a walk." Taking her by the hand, they walked around the beautiful grounds for a few minutes and then casually back to the car. They got in the car and started down the River Road again. Millie seemed more relaxed. As they reached Hwy 22, they turned left towards Sorrento, crossing the Airline Highway at Sorrento, on up Hwy 22, to the French

Settlement and a quaint little seafood restaurant. Parking, he looked at Millie and said, "Let's go eat, darling. It's good food, it's quiet, and nobody will bother us." She finally smiled as she got out of the car and they went inside.

After lunch, she was obviously excited for the next stage of the afternoon. They pulled into the Holiday Inn on I-10. Blackie got a room in the back to give the car a little bit of privacy. Two steps into the room Millie turned around and threw herself into his arms. As he pulled her down onto the bed, their clothes could not come off fast enough. She rolled Blackie over on his back and started kissing him all over, straddling him, looked down and said, "if I had this everyday, I'd never be depressed." Blackie looked up and said, "if I had this everyday, I'd never go to work." After an hour of intense lovemaking, they drifted off in each other's arms. When nature woke Blackie, it was nearly four o'clock. As he gently kissed and caressed her awake, he said, "We better head back toward town, or you're gonna be late for gettin' off time." She was much more relaxed as they drove back to her car, cuddled up with her head on his shoulder. When he opened the door of her car, he took her arm and turned her toward him, gently kissing her on the mouth and taking her in his arms and saying, "I have to do this now, so I don't run the risk of embarrassing you if somebody saw us in town. So this is your 'see ya later' kiss, earlier rather than later."

She looked up at him, smiling, giving a long leisurely kiss back. "I know I can't call ya at home, but I'm gonna get an apartment here in town and a phone, just so you can call me locally whenever you want to," Blackie said, taking her hand and squeezing it.

Millie looked back, smiling. It was hard to figure out what the look was, if it was shocked, surprised, or pleased, but it was definitely appreciated.

Blackie made a kissing mouth and shot out of the parking lot up to Capitol Boulevard, I-12, and home to his girls. It was just past five when he pulled into the driveway, which meant dinner was on the table and, sure enough, as he walked in, he was right! All the little daddy eyes turned toward him as they were just sitting down to the table. Sandy, getting up, said, "Oh, you're home!" as she came toward him.

In a defensive move, he handed her his briefcase, and said, "I have to go wash. I'll be right back." By the time he returned, they were all sitting at the table.

After dinner and small talk, Sandy started to clean up. Blackie said, "Come on, girls, I want to go over your homework for last week and your papers." After a couple of hours with homework, Blackie and the girls came into the den where Sandy had been reading and put on a movie. It was about midnight when Sandy woke him up and they carried sleeping little girls to their rooms. Once they were tucked in, Blackie came back to the bedroom to Sandy, standing naked beside the bed. He pulled her down on the bed and decided he'd fuck her brains out so she wouldn't be suspicious of him moving off to Baton Rouge. He didn't want to lose his babysitter.

During breakfast the next morning, the phone rang. Lu answered it. "It's Mr. Woody, Daddy."

"Uh huh. Uh huh, I don't know. I'll try to get to town later."

"Woody said, "how am I supposed to know if you're in town or not before I call again?"

"I'll call ya on the radio."

"Ok, good. This ain't gonna work if I don't know where you're at."

With that Blackie hung up and went back to breakfast.

About eleven, with the kids well occupied on their gym sets and swings, Blackie said, "I'm going to town and check on somethin'. I don't know when I'll be back," and then he got in his car and left. As he turned on I-12, he called Woody on the radio, Woody didn't answer. As he passed Walker on I-12 about twenty minutes later, he tried Woody again. This time Woody answered. Blackie said, "You know, if you put your radio switch to PA, it'll blast ya out of the house. Then ya can come out and answer it."

"Oh, I didn't know that. Are you going to be in town?"

"Yeah, for a while. Call me about ten tonight at my house."

"About ten?"

"Yeah, you're not gonna be up?"

"Yeah, but what will your ole lady think?"

"Who gives a shit as long as ya call?"

"Ok, man, no problem."

Blackie pulled over in Denham Springs and picked up a *Morning Advocate,* stuffed it all in the garbage can, except for the want ads, and drove to the Weights and Measures Office. There he tried to decide what the best part of town was, as he opened up the paper and started looking in the Apartments For Rent ads. After a few minutes, he marked about half a dozen one-bedroom furnished and started calling.

After a couple of minutes, there were only a couple of furnished available, and they didn't sound good. Before he went to look at those, he started calling the one-bedroom unfurnished. There were two or three of those that didn't sound too bad, so he decided to set up appointments at both. He thought all apartments should probably have a stove and refrigerator as he started calling. After a few calls, he had one appointment. This didn't make him very happy. He thought of David Martin's wife, in the real estate business. He called David's house and left a message on the answering machine. In the meantime, he went back to call on the one bedrooms, unfurnished. After spending a few minutes in the unfurnished ads, he saw that one was available. Blackie called David's house again before he left to go on the two appointments. The answering machine was still on and he left a message that he was on the air if they got back before he called again.

He didn't even keep the appointment on the furnished apartment because he saw that the neighborhood sucked when he got there. The unfurnished place didn't look too bad. It had a stove and refrigerator, but it was on the second floor. He decided that since it was just a temporary thing, it didn't really matter. He told the lady he would get back with her in a day or two. When he got back in the car, his message light was blinking. He guessed David was finally returning his call, so he pulled up to the first pay phone and called him. David answered the phone and Blackie asked, "Hey isn't your wife in the real estate business?"

"Yeah, her family owns Webb Real Estate, the biggest one in town."

"Does she handle rental property?"

"Here, let me let you talk to her."

"Hi Dave, I've heard a lot about you."

"I'm looking for a little apartment in town, just temporary. I don't know if that's beneath ya, but I thought ya might know a good part of town, whatever."

"We don't handle rental property; we just handle big stuff. But I'll be glad to take you around, show you areas, and help you."

"Well I found one, over here, right off of Highland Road. It's got a stove and refrigerator, but I'll have to get a bed. It's just for when I'm stuck in town overnight."

"We got all kinds of furniture in our warehouse, and you're welcome to borrow anything you need. If you want me to, I'll meet you and see if the price is right, or if it's in the right part of town. Are you looking at it right now?"

"Yeah."

"We live right by LSU. If you're by Highland Road, I can meet you, wherever you're at."

"Whatever."

"Go to the shopping center on Highland Road and I'll meet you there."

An hour and a half later, she had worked out a six-month lease, the lease was signed, she had arranged for furniture to be delivered the next day, and had told Blackie she would meet him there. He was sure that more would be delivered than furniture.

Blackie turned into his driveway pleasantly surprised that so much of his plan had come together. He hoped it would resolve his "wife" problem as he headed home to his girls.

Chapter 32

For the next week, Blackie spent every day moving into his new office. He spent every evening at his new apartment, trying to keep up with the sex drive of Mary Webb Martin, who Blackie knew, the day she helped him with the apartment, that she would be a regular BFI for his hormonal needs. Mary, a petite blonde with soft blue eyes and a pretty smile, had good legs and perky little breasts. She claimed she never wore a bra or panties because she never wanted to waste the time taking them off. She proved that on a regular basis, because every time Blackie got to the apartment, all she had on were high heels.

He was about to finish organizing the Agro-Consumer Division and looking forward to the weekend with the girls. He was surprised when the Commissioner and Jim Knotts showed up at the Airline Highway building Friday morning. The Commissioner said, "Pick out some people you can trust. I need you to go over to Mississippi and spruce up my trailer park this weekend."

Shit, Blackie thought. *I wanted to stay away from Sandy and he's gonna keep me away from everybody.* Blackie went to the phone and talked to Herman, Ronnie, Woody, Andrew, Stoogie, Tina, Nanci, and Denise. Herman LeMoine was the Director of Grading and Certification Division, a dark complected Louisiana coonass, of 5'11" and 160 pounds with an easy- going personality. Ronnie and Woody were already two of Blackie's "Golden Boys." Andrew Ney was one of Blackie's soldiers in the City and not yet on the AIG payroll. He was going to use him to requisition paint and other materials for the facelift on the trailer park. "Stoggie" Addison Merryweather, also one of Blackie's crew from New Orleans, had just been put on the AIG payroll as a no-show, but this weekend he would have to show. He'd been the main guy who hauled the tribute up to New York in the big rigs and looked the truck driver part with his 5'11", 230-pound body, ruddy face, and cigar hanging out of the corner of his mouth. He also spent time on his "hog," a Harley Davidson 74. Hell, he could have been part of a motorcycle gang. He looked enough like them. Tina Rathcke was an AIG secretary to Hermen LeMoine in Grading and Certification. She was a dark, petit little sweetheart who looked more Italian than whatever the nationality for Rathcke was. Tina's boobs were way too big for her body size, unless of course you'd seen them the time she was in a hot tub with Blackie when they floated along on top of the water. Blackie thought he better take another crack at that when he had time. Nanci Parker, whom Blackie had made his Administrative Assistant, was about 5'11", with long blonde hair, big blue eyes, and very white skin, a tribute to her Swedish heritage and on Blackie's list. Denise Guice was a typical Ascension Parish coonass, kind of a plain girl, with no tits and not much ass, with mousey brown hair and a few freckles. But she knew how to get on her knees. Like they say, there's somebody for everybody, and Ronnie had made her his playmate when he wasn't home with his family.

After Blackie lined them all up to meet at five Saturday morning, at I-12 and I-10 in Slidell. Herman and Stoggie were both driving State trucks and, along with Andrew, would pick up paint, paintbrushes, and other stuff to do the maintenance. Woody would take a carload, Blackie a carload, and the rest would ride in pickups. After breakfast at Denny's in Slidell, Blackie paid the check with a State credit card and then led the procession East on I-10 to Mississippi. Just across the state line, he pulled off the side of the interstate, got out, even though it was not quite daylight, no one seemed surprised that he took pictures of all the cars, trucks, and the people milling around the "Welcome to Mississippi" sign. Later, at the Cedar Lake Trailer Park, he took another roll of film of workers painting, mowing lawns, nailing up fences, and made sure to include license plates on the State cars and trucks. When they left that evening, on the way back to Louisiana, he pulled into the gas station on Hwy 49 and I-10 and had everybody fill up their cars on the State credit card. Then they went across the street and everybody ate. He made sure they all had their receipts that read, Hardee's Gulfport, Mississippi. It wouldn't take too many more fuck-ups like this, and the case would be over, Blackie thought.

The following Wednesday, just before quitting time, the Commissioner called him and said, "I need someone to fix a roof on one of my rental houses. It's leaking and looks like it's going to rain. Can you get somebody?"

"I'll try, where is it?"

"It's just an old slum house that blacks live in. All you need is a roll of black felt, a roll of roofing, some tar, and some roofing nails."

The only people Blackie could find that late in the day were Herman LeMoine and Tina Rathcke. He sent Herman in a State truck to get the roofing material, then he took Tina to his apartment so he could change clothes, get a blow job before he went to work, and pick up a throw-away camera for more pictures. Once they got to the job site, Blackie took pictures of Herman and Tina working, and the State truck and car, and Tina took pictures of Blackie on the roof. It was late before they got finished and, on the way back, Blackie thought, another nail in the coffin. How many nails does it take to seal an idiot's tomb?

Thursday morning, when Blackie got up, he realized that Tina must have left sometime in the night, knowing she would have to get clean clothes for work. He left the apartment and headed out to Rick's for a pancake breakfast. He met Millie headed in on Airline about two blocks before Rick's. Flipping around on Airline, he got her to stop on the side of the road. He said, "I've been calling you every day at your office, and some strange voice is on the end of the phone."

"Why didn't you ask for me? I take calls all day. You could be anybody. They don't know who you are."

"Shit, I didn't know. I was trying to protect the little innocence you have left. Let's set something up right now so we stop missing each other forever."

"What do you have in mind?"

"Come on back to Rick's and eat breakfast with me. The side of the highway isn't a good place to plan anything."

"She said, "I'll be late for work."

"Shit, my girls come in late all the time. Don't tell me your office is any different."

Laughing, she said, "Ok," and followed him back to Rick's.

"What's goin' on Friday with you?"

"The kids are going to their grandmother's for the weekend, and as usual, Bob is going to be out of town."

"Great. I've got an apartment in town that I've been trying to get you the number to for two weeks."

"I don't want to go to your apartment. I know more people than you know where it is, and someone could see me going in or coming out."

Blackie thought, *that's good, she won't ever catch any of those other squeezes when they're there*, then he said, "Ok, paranoia, I'll meet you at the shopping center at Florida Boulevard. I'll park by DH Holmes' front door. You park on the other side of the shopping center, walk through the shopping center, through Holmes, and come out. That way nobody can follow you."

"You must really be experienced at this. You know all the tricks."

"It's not tricks, baby. It's just common sense."

"Yeah, right."

As they were finishing their breakfast, he said, "are you sure it's ok for you to get calls at work?"

"Of course it's ok. I get calls all day. That's what Human Resources does. It handles complaints or job applications. It's all day on the phone," she said, adding, "don't send flowers there, though; everyone knows I'm married."

"Ok, I'll see ya about six or six-thirty?"

"Yeah."

"Are you going to show up?"

"Yes."

"Promise me you'll show up. Don't leave me in that parking lot all night."

"I'll show up, I promise, but don't leave if I'm late."

"Ok. Can I have a kiss good-bye, or do I have to wait until we're out in the parking lot?"

"You can't have one either place. There are too many people that know me here. You'll get your kiss Friday."

"I want a whole lot more than a kiss. Did you shave that thing yet? And I don't want you to wear a bra."

"I'm kinda afraid to shave. What will Bob say?"

"Well, you could keep him from seeing it," said Blackie, laughing. "Or you could tell him you got crabs and had to shave it," he said, laughing even harder, "or you could tell him it's for a bathing suit."

"You're such a smart ass. I could just tell him I shaved for you."

"He should understand that all right."

"I'm kinda afraid to go without a bra. I'm so big, my nipples show."

"Shit, that's what makes it look good. If you're too paranoid to take it off, leave it on until you get in the car, but take the god damn thing off before you get to me."

Blackie called and talked to Millie twice Thursday and, as he was dialing her number Friday morning, he thought, *shit, wouldn't it be just like the Commissioner to give me a job to do this weekend?* When she answered the phone, he said, "I don't know if I can wait till six."

"I can't either," she said. "I can't get you off of my mind."

"It's not your mind I wanna be on."

"I know," she said. "I keep thinking of that afternoon at the Holiday Inn when we fell asleep with you still inside of me."

"I'm standing out in the parking lot. If I don't hang up the phone, I won't be able to walk back to the car."

"You're full of shit. You better have some place discrete for us."

Blackie said, "of course," thinking, *I better get off my ass and find someplace.*

After hanging up with Millie, Blackie started calling motels close to Airline Highway and Florida Boulevard. Finally, after the third try, he secured a downstairs, outside room at the Holiday Inn right across from the shopping center. About five minutes to six, Blackie started circling the parking lot in front of DH Holmes, so he'd be able to jump into the first available place beside the door when someone pulled out. It was about 6:15 before he got a parking place. As he sat there daydreaming, it was nearly 7:00 before he looked at his watch again, thinking, she might not show. About fifteen or twenty minutes later, just as the sun was setting, he saw her come out of DH Holmes store looking just like she had robbed a bank. He started the car and headed toward her to save her paranoid exposure.

Millie got in the car, slouched down in the seat, and said, "This is too early; it's still light."

"Well, then, lay down on the seat and find out if your mouth can figure out what to do until it gets dark."

"You're funny."

Blackie pulled out on Florida and headed toward Denham Springs, and said, "If you don't stop that, I'm not gonna be able to drive."

She said, "I thought that's what you wanted."

"It is, but I can't concentrate on driving in this traffic."

She gave one more little tug and, laughing, said, "Are you still in control?"

As she looked up from his lap, Millie said, "Guess what happened today. The desks at H&R face each other. The woman in front of me heard me say 'discrete' to you on the phone and said, "what do you need discrete?"

"What'd you say?"

"I told her I was trying to have an affair."

"You what?"

262 • david steece's

"I told her I was trying to have an affair. I thought if I told her that, she wouldn't believe me. If I told her anything else, she'd probably think I was having an affair. This way she just laughed."

As they exited I-12 at Denham Springs, Blackie pulled to the far side of a daiquiri shop parking lot. When he put the car in park, Millie said, "What are you doin?"

"I'm gonna go get you a surprise."

"What do ya mean? What am I supposed to do?"

"Just lay there and rub yourself. I'll be right back."

When Blackie got back to the car with the strawberry daiquiri, she was sitting up. She said, "I was a nervous wreck. I figured if someone walked by and saw me laying down they would think I was nuts."

"You are nuts; that's what I like about you. Here, drink this; it'll relax you."

By the time they reached the Holiday Inn, the daiquiri had started taking effect and she giggled as they ran to the room.

While Blackie was taking off his coat and tie and unbuttoning his shirt, Millie kicked off her shoes, stood up on the bed, pulled the front of her skirt up and said, "Is this what you wanted?"

"Yeah, finally, an uncluttered woman."

After two hours of wild sex, Blackie showered, put on pants and a shirt, and went out to get them some ham and cheese po-boys. When he came back in the room, Millie had showered and was drying that long beautiful blonde hair. He put the sandwiches and drinks on the table, and when she walked over, she smelled like a bed of fresh roses. This interrupted their snack. A couple of soft kisses and the gentle caresses turned into feverish petting, which led to two more hours of passionate lovemaking and, finally, total exhaustion.

It was after 3 a.m., when they awoke with their bodies intertwined. Millie was obviously convinced she was in love and was never going to leave his side. Blackie figured he would never have to dial her phone again, that she would be calling him. When they left, Blackie gave her the number to the apartment, had her memorize the prefix and write the last four numbers down backwards. If he wasn't there, she was supposed to just say "it's me, just call me back," and leave a number that he could call. She agreed.

Much to Blackie's disappointment, 9:00 a.m. on Saturday morning after only three hours sleep, the phone rang. Groggily, he picked it up and said "Yeah."

"It's me. I miss you. Can I come see you? I'm not wearing a bra."

"Sure darlin'," he said, thinking, *I thought she wasn't comin to this apartment.*

After a pause, she said, "I have to have the address, honey."

"Oh, ok." Blackie gave her the address and hung up.

Five minutes later the phone rang again. This time it was Sandy. "What are we going to do with the kids this weekend?" she asked.

"I'm working today. I don't know about tomorrow."

"Well, they miss you. Do you want to talk to them?"

"Yeah," he said, and then, for the next twenty to twenty-five minutes, he talked back and forth to the girls, getting nothing done for the arrival of his guest. By the time Blackie got out of the shower, he heard the door open. Good thing he told her he'd leave it open, because if she had had to knock, he never would have heard her.

Blackie had been sleeping nude all his life, but he was sure everyone showered nude, so obviously, he was nude, and how does that song go, "What a Difference A Day Makes"—or she just wanted to match me, because off came the clothes and the next day of a torrid affair.

Chapter 33

Millie spent the night. On Sunday morning they had breakfast at Denny's before she had to go home, and Blackie went out to the estate to see his girls. As Blackie flew along on I-12, he decided he'd find a house in Baton Rouge, so he could save a lot of these trips and have more time with the girls. When he got to the estate, he told Sandy to pack the kids up for the day and follow them with her car, that they were going to look at houses and, when they finished, they'd have dinner in Baton Rouge, and Sandy could take the girls home while he did some work. You could see the excitement in the girls and hope in Sandy when he said "they" were going to get a house in Baton Rouge. He thought, *shit*. He knew he'd have to keep her on a string to take care of those little girls, but between Millie, Mary, and an occasional one-nighter, she might need to find a lover, because he might not have anything left.

Blackie called Mary when he got to the estate so she would have something to look at by the time they got back. They met Mary at the shopping center at Airline Highway and I-12. Blackie got in her car; the girls got in with Sandy. He couldn't very well cop a feel with the girls in the car with him, and they wouldn't all fit in one car. As soon as they turned out of the parking lot, Mary pulled her skirt up and said, "my husband asked why I shaved this, and I told him for one of my lovers. He just laughed and said, 'you never give me a serious answer do you?'" She said, "I innocently said what do you mean? and my husband said, 'You said you shaved for one of your lovers. If it was true, you would have said singular *lover*.' I just rolled my eyes. He thinks the only people that want to fuck are men and we just wait around till it's our turn. What I should have said to him was 'multiple lovers,' but he wouldn't have got that either."

The first house they looked at was much too small and didn't have a pool. The next two were kind'a traps on cul-d-sacs. Blackie always felt that if he needed a way out in a hurry, a cul-d-sac wouldn't be the right way. The fourth one was on Coronado, had a master bedroom of twenty-five by forty feet, with his and her baths, hers with a tub and a bidet, his with a stand-up shower and a sauna. Both had large dressing areas with individual cedar closets, and the other end of the room opened up to a twenty by sixty-foot balcony that overlooked a beautiful garden on one end, an Olympic sized pool, and a good-sized back yard on the other end. The entire back yard had an eight-foot-high wooden fence. There were four bedrooms downstairs, with three and a half baths, a formal living and dining room, a huge den, a study, game room, sewing room, and a large year-round rear screened-in porch. The kitchen had all the amenities, including a Sub Zero refrigerator, a relatively small utility room, but adequate. Mary said she thought he could buy it for a little under $200,000. Blackie said, "go offer them $150,000, but the sale's gotta be now!" After a couple of counter offers, the sale was set for the next week for $187,500. The house was already empty. Mary, with the Webb connections behind her and no financing involved, thought if they placed the money in escrow, she was sure she could get permission for them to move in prior to the closing and she would know by Monday evening. Blackie then suggested she call her husband and they would all meet at the Village Inn Restaurant to celebrate. After dinner, Blackie kissed the kids and Sandy goodbye, and they headed back to the estate. Mary and her husband had left the restaurant at the same time and, not much to Blackie's surprise, a nude blonde Mary was propped on his bed working on the paperwork for the house when he got to his apartment. When Blackie walked in, he said, "Oh my god, I'm too tired to shower after today." Looking up with her devilish eyes, she said, "That's not a problem. I'll lick you clean." he got off the bed and undid his belt and pulled it out of his pants.

Blackie had no idea what time Mary left but the ringing phone at 7 a.m., thank God, woke him, because he was at least an hour late getting up. He threw himself together and headed to the office, deciding he'd send Nanci or somebody out for some eggs and coffee. The new office was still a bit of a mess, but, with a little screaming, it should be organized by the end of the week.

Blackie called Sandy from the office, told her to get the movers lined up, run over and get the utilities turned on, etc. Sandy, sweet as usual, said, "Honey, when am I gonna see ya?"

"Babe, I'm real busy with this office move and all. You take care of the house. That's what wives do," he said, as he hung up the phone. *God damnit*, he thought, *give me a fuckin break. I'm trying to keep two squeezes happy, not to mention me. She's there to take care of my kids. I ain't got time to run over there an fuck her twice a week. Fuckin women!*

Chapter 34

Sandy got the new house organized, the girls' fall clothes for school and their school papers ready, while Blackie settled into the new office. He got deeply involved in AIG, including organizing the eight divisions by getting them up and running smoothly, and inspecting all the scales in the state for the first time, since the law was enacted in 1952. By moving his office, and several of the other administrative offices, plus the eight regulatory divisions, he had a lot less contact in the Capitol. Because of Blackie's stubbornness in refusing to get himself caught in the remote chance of entrapment, the Commissioner hired an old political hack and Judge William Hawk Daniels to help him in his money raising capacities. Blackie had known Hawk for a long time. He'd been a traffic judge in Baton Rouge and had a reputation for being a little nuts. He would admonish people from the bench, arbitrarily fine them one penny, or, on other occasions, a ridiculous amount. On more than one occasion, in open court, he would flip a coin and let the defendant call it. If the defendant called it right, he was found not guilty.

The Man was on Blackie to get more on the malfeasance in the Commissioner's "deals." Blackie started going in the field snooping around. He found some disgruntled sugar cane farmers, rice growers, and milk processors, who were complaining about being touched up for $10,000 each by the Commissioner and the Hawk. After a few visits in the field, Blackie realized that, at the pace Hawk was going, it wouldn't be long before Blackie would be replaced like a fat wife. Blackie got the name of a couple of disgruntled growers and the squeezed-out Holmes Johnson, former head of Weights and Measures, the Irma Tucker fiasco, and leaked the names to the Baton Rouge newspaper investigative reporter Paul Bartels. That stirred up some headlines but seemed to die down after a day or two.

Blackie believed Dr. Reed Grigsby to be an honest man and knew that the Commissioner had hired him to push him out front to improve his credibility. He also believed he had to do something to get a fight going and get the government involved in the investigation. Blackie used an anonymous leak that Reed Grigsby's division was taking kickbacks for licenses to a weaker reporter whom he knew, unlike Paul Bartels, was too lazy to check out the details. The story sent Reed screaming to the Capitol and was the first crack in the protective shield around the Commissioner. This lit a fire under Paul Bartels again, who then interviewed Holmes Johnson and Irma Tucker but didn't get the results Blackie hoped for. Both of them called Blackie and the Commissioner bad guys but named Blackie as the one who was the wire-tapping, gun totting, strong arm. Talk about rocking a boat full of seasick people! Blackie knew to finish his job he'd have to keep from being terminated. He'd have to do something to keep the Commissioner from cutting him loose, because he knew the Commissioner would not take the heat. Blackie had the $10,000 bribe, three out-of-state and one local incident of AIG employees working on private property and, if the government was smart enough to make the sugar cane farmer and rice grower and the guy that had the kickback on the milk processor, that should be enough to take this fucker down.

Blackie told The Man, what his plan was. The Man, said, "You've got to stay a while longer. Can't you get close to someone in Human Resources to see if he's got anybody ghosting on the payroll?"

Blackie laughed to himself, thinking, *I actually been inside of somebody in H&R a bunch of times*, but he asked, "What do you mean somebody in H&R?"

The Man said, "You'd have to be with somebody, either at the top or the first assistant. Not just one of the employees."

Shit, why couldn't Millie be the boss? Blackie thought. "I know somebody in H&R and I know Connie LeBlanc is the boss, but I only met her once."

"Listen, Blackie, quite making excuses. You've been doing this for twenty years. Get next to this Connie person and get it done. You're acting like you're fucking one of her employees and afraid she'll find out and be jealous."

Blackie rolled his eyes and thought, *if you only knew.*

The two men chatted a few minutes about their children.

Blackie told him that he thought Teri was going to continue on for her Masters in head shrinking. Would that make her like an Italian cannibal? Bitsy was going to be a freshman, studying biochem. Rae would be a first grader studying advanced baby carriage rolling, since that was the only foundation she had. The Man's daughter was also working on a Masters Degree, and his son was a sophomore. How time flies.

Blackie got back to Baton Rouge and was a little surprised and pissed when his administrative assistant, Nanci Parker, brought him a phone message from Paul Bartels. Nanci walked back to her office and Blackie watched her ass move under that tight skirt. He thought, *she's gonna make me break that rule about dipping the pen in the company ink if he wasn't careful,* then he called out to her, "Get him on the phone." As Blackie pondered how he'd deal with Bartels' questions, the intercom buzzed, and Nanci's voice chirped, "He's on two."

"Mr. Bartels? David Steece here. What can I do for ya?"

Bartels said, "Have you read the last two stories I wrote, and do you have any comment?"

"I did, and my first comment is that I'm surprised that a man with your reputation as an honest, fair reporter wouldn't have called me and asked if I had a comment before you wrote the stories."

"Well, I did say in the story that you hadn't been reached for comment, and to be perfectly honest, your reputation in New Orleans pretty much made me think you wouldn't have a comment that would be worth printing."

"Now see! I've always heard you were a fair journalist, and rumors are just that, Paul, rumors. They had a rumor going around that Vice President Johnson killed Jack Kennedy and that was just bullshit. When I was in the third grade, they told us that the moon was 175 light years away, another unfounded rumor that was actually being taught to children in school. So rumors are just that—rumors and nothing more."

"Well, what is your comment then?"

"Have you ever heard of the 'Cui bono'?"

"Cui bono? No I don't think so, what is it?"

"It's something I read about an intelligence officer. I don't remember what book it was in, but it makes really good sense. The first rule he used in all investigations was 'To Whose Good' to gain anything large or small? Now in any type of extortion, gambling, or any other alleged criminal activity, the first rule would be 'Who benefits?' Wanna go off the record for a minute Paul?"

"Yeah, I guess so, for a minute."

"Take the Holmes Johnson story. He was an old bureaucrat who'd been reappointed every four years, forever, and just got stagnated and hadn't done his job in years. I came in here, and you can check this out, turned that division around, checked every scale in the state, and that hadn't been done since the law was passed. You didn't really expect him to say something nice about me. I busted up his playpen. With the Irma Tucker case, the other case you wrote about, another old bureaucrat who worked in the printing department, didn't know a letterpress from a typewriter and, as far as I know, I only saw her once. I think it was when I took her the separation check. She had already resigned if I remember right. I don't know why anybody would believe I had to carry a gun to give somebody a check."

"So what are you saying? They're both lying?"

"No, what I'm saying is dig a little deeper. Follow the Rule. Who benefits? I didn't make any more money, get any time off, or fill either one of their positions. So what did I have to gain?"

"OK, but we're going back on the record."

"OK, Paul. "

"I've heard rumors that people who are being regulated by your divisions are getting tapped for huge 'alleged' campaign contributions."

"Paul, go to them, these people with the rumors; ask them if they've ever met me, if I've ever asked them for a dime. If they say yes, I'll be glad to take a polygraph with them."

"Are you telling me you've never asked anybody for campaign money for the Commissioner?"

"That's what I'm telling you, Paul."

"Well, in the District Attorneys Race in the City, it's rumored—"

"There you go again, Paul, rumors. I don't have any comment to make unless you have documentation other than some vindictive rumor. Let me add this. I'm gonna give you my home telephone number; its unlisted and you can call it anytime day or night, and if I know about your question, I'll answer you and it'll be the truth."

"Mr. Steece, I'm gonna run this story pretty much how we talked. Is that going to upset the Commissioner with you?"

"My job is to run the eight regulatory divisions. They're here to serve the three million-plus people in Louisiana, and I'm doing my job the right way and the honest way. If any cow chips land on somebody else, that's not my problem."

"I don't think the Commissioner is going to agree with you, Mr. Steece."

"I guess we'll have to wait and see. Anything else, Paul?"

"No, thank you for your time, Mr. Steece."

As Blackie hung up the phone, he thought, *that should start the ball rolling.*

Blackie pondered whether to call or just drop in to see Millie at the H&R's office. And how in the Hell was he going to get close to somebody that he only met once and ran the same division that his girlfriend worked in? As Blackie sat trying to figure out what to do, Nanci walked in and said, "I've got an application that Connie sent over for a clerk typist."

Blackie took the application and told Nanci to show her in. He thought Vicki's twin had just walked in. Although she looked a little younger than Vicki, she had the same porcelain skin, raven black hair, big blue eyes that didn't hold your view very long because of the rest of her body.

Nanci introduced Geri and left. Geri sat down on the chair in front of the desk, crossing her long legs, making sure Blackie got a good view of them. After a few minutes of standard questions, she leaned forward, unbuttoned one of the buttons on her already too low blouse, and said, "I really need this job bad. I'll do anything I have to do to get it and as often as you want me to ta keep it."

Blackie said, "Hon, I don't fool with the women who work for me."

She said, "I understood your staff was filled. Connie is a good friend of our family, and she said you had openings in other divisions. If I got hired for one of those positions, I wouldn't be working directly for you, would I?" She coyly added, "I know a man of your talent and experience can then work out the details so I can keep you satisfied."

Blackie said, "How do I know you're not trying to set me up for some newspaper story?"

Geri stood up. "There's a camera right there on the corner of your desk. Take a picture of this and see if anybody thinks you made me pose. She stood back and pulled her skirt up above her waist, revealing nothing but a clean-shaven body. "Or this," she said, as she dropped her skirt and pulled her blouse open showing her braless breasts. "I'll pose any way you want me to, any time your want me to, so you'll feel safe. I promise you can trust me, and I really need the job. Plus, I really think you're a sexy man." Geri sat back down.

Blackie got up, walked over to the door going to Nanci's office and turned the lock, came back, and stood in front of her. Five minutes later, Geri finished showing one of her exceptional talents.

Blackie walked over to Nanci's door, turning the lock and opening it in one motion, asking Nanci to come in at the same time. "This is a friend of Connie's, and she seems qualified for the clerk typist position. Find a place for her and see if you can get her set up to start work tomorrow."

As Nanci and Geri left the office, Blackie said, "I'm gonna be down at H&R for a while; call me there if you need me."

He got off the elevator and walked into the H&R general offices. Since he'd never been there before in person he was a little surprised to see several rows of typists. It reminded him of an insurance office. You could see two glass cubicles in the back and, about half way back on the left-hand side, a pretty blonde head that he recognized. As he started back to what he was sure was Connie's private office, he decided he'd let Connie introduce him to her staff, instead of speaking to Millie as he made his way through the desks. He tapped on Connie's glass door. She looked up and motioned him in. As he entered, he said, "How ya doing Ms. Leblanc? You buying the coffee?"

"Mr. Steece, it's too hot for coffee. How about a coke?"

"Naw, I don't drink carbohydrates. How about Dave instead of Mr. Steece?"

"That's fine. How about Connie instead of Ms. Leblanc?"

Blackie, although he'd only met her once, obviously hadn't looked at her very well. The Leblanc, denoted coonass, but she was anything but. She had beautiful skin, dark brown eyes, and dark curly, almost black, shoulder-length hair. He couldn't see her legs since she was sitting behind the desk, but if they looked as good as her chest, this wouldn't be such a drudgery after all. Connie gave him a big red-lipped smile. "Ok, Dave, if you really want coffee, I'll have one of the girls make you some."

"Nah, that's just a conversation piece. I really came over to thank you for thinking of us in our need for a clerk typist and for sending Geri over to fill one of the posts."

"I really don't know her that well but I'm good friends with her sister and brother. So you hired her?"

"Well, my staff's full but I gave her to Nanci and told her to place her somewhere. She'll start tomorrow."

"That was sweet of you. I believe she really needs the job."

"This looks like a pretty big operation. How many people do you have on your staff?"

"Eight, plus my assistant. Come on, I'll introduce you." With that, Connie introduced him first to her assistant, then, from one desk after another. Blackie shook hands with each lady and, as he shook hands with Millie he gave her a little finger scratch, thinking of his high school days. As Connie walked him to the elevator, Blackie looked over his shoulder and thought, *oh, my god, all this meat and no potatoes.* Connie brought him back to reality, saying "Thank you for coming to see us, Dave."

"You're welcome, darlin'. I know you handle all the Civil Service testing and basically screen everybody we hire. I'd really like to learn more about it. I'd like to take you and your husband to dinner one night."

"Jimmy and me? Noooo, Jimmy is antisocial."

Blackie smelled an opening. "I'm married to one of those, too. Maybe just you and I could go to dinner." With that, he got another smile as Connie took a half a step closer and she extended her hand. "I'd like that, anytime, but call me here the day before, would you?"

As Blackie rode down the elevator, he thought, *this might be easier than I expected.* He decided at the last minute to stop and see Jeannie in the Commissioner's office and do a little recon on Connie. As he walked into her office, she looked up from the typewriter. "What brings you to see us?"

"I just met Connie Leblanc, really for the first time to talk to her. You know the history on everybody—what's she like?"

Jeannie said, "I hate to gossip, but I'm sure you'll find out anyway and be mad at me for not telling you. She's married to an alcoholic who doesn't work. She's got a couple of kids about to finish high school, and I think once they're gone, her husband will have to find someone else to buy his booze."

Blackie raised one eyebrow, and said, "Oh, so she's probably got a boyfriend."

"I don't think so. I've never heard that. Isn't she a little bit old for you? If I remember right, you told me you like middle-aged women. You also told me that most of the old people we knew were fifty; therefore, middle age would be twenty-five. Connie, at very best is thirty-five and maybe even forty by now, which would put her way over in your world."

Blackie laughed. "I was only asking because she hires all our personnel, and you know if twenty-five was the limit, that would knock you out of the running, because you're thirty, and you're number one on my list."

"Yeah, yeah, what else do you want, you big flirt?"

"I just told you, your body."

"Not today."

"How about tonight?"

"You're impossible. What do you really want?"

"You got anything going out to Airline? I'll take it and save you a runner."

"Yeah, there's some mail over there."

Blackie walked over and picked up the mail. "I don't see no checks or love letters for me in this mess," he said, as he was leaving.

As Blackie waited for the elevator, he thought about going up to see CRII and, as the elevator dinged, he decided it would be a good idea.

CRII's secretary showed Blackie right in. The two men shook hands and CRII said, "What's going on exciting?"

"I don't know; this guy's kinda a loose cannon. You think there's a remote chance it could be dangerous?"

"I don't think so, but you never know. You think he's going to crash?"

"I don't know. The papers are just starting on 'im. If he can't clean that up, the next thing will be the Grand Jury. If he fucks that up, then it'll be a trial and jail."

"I guess its something to think about. We get enough heat up here. I really don't have time to think about the Commissioner."

"I wasn't worried about him. I was worried about me. The last two stories splattered on me as much as they did him."

CRII laughed. "When you walk around in shit, you know you're going to get some on you."

Blackie laughed. The two men shook hands and he went back to the elevator.

As Blackie started back to his office, his mind drifted back to the Grand Jury comment *when, a few years ago, he'd been called. When he entered the Grand Jury room, he was asked to raise his hand and swear to his name and address. He'd crossed his arms and refused to speak. After two or three attempts to have him sworn in, the US attorney ordered the US Marshall to escort him over in front of a Federal Judge. Although your attorney cannot be present with you inside the Grand Jury Room, they're readily available in the room right outside. As*

Blackie was being escorted, Jamie, ready and waiting, fell in right beside him. When they stood in front of the Federal Judge, the US Attorney said, "When we tried to swear him in, he refused to speak."

Jamie, addressing the Court, said, "Your Honor, I have a copy of the law here and the way I, actually we, interpret it and the way it's spelled out is you must swear under oath to that of which you know, only of your own volition, with absolutely no variation, or face the charge of perjury. Now I know this gentleman to be called David Steece, and some other nicknames, but I cannot swear nor attest to his name under oath, and I see no way he can, since I wasn't there at all and, at birth, he did not have the capacity to know if the name he has was actually the one given him then.

"We know that's not his name from birth. He's a gangster," The US Attorney screamed. "They all change their names.

"THAT'S RIDICULOUS!" Jamie cut in. "I object, your Honor,"she said, taking out another case that set a precedent. Years ago there was a company called LL&T, Inc. Louisiana Loan and Thrift, Inc. When incorporated, they had gotten some advice from P.F. Jack Gremillion, the Louisiana State Attorney General at the time. Unbeknownst to him, the founding corporate officers had put a few shares of stock in his name without ever mentioning it or telling him of that as a reward for his advice. Many years later when LL&T, Inc. failed, and eventually went bankrupt, Mr. Gremillion was called and asked the specific question, "Do you or have you ever owned stock in LL&T Inc?" His answer, of course, was no. This US Attorney's office, though staffed by different personnel at the time, indicted and convicted Mr. Gremillion for perjury. I've got to advise my client not to answer any questions unless he knows of his own volition that they are true and correct.

"This is ridiculous," The US Attorney screamed. "He's a gangster—I mean an alleged gangster."

"That's another thing, your Honor," Jamie said. "My client's a salesman. He doesn't deny being of Italian descent to the best of his knowledge, but that doesn't make him a gangster. According to the law," she said, removing another copy from her briefcase, "he's supposed to be in front of a jury of his peers. He tells me there's eight black jurors in there, both female and male of different ages, a half a dozen fifyish white females, and what he termed to be either a cab driver or a longshoreman. Nobody 6'3", 235 lbs, 31 years old, Italian American who's a salesman or for that matter even an alleged

gangster. Not one person fits his peer description on the entire grand jury."

*The US Attorney, now sputtering like a bad outboard motor, threw his glasses down and pleaded "**Your Honor!**"*

The Judge said, "I've never heard of such a thing, but I assume that if I rule against you, the next step will be the appellate courts. Am I correct?"

"Absolutely," Jamie said, "And after that the Supreme Court."

The judge, addressing the US Attorney said, "your solution might be to stipulate to who you think he is and Mrs. Veverica, if they try to get a few grand jurors close to his peers, I don't think you're gonna win that one. This hearing's over for the day."

The US Attorney told the Marshals to take him back to the Grand Jury Room.

Back in the Grand Jury Room, the US Attorney, obviously flustered, addressed the jurors by saying, "We're going to stipulate to David Steece's name and address. It's just too complicated to try to explain to you. Now, Mr. Steece, do you know Larry Heaslip?"

Blackie smiled and crossed his arms. The US Attorney's face, as red as if he'd been out in the sun for a month, took his glasses off and, nearly screaming, said, "Do you know a man allegedly called Larry Heaslip?"

Blackie smiled at the jurors and said, "I think I might know a couple of people that might be called that, but I don't know if that's really him."

The US Attorney's nerves were obviously worn to a frazzle. "Are we going to do this every step of the way?"

Blackie said, "You're just trying to set me up, I think, but the bottom line is 'of my own volition' I don't know anything. Oh, that's not the truth. I don't like you. I know that."

The US Attorney, now completely out of control, said, "I'm going to get you if it's the last thing I ever do!"

Blackie leaned toward the court stenographer and said, "I hope you got that all down. I believe that was a threat."

"You're excused!" the US Attorney screamed.

As Blackie stood, he looked at the grand jurors menacingly and said, "All ya'll heard this of your own volition, and when it comes time to testify under oath, I'll expect you to tell the truth."

The US Attorney, now screaming to the US Marshal said, "Remove him from this Court Room!"

As Blackie and the Marshall started to walk out, Blackie said, "That guy needs what I think they call a Valium, something to calm him down; he's a nervous wreck."

The US Marshall, half smiling, half whispered, "You did it again. I knew you'd get out of it somehow."

As they approached Jamie, Blackie said, "Come on darlin'. They kicked me out." Turning to the US Marshall, he said, "If you need anything, let me know."

Blackie decided to start the weekend early, go straight home to his girls, and check in with Nanci by phone. As he got out of his car, he could hear shrill voices and splashing water. He knew tonight would be fun.

Blackie called Nanci from his home phone. She told him Jim Knotts had called, as had Paul Bartels, Mary Martin, Millie Odom, and the new girl Geri. He told Nanci to return Paul Bartel's call and say he'd be back Monday and that he was leaving for home and would not be able to get him the message. He wondered what to do about Millie. He finally decided to have Nanci call her and ask if she wanted him to call her from home, go to a pay phone, or wait until Monday. He figured Nanci already knew or suspected what was going on between him and Millie. He told her to call Mary and give her the same message she'd given Paul. He took Geri and Jim's phone numbers and said he'd handle those two.

When Jim answered the phone, Blackie said, "Anything important?"

"The Commissioner just talked to me a little while ago, acting like he was trying to feel me out to see what was going on. He thinks somebody high up is leaking to the press. That means me, you, Cuz, Hawk, Charlie, and Meadows to pick from since nobody else knows what's going on."

Blackie said, "Shit, I don't know nothing. Him and the Hawk been doin' all the hustlin'. I wouldn't believe it was you if you said it was, and I think Cuz is straight. That leaves shit-for-brains, his hack Hawk, and his two idiot cousins Charlie and Meadows. I don't know if any of them would leak, but I'm positive that they're stupid enough to make a mistake or just randomly brag while they're bullshitin'."

"Yeah, that makes sense, but I don't want to, and I'm sure you don't want to get caught in the crossfire and lose our jobs."

"Fuck him. I ain't gonna lose mine. I bought two medium, one small, and one huge insurance policy when he was runnin' my ass around doin' his private shit."

"Oh yeah?" Jim said. "Will they protect me too?"

"I don't know, probably, but they will damn sure take him down if he fucks with me."

Jim said, "That's cool. I'm gonna snoop around and see what's going on. I'll get back with you."

While Blackie was putting on his bathing suit to join his girls, Sandy stuck her head in the bathroom. "Nanci's on the phone."

"I'll take it in here, go hang the other phone up." Blackie held the phone against his ear until he heard the extension click off.

"I called Millie. She sounded kinda' like the priest caught her asleep during Mass, or her husband was on the extension while she was talking to a boyfriend. Got a little something going there, boss?"

"Come on, Nanci, we're casual friends, you know that."

"Yeah, yeah, I like you. I'd never give you up. Don't worry about me. She said you'd have to decide where to call her and when and that she'd be alone all weekend."

As Blackie put one foot in the pool to enjoy a splash with his girls, the phone rang again. He got to it on the third ring. "This better be important," he warned.

"I don't know, but Paul Bartels called again, and I put him off by letting Vicki take the call, and Geri called again. What do you want me to tell her? You're still not back."

"Don't tell 'em shit. Go home. Leave. Get outta' there."

"Sounds good to me. What about Vicki and Jana?"

"Tell them to go, too. Let Rosemary and Tina answer the phones, and they don't know shit—just to take messages. That means everybody. If God calls, tell him I'm on my way to Heaven." Hanging the phone up crossways so callers would only get a busy signal, he turned and dove into the pool.

Chapter 35

Blackie got to the office about 8:30 Monday morning and, as he sat down at his desk, Vicki brought in coffee and donuts, and Nanci brought a stack of phone messages. They both sat down in front of his desk as Blackie chewed on a glazed, sipped his coffee, and sorted through the messages.

"Nanci, you get Jim on the phone for me; you call Cuz, see if you can find out what he wants and stall him. Tell him I'm in a meeting. Come back and tell me what Cuz says and then do the same thing with Hawk. Meadows wants an appointment to see me? Find out what he wants."

Nanci interrupted. "Jim's on one."

"Vicki, go do Cuz and come right back," Blackie said, as he picked up the phone.

"Hey, dude."

"What's up, cowboy?"

"You tell me, it's your nickel."

"How about lunch. I wanna talk to ya about those insurance policies."

"OK, I gotta a pretty full plate. Can we do it someplace out in this area? How about the Chinese Inn—11:30?"

"11:30, cowboy, see ya then."

Vicki came back and said, "Cuz wants to talk to you about the budget."

"OK, Nanci, get me Paul. Vicki see if you can find out what the Hawk wants." In less than a minute, Nanci said, "Mr. Bartels is on line three."

"Dave Steece here, can I help ya?"

"Mr. Steece, we got a statement from David Martin saying that Holmes Johnson had an extensive amount of surveillance equipment and that it's come up missing. When I talked to Holmes Johnson, he said he never had any surveillance equipment; you did all the wiretapping. The surveillance equipment was left over from the Dave Pierce era.

I know you told me you didn't know anything about wiretapping, but do you know anything about previous equipment?"

"Not a thing, Paul. Not present or former."

"It's rumored that a story is going to break in the Shreveport paper about some rice growers, maybe not from that part of the country, but that's where it's comin' from, that have been shaken down for campaign contributions."

"Like I told you the other day, I don't know anything about any farmer of rice, sugar, or any other kind of farmer that's been solicited."

"I also spoke to the Commissioner and asked him about your comment, 'let the chips fall,' and he had no comment."

"I guess that's a non-denial denial, isn't it?"

"So the questions I've asked you today are what? No comment?"

"That's right, Paul, no comment."

When Blackie hung up, Vicki was standing in front of his desk looking puzzled. "I'm really not sure what he said, boss, or I guess I know what he said, but I don't now what he meant."

"Huh?"

"I think what he said was, 'The man's way to settle differences, like calling somebody nuts or a hack, would be to meet him on the Mississippi Levee and have a dual at dawn with shotguns."

"Are you kidding?"

"No, that's what he said word for word. I tried to write it down as he said it. He also said you were avoiding him by having me call him back."

Blackie laughed. "Jesus, did he say he wanted to flip a coin to see who went first?'

Vicki looked even more confused. "What?"

"Never mind, hon. Just go on back to work."

As left the room, Nanci said, "You obviously didn't call Millie or Geri back. They both called twice this morning." She added a knowing little arched eyebrow.

"Bullshit. Get Millie on the phone and what the hell does that other girl want?"

As Blackie mulled over the Paul Bartel's conversation, Nanci, poked her head in and said, "Millie's on two. Do you want me to call Geri?"

"Yeah, yeah," he said, as he picked up the phone. "Yeah, darlin'?"

"Well, finally, I thought you were avoiding me or probably you dumped me for my boss."

"C'mon, darlin'. I went to see Connie on business. Then had to play daddy with the little girls all weekend. I knew if I called you, I'd end up with you straddling my face and I'd never get back to my girls." That softened her to the point where he could almost see her smile over the phone. She said, "Tonight then?"

"How about a matinee about one o'clock this afternoon—take a late lunch?"

"Hmmm, I guess I can do that then," she said.

"The key's under the mat."

"Ok."

Blackie made a mental note to make sure he went by to put a key under the mat before he met Jim for lunch. As he hung up, Nanci said, "Geri wants to thank you for the job."

"Ok, tell her I'll get back to her when I can. I have a full plate."

"I told her."

Right then Vicki came back in and said, "I talked to Jimmy Meadows, and he wants to talk to you about a new position."

"Jesus, are you serious? He can't handle the one he's got now!"

"I know, I told him I'd put him in your appointment book just as soon as you had an opening, but with the budget happening, it wouldn't be right away."

"Good girl. It's hard to believe you're smart and beautiful. I knew there must be a reason Cuz kept you around."

Vicki turned bright red and said, "Anything else right now?"

Blackie leaned back, laughing. "Yes, but I don't fool with the help."

Nanci laughed as well. "Talk about bullshit. If we took our clothes off right now, he'd have a heart attack trying to figure which one of us to get first."

Vicki really got red then, bowed her head, and went back to her office.

Blackie walked to the back of the building taking Nanci along to take notes while he visited with his department heads, giving Nanci the requests for leave, vacation, etc., to handle for him. By the time they got back to his office, it was 10:45. He told Nanci and Vicki to hold the fort down, that he was going to a luncheon meeting.

As he swung by the apartment to drop off a key, he wished there was some way he could be sure that she wouldn't make a copy waiting for him. He decided that she wouldn't have enough time for that, thinking it would not be a good idea to have Millie and Mary there at the same time, although he wasn't sure Mary wouldn't welcome a threesome. As he turned into the parking lot, he thought maybe he would have Geri meet him over here and try out the other end of her when he had time.

Blackie turned into the Chinese Inn about 11:20 a.m.. Inside, he recognized State Representative Martin and, knowing he was on the Agriculture Committee, stopped and schmoozed a little bit before he went to the booth in the back corner. He barely sat down when Jim scooted into the seat across from him. They shook hands as the waitress asked what they wanted to drink. Blackie ordered unsweetened ice tea and Mo-Goo-Gai-Pan. Jim ordered the same thing.

Jim said, "Evidentially, somebody, I'm assuming the Commissioner and maybe Hawk, or one of his other hacks, have put the arm on a farmer who is friends with Bob Wright. Do you know him?"

"Yeah, I know of him. He's a maritime lawyer over in Lafayette, and his reputation is supposed to be squeaky clean."

"That's who he is and that's his reputation. He was also a law school classmate of the Commissioner. They're pretty good friends, and he was a big asset in the campaign, not only with his fund raising, but his reputation got a lot of good honest votes."

"What's your point, Jim?"

"The allegation is that, at some kind of a coffee, tea party, cocktail party, or something, he says the Commissioner said, "Give me ten grand or you don't get a license." The farmer flipped out, of course, and went to see Bob Wright. I guess Bob didn't believe him, so supposedly the farmer talked to some newspaper friend of his in Shreveport, and now they're digging into it."

"Is that the leak we were talking about last week? That ain't no leak. That's a broken dam."

"That's it."

"Why the hell would he think you or I—we don't have anything to do with those people over there."

"I know, but ya gotta have a fall guy. Remember how Nixon dumped Spiro Agnew?"

"Yeah, I remember, then Nixon got booted out anyhow."

"That's why I wanted to know how good your insurance is."

Blackie thought a minute, *fuck it, let's get this over with.* "I got pictures of Civil Service State Employees using state bought materials, driving state cars and trucks to Mississippi, working on a trailer park that the Commissioner and some Biloxi politician own in Biloxi, Mississippi. I got the same shit on a rental house of his in Baton Rouge."

"You said you had three insurance policies."

"I got another one of me and another guy in Mississippi collecting money."

"Campaign money?"

"No, money from that fuckin' trailer park. I got the receipts. It's still state employees, driving state cars, burning state gas in the wrong state."

"Yeah, man. Sounds pretty good. Can I get the pictures?"

"Sure. It'll take a few days. I got abut ten attorneys that are gonna mail 'em to everybody from the *New York Times* to the *San Francisco Examiner* and everybody in between, including every TV station and newspaper in the State of Louisiana, and will mail a few to Biloxi. Bring that fucker down too."

"God damn, you sound bitter."

"I'm not bitter. I came down here to do a good job. Moved my family, bought a house. I'm not going to be the fall guy for some half-wit."

"Calm down. I'm your friend."

"Nobody's my friend when you're fuckin' with my little girls. Another thing, fuckin' Hawk Daniels called my office this morning and challenged me to a fuckin' duel. I'll duel him with an .88 from behind a billboard. Fuck him and his threats." Blackie suddenly realized that he had gotten so loud that half the restaurant was staring at him, and the waitress had stopped about four feet from the table with their food in her hand, like she was afraid to come the rest of the way.

As the men finished their lunch, Jim said, "Let me handle this. I'll find out what the hell that Hawk Daniels shit is and tell the Commissioner he has to find another scapegoat."

In the parking lot, the two men shook hands. As Blackie wheeled away, he started to think, *it's pretty hard to figure out what side Jim was on in that conversation. There might have been a lot of CYA in there. If I had only one set of pictures and had given them to him, I'd be twisting in the wind tomorrow. Anyhow, the hell with that now.* He was on the way to the apartment and he'd let Millie work out all his aches and pains.

It was 4:30 before Blackie got back to the office, and he was glad to see the rest of the day there had gone pretty well. However, he barely got in his chair before Nanci said, "Geri's on the phone—again."

"Alright, let me take it." He picked up the phone. "Dave Steece here," he said. "Can I help you...just a minute...Nanci, do I have any other calls now?"

"I get it, you can't talk. I'll be at the McDonalds on Government at 5:30 and I'll wait until you get there however long it takes. Now you say 'you're welcome' for getting me the job and they'll think it was a legitimate call."

Blackie said into a dead phone, "you're welcome. I hope you like your job." He thought, *smart little bitch; she's done this before. She might be fun after all.*

Blackie sat in his office alone after everyone had gone home until about 5:15, trying to figure the angles as to what was going on, deciding that he better put that .44 back on his hip and not depend on this little ankle gun for his only source of self preservation.

It was about 5:40 when he pulled into the McDonalds on Government. He walked up to the counter and ordered a cup of coffee to go. Glancing around, he saw Geri in a halter top, shorts, no make-up, and a pony tail. Damn, she didn't even look fifteen. *It's amazing how some of 'em want to look older while some of 'em want to look younger,* but he thought it was strange that a twenty-year-old would want to look younger. As he walked out with his coffee, she followed discretely. He tossed the coffee unopened in the first garbage can he came to, drove out of the parking lot slow enough so she would have no trouble following him. As he turned onto Foster Dr. over to Highland Road, he picked the speed up until he reached the apartment parking lot. He got out of the car, and going into the apartment, left the door ajar. As he was taking his coat and tie off, Geri stepped in and closed the door behind her. Reaching behind her back, she pulled the bow on her halter top and it fell to the floor. Damn, he hadn't noticed how young her tits looked the other day under that lighting in the office. With no makeup on and those huge nipples that barely stood out, she looked like a kid. As she was pushing her shorts down, he said, "wait a minute darlin', you got a driver's license?"

She stopped with her shorts around her knees and paled a little, "Yes, why?"

"I want to see it."

"I don't have any tickets if you're gonna check it for holes."

"I'm not checking it for holes, I'm checking it for dates."

Geri stood frozen for a minute. Blackie said, "Give me the license, NOW." As she stepped, her shorts went to her ankles and she kicked them off going to her purse. She turned around with her wallet in her hand and said, "Fuck me first, then you won't care how old I am. All older guys like young girls, that's why I dress like this."

"Maybe, but you look too young. I'm afraid I have daughters older than you."

"You didn't care the other day."

"Give me that driver's license. Jesus Christ, Geri! You're just sixteen years old."

"I know, but I'm as good as any older woman and better than most."

"Get your fuckin' clothes on, NOW. There's not a shortage of pussy in my life and, even if there were, I wouldn't fuck a sixteen-year-old. When you filled out your application, didn't anybody check it?"

"Miss Connie knows how old I am. When she made a copy of my driver's license she changed the year by two years and made a copy of the copy."

"So Connie knows you're sixteen and helped you forge your papers for Civil Service? I don't fuckin' believe this."

"Don't get Miss Connie in trouble. My brother and sister will hate me. She did it for them."

"Miss Connie? What were you gonna say when I was fuckin' ya? 'Fuck me harder Mr. Dave?' Get your god-damn clothes on before I cut you up and put you in a dumpster. If you ever tell a soul you were in this apartment—"

"I won't, I won't, I promise I won't."

"Get the fuck outta here and don't call my office again—ever!"

Calling over her shoulder as she went out the door, she said, "Am I going to lose my job?"

Pissed, Blackie ran to the door and hollered, "Wait a minute." He ran down the stairs to her car. "Gimme your driver's license!"

As she handed him the license, she said, "What are you gonna do?"

"You just fuckin' sit right here. I'll be right back." Blackie jumped into his car and went to the closest Time Saver, dropped two dimes into the machine and made two copies of the driver's license. When he got back to the parking lot, he handed her the license and said, "If I hear one peep about this from anybody, including Connie, you'll be fired."

"You mean I still have my job?"

"Keep your fuckin' mouth shut and get to work on time in the morning."

"Oh, thank you!"

"Just shut up and get the fuck outta here."

Blackie went back to the office, started to call Nanci, remembering she was married to an idiot, changed his mind and called Vicki. "Where do we keep personnel files that come over from H & R? The applications?"

"The applications and information that Connie sends over are filed in Jana's office, alphabetically. The current information is kept in whatever division they work in. Why, is there something I can help you with?"

"Naw, I was thinking what you said about Jimmy Meadows wanting a promotion. I was going to look at his file."

"Oh, that won't be in there. He's unclassified. He would be in a file in the Capitol, in Administration, with all the unclassified personnel, like you, Mr. Knots, Mr. Kidder, David Martin, people like that."

"Ok, thanks. By the way, did you actually say Kidder's name right next to me?" Vicki sputtered, but Blackie laughed and said, "I'm just kidding you," and hung up.

Blackie had keys to everything in his desk, but it took him fifteen minutes to find the keys to open Jana's office and another fifteen to find the right one to the file cabinet. Lo and behold, when he got the drawer open and pulled Miss Geri's file out, the copy of her driver's license, instead of showing 1962 like Blackie's copy, the copy said 1960. Not a bad forgery, but he could tell it had been altered. Blackie made a copy for himself and put the file back, locked everything up, and went home to his girls.

As Blackie pulled into the driveway, he recognized the blue Chevrolet Classic parked there as belonging to Mary. He guessed she got tired of waiting for his callback. Well, he was home for the night with his girls. All she'd get would be a couple of sneak feels. If she wanted more, she'd have to get on his sex schedule, which he was having a hard enough time keeping up with. Hell, she was fuckin' half the people in Baton Rouge. She sure didn't need him. As he walked in, he was greeted by, "Hi, honey," from Sandy and "Hey good lookin'," from Mary, as they both got up from their coffee.

He said, "Hey, I'm glad to see you got each other to keep company, 'cause I got a meeting to go to. I gotta go change clothes." They sat there looking like two blow-up dolls as he walked away. As he climbed the stairs, he thought he'd heard rumors that Mary liked to muff-dive. Maybe she'd teach Sandy and that'd keep them both off his back.

In his bedroom, Blackie took his coat and tie off when Lu, Rae, and Alley screamed in. Lu said, "Teri called. And Mom said it was correct and long distance. But it sounded just like a regular phone to me. She's gonna bring us all presents when she comes, but I don't member when she's comin'."

"Yeah, what did you say to her. Alley?"

"I told her how to spell Baton Rouge and told her the Indians named the town after a deer." Blackie shook his head and picked up the baby. "And you?"

"I want a new baby doll, but I don't wanna wait till she comes. Can I have one now?"

Blackie thought, *God it's so hard to believe that these lil angels are gonna grow up, get married, and drive some idiot nuts, and I'll probably have to kill the son-of-a-bitch for cheating on 'em. I wonder if that's called a double standard?* Maybe husbands don't cheat on angels. It wasn't long before he heard Mary's car back out of the driveway, and he felt the pressure that unsolicited sex lifted. After dinner, they hung out and watched the movie. Blackie fell asleep before it was over.

The next morning, as soon as Blackie got to the office, he called Connie.

"Ms. LeBlanc, can I help you?"

"Yeah, darlin', it's Dave Steece."

"Oh, hey, I didn't know you placed your own calls or I wouldn't have answered so—"

"What—professionally? I want to see ya for lunch today. Can you handle that?"

"Sure. Where, when?"

"How about the Chinese Inn about 11:30?"

"Ok, is it going to be a long lunch? I need to tell my staff how long I'll be gone."

"I don't know. Kinda depends on you."

"Ok, I'll handle it."

Blackie answered a few routine AIG letters and headed for the Chinese Inn.

Chapter 36

Connie LeBlanc left her office five minutes after she talked to Blackie, drove straight home, hoping Jimmy would be either passed out or gone or both. When she arrived, she was lucky that he wasn't there. She went straight to her bedroom, unbuttoned her work-shirt jacket as she walked to her bedroom, throwing it on the disheveled bed. Kicking off her low heels and her skirt, she turned toward her closet. Connie knew she wasn't beautiful, but she considered herself above average with the right hairdo, make up, and clothes, she could hold her own with any forty-year-old. And that's exactly what she intended to do. She didn't know where Blackie was going, but she knew he was a climber, judging from the short time he'd been there, and she planned on getting on his coattails. She tossed her plain white bra on the bed, selected a black half-cup push-up. She knew this would enhance her large cup size. She took her panty hose off, got a pair of black thigh-highs she'd been saving since her last lover had gone back to his wife. She selected a taupe skirt with a slit up about the middle of her thigh. The strappy sandal heels would make her calves more distinct. She picked out a short-sleeved, bright-yellow blouse with a ruffled front. Buttoned and unbuttoned the third button down several times, trying to decide between more or less cleavage, finally settling on more. She put on gold hoop earrings, dumped her wedding ring for a dinner ring that had been her mother's, and a gold watch. A dash of Channel and she was out the door. The five minutes she'd spent in her office after she'd talked to Blackie, she'd spent talking to her special friend at the beauty parlor who was going to squeeze her in to touch up her hair, her makeup, and her nails. She'd been shopping for almost a year since she'd been dumped when she'd given her lover an ultimatum. He'd chosen the wife and she went back to the drunk. This time, she was going to do it differently. If she got him, she'd take three or four nights a week. That was a hell of a lot better than none. She'd just passed her fortieth birthday and knew she had to get her talons into something substantial or she'd end up old, gray, and probably fat like her mother had. This was not something to look forward to.

Blackie got to the Chinese Inn a little early again, and was a bit surprised to see Connie waiting just inside the door in what he could hardly call "office dress." She actually looked good. He'd turned around and looked at the parking lot to make sure this wasn't evening and this wasn't a club and they weren't going dancing.

Connie took his arm as the hostess led them to a booth in the back. Blackie grinned at her. "You look ravishing."

She smiled up at him. "I thought you might want to ravish me."

"You say anything else and we're gonna miss lunch. You're not just playing me are you?"

"No, I'm a 'no strings' girl who thinks you're a sexy man and would love to work something out with you on your schedule."

"God, where have you been all my life? I been looking for you since I was nine years old."

"Connie squeezed his arm as they reached their booth. "I can promise you that you won't be sorry."

The same waitress approached their table and Blackie said, "She looks a lot better than my lunch date yesterday, huh?" The waitress nodded shyly and stated, "I bet you won't yell at her like you did him either."

"Who'd you yell at yesterday?" Connie's asked.

"It was some girl that turned me down."

"I know that's not true; the waitress said it was a man."

"Yeah, I know. I'm kidding. I was just expressing myself loudly. He is a friend."

The waitress still waiting for our order, said, "If he's your friend, I sure don't want to be your enemy."

Which caused Blackie to laugh, leaning back, looking the waitress up and down. "You're way too pretty to be an enemy. I want Moo Goo Gai Pan and unsweetened tea again. Connie?"

"Mandarin Chicken and sweet tea with extra lemon."

As they waited for the lunch, Blackie asked, "How soon do you have to be back?"

Connie smiled. "I don't. I'm the boss and I run my ship like Admiral Halsey."

"I know you got something to do with personnel but what exactly do you do?"

"Every Civil Service Employee touches my desk. George Hammler is the head of Civil Service, but he's a bureaucrat and couldn't pour piss out of a boot with directions."

"You mean if I wanted somebody on the payroll or for that matter anybody wanted somebody on the payroll and you were open to it, you could do it?"

"I just told you I run it. Can't be much plainer that that. You aren't asking me if I'd do something illegal are you?"

"No. I was just kinda wondering how it works."

"You take the test, I interview you, do some background, check your references, place you on the register. When the department asks for a particular employee, I go to the register and send them two or three qualified applicants."

"You mean like Geri that you sent to us?"

"She was a special case. She's the sister of a couple of my very good friends."

Right then, the food arrived and they changed to light small talk as they ate. When lunch was over, Blackie said, "I'm a little hesitant with what's next. With all your power, I don't want to get in trouble."

Connie reached across the table and said, "I told you, you aren't going to get into trouble with me. I'm interested and I thought you were also by the way you looked at me."

"What's the next cliché? Your place or mine?"

Connie threw her head back and laughed. "I think neither would be appropriate, since we both have spouses there."

Blackie decided the apartment was out at this stage. He didn't trust her enough for her to know where it was. "I guess the safest thing for your reputation is for me to go get a room. Where can I call you with the number?"

"Where did you have in mind?"

"I guess the Belmont."

"I'll follow you there and just wait at the Burger King across the street. I'll leave my car there and you can come and get me."

"That's a great idea."

Blackie pulled into the Burger King parking lot. Connie had parked in the back among all the employee cars and just got in with him. When they pulled into the Belmont, Connie literally attacked him when they entered the room, throwing clothes in all directions like one of those Hollywood movie scenes. Blackie knew that he had to act like he was enjoying her passion or he would never be able to use her for what he planned. At ten, he dropped Connie off at her car. Blackie, exhausted, pulled out of the Burger King parking lot, thinking, *my God, now I have three oversexed nymphomaniacs on my hands and a wanna-be wife who requires some servicing. I'm not gonna have enough energy if a one-nighter happens to come along.*

As he turned into his driveway, he realized how badly he had been neglecting his girls. None of these damn women were worth five minutes with these little angels. Somehow, he had to get more time with them. When Blackie walked into the sparsely lit den, he found Sandy dozing in a chair and the TV tuned to snow. She rose up and said, "Nanci called. Paul Bartels, Jim Knotts, and somebody else that identified himself as being with the FBI called you at the office." Blackie could see the anguish in her face as she raised her eyebrows without needing to say, "Where have you been?"

Blackie took the paper from her hand. "You know I can't tell anyone where I've been when I meet The Man in New Orleans."

That seemed to satisfy her, and she smiled at him. "If you haven't had dinner, I'll fix you some while you return your calls."

"That would be nice, babe. I haven't had time to get gas, much less eat." He noticed that both Paul Bartels and Jim Knotts had their home phones down along with their office numbers. He figured the FBI was too important to be called at night. All he left was the office and extension number. He called Jim first. A sleepy voice answered on the fifth ring. "Hello."

"Did I wake you?"

"Hey, cowboy, where ya been?"

"You know."

"Oh, chasing some squeeze and can't talk?"

"Ya got that right."

"I wanted to give ya a heads up. The FBI agent called the Capitol this afternoon and tried to get your home phone."

"Shit, they're supposed to be great investigators. Ya mean they can't find out where I live?"

"I'm sure they can. I guess they wanted to do it the easy way. I just wanted to let you know that, when the Commissioner found out they were looking for ya, he went nuts."

"Well, that must have been about a three-second trip. Ya got any idea what they wanted?"

"Nah, probably want to give you some sort of award for 'Mr. Personality.' You really don't have any idea?"

"Not a clue, but with dumb shit and the goofas guys running around, there really is no telling."

"Are you going to call them back tomorrow?" Jim asked.

"Yeah, if they don't call me first."

"Ok, man. Let me know what they say. I'm going back to bed."

Blackie took off his tie, tossed his shirt in the utility room, and walked back into the breakfast area. Sandy had just set a plate of potato salad, deviled eggs, and a ham and cheese po-boy on the table for him. "You wanna spin me up a vanilla shake with three or four raw eggs in it?"

"Sure honey," she said.

As Blackie stood in the shower with the water beating on his back, he wondered what the FBI could want. Were they trying to get him? Did they think he knew something about the Commissioner and he'd roll, or was it a political witch hunt? There had been rumors for years that the Government had been after Hawk Daniels to disbar him and get him off the bench. Maybe he brought the extra heat on, and then Jim Knotts had wiggled out of going to prison with the Commissioner of Education Michot when that fiasco had fallen apart. That would be another possibility, not to mention that most of law enforcement had spent years trying to convince Blackie that he was a gangster. Add the Commissioner, who Blackie knew was a dumb shit and shaking people down, and the bobsey twins going around doing who knows what, that would be a pretty big feather in a hat if they could get all of them.

As Blackie was toweling off, he felt a pair of hands sliding up his chest from behind and pulling him into a pair of pointed breasts. Sandy whispered in his ear, "I put Vitamin E in the deviled eggs and in the malt." He thought, *oh shit, ole buddy, don't fail me now. You're gonna have to perform this feat one more time tonight, so my little angels will have a loving mom tomorrow. Wouldn't it be nice to find somebody he wanted to fuck to be his wife and the children's mother? Maybe someday.*

Chapter 37

As Blackie backed out of his driveway admiring the crepe myrtles, he wished he was taking his girls on a drive through the azalea gardens in LaCombe today, instead of putting up with car fumes, politics, and greedy dumb shits. They could fuck up anything. Agriculture should work toward making the state more beautiful.

Vicki met Blackie at his desk with his usual two donuts and coffee. Nanci had her hand full of the usual phone messages. Grinning at Nanci, he said, "Flip a coin and start returning calls. Let's get this shit over with."

A minute later she said, "Mr. Hahn with the FBI on line three."

Blackie picked up the phone. "Dave Steece."

Hahn identified himself and said, "We'd like to have you come down and talk to us."

"Ok, what time?"

"One o'clock would be fine. We're in the Federal—"

"I know," Blackie said, cutting him off. "You're downstairs in the Post Office on Florida Boulevard."

"Oh, you've been here?"

"No, but everybody knows where the Feebees are."

"Feebees? What's that?"

"That's what everybody calls you 'gray-suit, conservative-tied, wing-tipped cordovans."

"Really?"

"Yup, see ya at one o'clock, feebee," He hung up. "NEXT!"

Nanci said, "Paul Bartel's on four."

"David here, Paul. If we keep spending this much time together, when it ends, one of us is going to have to pay alimony. What can I do for ya?"

"I have information that the FBI is interviewing several agriculture employees and that you're one of 'em. You want to tell me what they want?"

"No, 'cause I don't know, and I don't know if I would if I did know."

"So your answer is 'no comment'?"

"My answer is I don't know. Who else are they going to interview?"

"Oh, so you admit you've been interviewed or you're going to be interviewed?"

"I don't admit nothin', except I love my five girls."

"Would you tell me when you're going to be interviewed?"

"Why don't you ask the source that told you its gonna happen, and then we'll both know. Anything else, Paul? I have about a hundred phone calls to return."

"Ok, I guess I'll just go sit in front of the Federal Building and see who comes and goes."

"Hey, that's an idea. There's a lot of postmen going in and out of that building. Maybe I should just go rent a postman's uniform, if I ever have to go. I'll just wear that and no one will know it's me." As Blackie looked up, Nanci was standing in front of him with the words, *Commissioner on line three*, written on a piece of paper. "I gotta go Paul," Blackie said, and hung up, pushing the line three button at the same time. "Yes?"

"This is the Commissioner speaking." *No shit*, thought Blackie. "What can I do for ya?" he asked, thinking, *drown ya, give you a brain transplant, push you out a window?*

"I understand that you're going to the FBI for an interview today. Can you tell me what time that's going to be?"

"One o'clock."

"I'm gonna send an attorney with ya."

"I ain't payin for no attorney."

"You don't have to pay. I'm paying. I just want to make sure your rights are protected."

"Who is this guy? I've probably forgot more about my rights than he knows."

"Oh no. He's a prominent criminal attorney. I'll have him meet you there at one o'clock."

As Blackie hung up, he thought, *shit, this will be a fiasco.*

"Jim Knotts on line one," was Nanci's next announcement.

"Hey, Jim."

"The Commissioner get you? He's been driving me crazy for the last hour."

"Yeah, just talked to him. I've been in my office all day. He could have called me there. He don't know where that's at?"

"I don't know. He's pretty nervous. What did the FBI say?"

"They said come down and talk to them at one o'clock so we could exchange pleasantries. Who else have they called?"

"I know they're going to talk to me and Hawk, and I don't know who else from AIG."

"What time you going?"

"I'm going at 11:00."

"You taking an attorney?"

"Yup, the Commissioner is paying for one."

"Me too. Probably the same idiot. Give me a call after ya go."

"You're alright with this, huh, Blackie?"

"Yeah, I'm fine. I haven't done nothin'."

"Ok, keep it together. I'll talk to ya later."

Vicki came in and said, "you want me to order your lunch, or are you going out?"

"Nah, order me a ham and cheese po-boy. I'm gonna eat here with the peons."

"Ham and cheese po-boy with no tomatoes, right? And unsweetened tea?"

"You got it darlin'. You gonna make somebody a good wife, girlfriend, or secretary some day," Blackie said, grinning as she headed back to her office.

Just as Nanci came in and said, "What's going on with the FBI?" Blackie's private line rang. He picked up the phone. "Go type a letter, look pretty, or something, until I get through with this call. Close the door behind ya." Then he turned his attention to the phone. "Yeah?"

Millie's voice purred, "Honey, when am I going to see ya? I miss ya."

"I know. I'm up to my ass in alligators. Call me on this line around five o'clock, and I'll try to be here."

"I called several times yesterday, but Nanci answered every time."

"Did you hang up or hit on her?"

"You're not funny. I'll call you back at five."

Blackie had barely hung up when Nanci said, "the Commissioner's on two."

He thought, *Jesus*, as he picked up the phone. "I just wanted to make sure you knew you didn't have to answer any questions," the Commissioner said.

"I know how to talk to the FBI. I've been doing it for years. Don't get nervous."

"OK, everything will be fine; just let the attorney do the talking."

"I'm not going to let some attorney talk for me. If he wants to be there, that's fine, and if you want to pay him that's fine, but I talk for myself."

"Ok, I just wanted to let you know that your job's secure."

No shit, Blackie thought, as he hung up the phone. As he got up to go to the bathroom, his private line rang again. "Yes?"

"Do you know who this is?"

"I will if you tell me what kind of car you drive."

"A blue Chevy Caprice Classic."

"And who's your husband?

"You know who my husband is you smart-ass."

"Ok, ya failed that question. Try this one. What number am I on your list of lovers?"

"You're the one with the biggest dick!"

"Awww, I bet you tell everybody that."

"Naw, you're the only one that makes my jaw sore."

"Oh, now I know who you are."

"You are a smart-ass. When are you gonna let me make my jaw sore? I haven't seen you in a while."

"Now let me see where you are on my calendar. I'll see when your turn's comin."

"Damn you! You are a smart-ass! How many women you fuckin' right now?"

"None. I'm talkin' to you on the phone. Well, I know you're in a private office, alone, because I can't even answer some of these questions, and how did you get this private number?"

"I got connections."

"Yeah, yeah, you probably stole it outta your husband's index."

"Seriously, I want to see ya."

"Seriously, I'd love to see ya when I have time. You love going by and talking to my wife. Go see her. She'll tell ya I don't even have time to talk to my kids."

"I know. I sat with her till eight o'clock last night. You were out plantin' somebody. I'm not greedy or jealous. I just want a turn."

"Hey, I know, I'm serious. When I get a minute, you're next."

"You are a smart-ass! Write down my private number at work and use it!"

As Blackie hung up he thought, *hmmm, Sandy didn't mention that Mary had been there for three hours with her.* He'd have to slow Mary down from going to his house so much or, eventually, he'd get caught in a lie. This time he took the phone off the hook while he went to the bathroom. When he came back and hung it up, it rang immediately. He thought, *shit,* he needed a secretary for the private line. He should have guessed it would be Connie.

"Hey, honey, I haven't heard from you this mornin' and this phone has been busy constantly."

Hey darlin'. I haven't had time to pee. I took it off the hook when I had to go to the bathroom."

"Well, that's why I got a busy. How long were you in the bathroom?"

"About ten minutes."

"Well, you were doin' something more than peeing."

"You're right, I was getting rid of the Chinese from yesterday," He said, thinking that would cover the call to Mary. Too many people had this phone number. Connie purred in his ear about how she missed him and he purred back, only his was a lie. *Please God, let me get home and have some time with my girls and get away from these crazy broads. They're fun to fuck and the blow jobs aren't bad, but this lovey dovey shit I just ain't got time for.* Blackie waved frantically to get Nanci's attention and made the motion so she'd know he wanted to be interrupted.

"Mr. Steece, I hate to bother you on your private line, but you have an important phone call. Shall I tell them you'll call back?" She made faces at him trying to get him to laugh.

"No, tell them I'll be right with them; put them on hold. See, darlin'—no rest for the weary."

Connie murmured into the phone, "More like no rest for the wicked."

"What? That hurts."

"I'm just teasing. I know you're busy. I miss ya, honey. Call me."

"I'm going to an important meeting downtown at one o'clock. It should last several hours. If I get back after five o'clock, I'll answer this phone. You'll have to call me 'cause I have no where to call you."

"I could wait in my office and you could call my private line."

"That wouldn't be right. I don't know how long I'll be tied up."

"Honey, I don't mind waitin for ya."

"I know, but I don't know how long it'll be. Just keep trying me here after five, and if I get through at any reasonable time before I go home to my girls, I'll come back here so I can answer your call."

"It's just so hard after yesterday. I never felt like that before."

"Me neither, darlin'," he said as he hung up, thinking, *shit, I don't even remember what it felt like. That was yesterday, give me a break.*

Just then, Vicki walked in with his sandwich and drink with Nanci right behind her. Blackie said, "Save us all a lot of grief. If I'm not here, just don't answer this phone. Turn the ringer off, down, or whatever you have to do to give you peace of mind."

"Ok, but it rings a lot."

"Pretend you're home and mad at your husband. Put a pillow over it."

Vicki chimed in. "I don't have a husband."

"Well, I can give ya a little pre-husband training if ya want. At least the sex part. I don't know about the cookin'."

Vicki, realizing that she had put her foot in it, turned her blushing face away and mumbled something unintelligible.

As Blackie took a bite of his po-boy, he said, "Ya'll can come in here and eat if ya want to. I won't hit on ya, promise. I don't want to eat alone."

Blackie pulled into the Federal Courthouse parking lot at two minutes to one. No use spoiling these people, he thought, by showing any fear, just a normal amount of respect. As he walked into the corridor, he saw some overweight gray suit sitting on a bench outside the FBI office and assumed this was his guardian angle. God, he hoped he wasn't in any trouble. This guy looked like an idiot. He stood up and said, "Are you Mr. Steece?"

Blackie thought, *yeah, wouldn't you know if you're going to represent me?*

"Yeah, who are you?" The guy mumbled some name he had never heard before and said, "I'm your attorney."

Blackie said, "You're not my attorney. If the Commissioner wants to waste his money and your time, that's up to you and him. My attorneys are Harry R. Cabral, Jr., and Jamie Veverica, and they're in New Orleans. If I felt like I needed an attorney that's who'd be here, not you."

Just then, the door opened and Blackie figured they either had a camera or a bug and had heard the conversation; they knew he was out here and figured they needed to save this guy. The guy who opened the door identified himself as an FBI agent and mumbled some name that Blackie didn't get nor did he care, asking, "David Steece?" When Blackie nodded, he said, "this way please."

Num-nuts fell behind Blackie. "I'm Mr. Steece's attorney," to which Blackie said, "No he's not. The Commissioner sent him, and the Commissioner's payin' him. I don't need no attorney."

The agent said, "If you don't want him in here, we'll make him leave."

Blackie said, "I don't care if he's in here. He's just here to report back to the Commissioner whatever I say. And I ain't got much to say, so that ain't no problem."

Both men looked a little bewildered and the agent said, "Ok, ya'll have a seat right there." Blackie took a seat in front of a metal desk and the Commissioner's attorney took the seat beside him. Blackie thought, *shit I hope our tax money's going to salaries, 'cause it sure ain't going to decorations or furniture.* He looked around the room, which was about 12' x 12' with a single desk, two steel vinyl covered chairs that Blackie and the attorney occupied, and one cheap swivel arm chair on the other side. The room was painted a terrible off-green color with a calendar on one wall and a picture of the White House on another wall and, staring down behind the interviewer's seat was a picture of J. Edger Hoover—gray suited, of course, not in his infamous pink crinoline. No truth in advertising, here. He knew from rumor and reputation that he had as big an ego as one of Blackie's young soldiers that had not risen above soldier status, yet, and was still on the climb. Blackie thought of all the stories related to the director allegedly by his own agents, like his daybreak attempts to walk on water, witnessed only by his associate director Clyde Tolson, who was also supposedly his roommate and lover. But you know how gossip is—it had Blackie being a gangster. Maybe ole John Edger wasn't queer after all. Only Blackie and John Edgar knew the truth about themselves. Just then, the agent walked back into the room with a legal pad and two #2 pencils, both sharpened. Blackie figured they wrote in pencil so that Hoover could correct any mistakes they made and the answers to the questions, the way he wanted them to sound. Anyhow, that was the decor for the room, two chairs, a swivel chair, two idiots, two pencils, a calendar, a picture of J. Edgar Hitler, a legal pad, and a nice guy—*me,* Blackie thought. The interview couldn't go all bad with that, he thought.

The FBI interviewer said, "We have some history with you, Mr. Steece, so we're going to stipulate your name. The address we are going to use is the Dept of Agriculture Building on Airline Highway. The Commissioner's attorney looked completely bumfuzzeled at this statement, and Blackie thought, *shit, they know about that Grand Jury testimony.* The interviewer than asked, "Have you ever threatened, through any of your enforcement divisions, to refuse to give or suspend any licensing in lieu of campaign contributions?"

The Commissioner's attorney said, "You don't have to answer that."

Blackie turned and glared at him and said, "You're NOT my attorney. You can sit here and listen if you want, but don't talk or give ANY advice. Do you understand?" Dumb-fuck looked shocked.

The interviewer again said, "If you don't want him here, we can make him leave."

"No, he doesn't have to leave, he just has to learn to act like a wife and shut up when he's told to and listen." Dumb fuck again looked shocked, red-faced, and embarrassed.

The interviewer shrugged and said, "Do you remember the question?"

Blackie said, "Yes, I remember the question, and the answer is no."

"Are you telling me that you have never used the power of the office to get money, campaign money?"

"That's what I'm telling you. No, I haven't. I can't speak for anybody else, but no, I haven't."

"Have you ever gotten any type of gratuity through threats or intimidation?"

"No, I haven't."

"How about the Dept of Agriculture?"

"How the hell would I know? You're asking me about me and the answer is no, I haven't. I don't know what anybody else has done. As far as I'm concerned, everything else is just rumors. Kind'a like your boss, everybody in America has heard rumors about him, from being a dictator to being gay. Kinda like my rumors, just rumors."

The interviewer stopped writing and started to sputter, then said, "You ever carry a gun?"

"That's a stupid question. Ever is a long time. I've taken my girls hunting, yes. I've been commissioned with law enforcement and carried a gun, yes. Do you ever carry a gun or do you run around chasin' bank robbers with no gun? They're common tools of modern life. Even if you don't like them, it behooves you to know how to use one and, occasionally, carry one. In the Marine Corps, it's called a weapon, and it's part of your body. In the Army, Navy, and Air Force it should be, but that's their problem. I've answered you, did you answer me? Do you ever carry one?"

Now the interviewer was sputtering openly. The Commissioner's attorney was in complete shock. Just then, a second agent stepped into the room. He handed the Commissioner's attorney a folded piece of paper and said, "You've now been subpoenaed, and this interview is over."

Blackie stood up and said to the second agent, "I told your buddy here and this guy, pointing at the Commissioner's attorney, and now I'm telling you. That's NOT my attorney. If that subpoena's meant for me, you hadn't effected a good service, because everybody besides you, and now you, know he's not my attorney." The agent snatched the paper out of the Commissioner's attorney's hand and handed it to Blackie. "Now, you're subpoenaed."

Blackie opened up the paper, read off the United States of America vs. the Commissioner, and when and where to appear before the Grand Jury. "Got it. By the way, your buddy here never answered me in our question and answer session whether he carried a gun or not, do you?" He now had two sputtering agents. "Shouldn't you have searched me if you really wanted to know before you let me in here to see if I was armed?" he asked. As he started out the door, both men were looking at each other a little lost. The Commissioner's attorney caught up with him in the parking lot and said, "You didn't treat me very good in there."

"I didn't invite ya, I didn't hire ya, and you don't listen. Considering those three things, I think I treated ya pretty good. As far as I'm concerned, you're an intruder in my personal life and whatever part of me here concerns the Dept. of AIG. Once more, considering those things, I think I treated you pretty good."

As Blackie turned into his office parking lot, he saw both the Commissioner and Jim Knotts' cars. He made a U turn and drove straight over to his apartment, where he called Nanci at her office. "What's goin on darlin', or can anyone hear ya talkin to me?"

"No, I'm okay; they're both sitting on the couch in your office waiting for you."

"Do you mind lying a little for me darlin'?"

"No, not at all."

"Tell them I just called from downtown, that I just got out of a meeting, that I haven't had time for lunch before the meeting, so I was going to go have my lunch and I 'think', be sure you emphasize 'think' I was going to Rick's Pancake House out on Airline Highway to eat. After lunch, I'm either going home or going to get drunk. At this point, I don't know which one I'm going to do. Tell 'em that."

"That's easy, where's the lie?"

"I had lunch with you and Vicki, remember?"

"Oh, yeah, well that's not much of a lie."

"Also, guess where I'm not going."

"Rick's. Right! And then you're not going to get drunk or go home."

"You're right three more times. Go give them the good news. I'll call you on my private line in about five minutes. If they're gone answer it, if not let it ring. If they try to answer it, say, "Whoa, I never answer that phone. He gets really upset if anyone touches that phone. I know you're the Commissioner. I just thought I'd mention that."

"Ok, do you want any of your messages?"

"I'll listen to them. I don't know if I want them."

"Paul Bartels, Gus Weill, and Dr. James Dudley Day. Isn't he that famous plastic surgeon?

"That's him darlin'; he sewed up my neck. That's why I look so pretty. OK, I might call 'em back from here or I might not. Go work your magic on those two people."

"Ok, ya want me to call you back when they leave, if they leave?"

"I love ya darlin'. Nice try, but you're not gettin this phone number. Sorry.

"OK, Perry Mason."

"OK, Della Street, I'll call ya back in five minutes." Blackie hung up and went to the refrigerator to get a glass of milk, wondering what the hell Jim was doing with "shit for brains?" Five minutes later, when he dialed his private line in his office, Nanci answered it on the first ring. "They left immediately. Jim wanted to go back to the Capitol, but the Commissioner wanted to go to Rick's to see if you were there. When they don't find you there, they'll probably go back to the Capitol."

"Ok, I'm not going to Rick's, and I'm not going home. I'm going straight to New Orleans. Call Sandy and tell her to tell the kids they can call me before they go to bed at Mom and Pop's. I'll end up there for dinner after my meeting." Blackie hung up, called Jamie, and briefed her on the Grand Jury subpoena and arranged to meet at her house in about an hour. He then called Mom and Pop to see if they'd be home for dinner after he met with Jamie. With everything said, he turned the Plymouth south on Highland Road at a reasonable speed, but he knew that, when it intersected with I-10, he was going to skin it back because to get to Jamie's house in an hour required at least a hundred miles an hour.

Chapter 38

Blackie had pondered the idea of Jamie or Harry, when he first left the FBI office. He had to decide between them, only because the fact that she was a part-time lover always frightened him. Most women who had been his lovers had always got pissy jealous when they found out about one of their rivals. Jamie, however, was in her second marriage to a really nice guy, and Blackie had finally become comfortable with their sex life. Maybe now she could become what he wanted in a woman. He could spank her ass, hold her head down, and then take her around his close friends and treat her as the very special friend and competent attorney that she was. None of the three things ever mixed. She was definitely an exceptional woman and probably could be the one who could be the mother to his kids and the wife he longed for if he could give up everything else in his life, which of course he couldn't.

As he turned off Hickory and pulled into the last driveway of Jamie's four-car garage, he hoped his plan would work. Jamie had a private office in the front of her house. She opened the door as he approached, smiling up at him with that questioning look she always had. "Is this all pleasure, all work, all business, or some of both?" They both always loved the latter if time would allow. As he entered her office, she pressed up against him and gave him a light kiss. He reached into his coat pocket and handed her the subpoena. She stepped back and lifted the glasses that hung around her neck on a gold chain, with a little furrow formed in her brow as she read. She let her glasses hang again as she dropped her hand with the paper to her side. "Does he know about this?"

"He knows I was at the FBI office today. He sent one of his attorney friends to meet me. They initially handed him the subpoena, but it was folded. When I told them he was not my attorney, theCommissioner Gilbert y took it back and gave it to me. I'm not sure he has any idea of what it says. I understand the FBI interviewed several people, so I'm not sure they all got a subpoena, but they probably did."

"What do you want to do?"

"What we talked about. Let's give them the Monty Hall treatment. I'll give them the violations I know about, plus the extortion, work my magic, and try to get Westerlund to testify for them, appear before the Grand Jury, and not give them a bunch of shit like usual. All I want is not to get on the stand."

"That's a big order, honey."

"Darlin' you've been juggling yourself around my wants and needs for years. This is not harder than any of the other ones."

With that, she sat down with her legal pad and wrote the numeral one.

#1. "We'll tell them about the Westerlund bribe for $10,000. At the right time, we'll produce the original envelope that the bribe came in with Westerlund's fingerprints, Knotts, and probably yours."

"Right."

(THIS ENVELOPE IS IN THE FEDERAL COURT RECORDS)

"Let me see if I have the rest of this straight. You want to be put in a witness room alone with Westerlund. You're going to coerce him by saying you're going to testify about the ten grand. You're going to show him an envelope and allege it's the original with his fingerprints and tell him you're going to turn it over. That should flip him."

#2. "You're going to produce pictures, receipts for material, food, and gasoline, bought with Louisiana state credit cards while in Mississippi and an affidavit with names of the State employees from some or all of the people that participated and worked for the Commissioner and his Mississippi politician partner's property."

#3. "You're going to produce a statement from a New Orleans School Board employee and the name of another Louisiana State employee with you at the time you assisted the School Board Employee in Mississippi."

**BLACKIE AND A STATE CAR WITH TWO OF THE
AGRICULTURAL EMPLOYEES WORKING ON THE
COMMISSIONER'S CEDAR LAKE TRAILOR PARK PROPERTY IN
MISSISSIPPI (THE REST OF THE RECEIPTS AND PICTURES ARE
IN FEDERAL COURT RECORDS)**

Letter from Violet Hane Cinquigranno, New Orleans Public Schools

NEW ORLEANS PUBLIC SCHOOLS

Gene Geisert, Superintendent

August 2,1977

Commissioner Gilbert L. Dozier
PO Box 44302
State Capitol
Baton Rouge, LA 70804

Dear Commissioner Dozier:

Just a note to commend your staff, and extend my personal thanks to two of them. Unfortunately, their names are unknown to me.

Yesterday, in a driving rainstorm in Mississippi on I-10 several miles east of Hwy, 607 as I attempted to fill my steaming radiator, a car stopped and two gentlemen emerged into the rain to help. Such assistance should not go unnoticed. If you can identify them, by all means convey my personal gratitude to both gentlemen from the lady in the silver Impala.

Very truly yours,

V. CINQUIGRANNO /S/

VHC/cvs

Purchasing Department 4300 Almonaster Street New Orleans, LA
(504)288-6561 ext.428

#4. "Pictures of the Commissioner's personal rental property being repaired by Louisiana State employees, receipts for the material, and the employees names."

Tina Ratchke agriculture employee delivering supplies in a State Agricultural Truck to Commissioner's Spain Street rental property, Baton Rouge, LA
(other pictures and receipts in Federal court records)

#5. "Be available during the Grand Jury and the trial as a consultant for any and all witnesses, either for the Commissioner or the Government." She wrote the number six.

#6. "You're not asking for any immunity for this, you just don't want to testify in open court."
"Right darlin'."
"OK, honey. I'll talk to the U.S Attorney tomorrow. You know there's gonna be some fallout from the Commissioner on this."
"I could care less. Our whole plan from the beginning was to get him. I just thought it would be the State and not the Government that would try him."

Jamie got up, leaving her pad on the desk, walked around, and stood in front of Blackie, took his head in her hands, and pressed it against her chest asking, "Is there any time for me personally?"

"Darlin', I don't want to sound cold or mean or indifferent. If you get me through this shit, we'll go off someplace in the mountains, get a chalet for a week, and I'll fuck you till you're so sore you can't sit on the commode."

"Oooh, hope I can keep my mind on the case with that thought in the back of my head."

"Ya better. darlin' or it'll be uhhh—none," he said, as he kissed her on her forehead and left.

Blackie pulled into Mom and Pop's a little after six and walked in on a mashed potatoes, gravy, fried chicken, and corn-on-the-cobb dinner. For dessert, Mom brought out apple pie and a gallon of Golden Vanilla ice cream. As he chugged down a second helping of pie and ice cream, he hoped he'd fit behind the steering wheel to get home to his little angels. After some conversation about his brother Lynn, who was a sergeant in the Marine Corps, serving his second tour in Viet Nam as a door gunner, Blackie headed North on I-10, hoping to make it home in time to kiss his little girls good night before they fell asleep.

When Blackie walked into the office at 8:00 a.m., he could tell by the way Vicki looked that she was surprised he was there. Nanci, also with a surprised look on her face, came out of her office. "Didn't expect you!"

"Really? Why not?"

"You obviously didn't see the morning paper."

"Nope, do I want to? Why don't ya just make my day and read it to me."

Nanci went to her office as Vicki came in with the donuts and coffee. Nanci came back and read the headline from the morning paper: "FBI PROBES LOUISIANA DEPARTMENT OF AGRICULTURE." Blackie grinned at Vicki. "Do I need a food taster to try this before I take a bite of it to make sure it's not poisoned?"

Nanci said, "We didn't poison it, and I don't think the Commissioner's been out here today."

Blackie feigned shock. "You don't think the Commissioner would poison me?" he asked. Both girls rolled their eyes.

Nanci said, "I still got the same three messages I had from yesterday. Knotts, Bartels, and the Commissioner. You want to talk to any of them?"

"Who wrote that story, Bartels?" Blackie asked.

"Who else?"

"What does it say about me?"

"You don't want to read it?"

"I work for the Commissioner, what makes you think I can read."

"It basically says you have no comment."

"Ok, get 'im on the phone."

"Bartels?" Nanci asked.

"Well, I'd rather talk to Susan Hayward, but she's probably not available."

Vicki laughed. "What do you want me to do?" she asked, as Nanci went back to her office. Blackie looked devilishly at Vicki. "Not a good day to ask that question."

Vicki was blushing, as she went back to her office.

Nanci said, "Paul Bartels on line four."

Blackie picked up the phone. "You called?"

"Actually yesterday, but I guess you were out of pocket."

"Well, I'm here now, what did you want?"

"The comment about the FBI probe."

"I don't know what I could comment on, and I didn't know it was a probe."

"We know that four different AIG employees went into the FBI office yesterday. We called each one and no one answered our calls."

"Did ya ask the FBI what they were doing?"

"Yeah, they said, 'no comment.'"

"Well, that's something we agree on."

"You mean no comment?"

"That's right. I got another call comin' in, Paul," Blackie said and hung up the phone.

As Blackie attacked a second donut and sent Vicki after more coffee, his private line rang. He picked up the phone and recognized Jamie's voice at once. "I'm in the reception area of the US Attorney's Office. I want to make sure you want to do this, because once I do it, there's no turning back."

"No problem, darlin', let 'er rip!"

"I'll call ya back on this line as soon as I'm out."

"OK, darlin', see ya."

Nanci stuck her head inside the door, "Jim Knotts on two."

"I thought you were going to call me when you got out of there yesterday," Blackie said.

"Well, actually, I went out there to see ya."

"Yeah, I found that out this morning. That was after I left and you had somebody else with ya."

After a long pause, Jim said, "I couldn't get rid of him. He was pretty upset about the way you talked to the attorney."

"I told him and the attorney I didn't want him. It took two or three sessions to get it through their heads. What'd they ask you?"

"Mostly wanted to know why I was hired and what my duties were, and you?"

"They want to know if I shook anybody down for campaign money."

"That blunt?"

"Pretty much."

"What'd you say?"

"I told 'em the truth. No."

"Did they ask you any specifics?"

"Nope, just if I'd used the Regulatory Division to hold licenses for money." Then, brushing him off, Blackie said, "Ok, I got some more calls to make, Jim. Let me call the Commissioner. He's been calling me too."

Blackie called to Nanci to ask her to get the Commissioner on the phone.

Just as Nanci came back into the office, the private line rang. Blackie held up his hand to hold her off and answered the line.

Jamie said, "What we are trying to do is serve you with the same date and time as Westerlund. Do you agree that's the way it's gotta be done? Of course, they have to cancel the subpoena they gave you the other day."

"Absolutely, when's it gonna happen?"

"They're gonna try and serve him this afternoon."

"And then mine? And do you have all the details worked out?"

"Uh huh. I'll explain it to you later, and where do you think you should be served?"

"Ringling Brothers, Barnum, and Bailey."

"You want a big splash right there at work, in front of everybody?"

"Absolutely, its the biggest circus I've ever seen."

"Oh, you want a leak to the press?"

"And all their friends."

"OK, I'll call the TV stations too."

"Sounds great. I'll get some 'Underprivileged Children' tickets for the kids."

"I'm gonna call you back in a few minutes. Get whoever's in your office out so I don't have to talk in these circles."

"Let me know when they're comin' to town. I definitely want to go."

Nanci said, "I didn't know there was a circus in town. Oh yeah, the Commissioner's been holding all that time on two."

As Blackie picked up and said, "Sorry to keep you waiting Commissioner," he heard Jeannie's voice. "You didn't, I'm holding for him, just a minute, I'll get him.

"This is the Commissioner speaking."

Blackie thought, *not for long*, as he said, "I'm returning your call from yesterday."

"You were pretty hard on my attorney friend yesterday."

"Not really. I told you and him I didn't need him," which got Blackie a few moments of confused silence.

"Aaaa, Aaaa, when's your Grand Jury date?"

"I don't know, I think its Friday. I don't know, it's in the car. Ya want me to send somebody out to get it?"

"Friday. That soon?"

"Yeah, when did the rest of the people get subpoenaed?"

"Oh, other people got subpoenaed?" the Commissioner asked, obviously pretending ignorance. "Where'd you hear that?"

"Paul Bartels, but I don't remember if he said four or five others."

"You talk to Paul Bartels? I'm gonna have to put a memo out that nobody can talk to the press."

"That's ok with me. It'll save me a lot of phone time."

"Aaaa, what else did they ask you?"

"Your attorney didn't tell you?"

"Aaaa, well, I want to hear your version."

"They wanted to know how many people you made me shake down for campaign money."

"I didn't ask you to shake anybody down!" the Commissioner sputtered.

"What do ya call that thing at Zumo's Supermarket and Dorniac's?"

After about two minutes of silence, the Commissioner croaked, "Did you really say that to them?"

"Nah, I still need my job to feed my little girls, even though I'm sure I wouldn't be guilty of anything, since I only did what I was being told."

Completely exasperated, the Commissioner mumbled something and hung up.

As Blackie mulled over what he should do for lunch, the private line rang and it was Jamie again. "They're pretty sure they can effect service on Westerlund this afternoon. They wanted to serve me as your attorney of record, but I told them no, because you might change attorneys, that they better serve you directly. I also told them that if I were them, I wouldn't go out there alone, just in case there's trouble. I don't know if they believed that, but I think there'll be at least two of them. I also think I need to come to Baton Rouge so we can work out a little strategy on this."

Blackie laughed. "Ok, I think I know the kind of strategy you're talking about. I'll talk to ya tomorrow."

Blackie tried to decide on lunch, realizing David Martin was real close to the Commissioner, and it might be a good idea to spend a little time with his wife, since she might have some "pillow talk" the Commissioner had told her husband. Blackie dialed Mary's private line. She answered on the second ring, and Blackie said, "You know who this is?"

"You must want something," she said.

Blackie laughed. "I was thinking about a blow job and lunch."

"In that order?"

"Whatever is easiest on you. Where would you suggest?"

"Well, not many people know you around here, but everybody knows me."

"How about across the River in Port Allen. That's kinda off the beaten path, and by the way, I'm getting more popular around here every day. I made the paper again today."

"Yeah, I heard. Actually, I saw."

"Look, I don't want to put the state car in that motel. Why don't you drive over and pick me up—or better yet, you get the room, I'll park across the street at the truck stop, you take your clothes off, stand with your tits pressed against the window, and I'll walk around the parking lot until I see ya."

"How bout if I get the room, you walk across the street, and I'll be sitting by the pool."

"God, you women are so hard to get along with."

"Yeah, yeah, yeah. Hurry up, I'm getting horny just sitting here thinking about it."

Blackie walked into Nanci's office. "I'm going to a business lunch. If anybody wants to know who and where, tell 'em ya don't know."

Nancy rolled her eyes. " I heard that private line hang up; it's probably monkey business."

As Blackie crossed the Mississippi River, it brought back memories of the old days, the Gold Strip, and its main hangout, the Carousel Club.

Because it was a hangout for all the crews, muscle was needed all the time to keep them out of each other's business. He recalled how Tommy Spoon, a hard ass Capo at the time, had gotten in some shit and how, after the argument had spilled outside, someone had called the Sheriff's office. Three West Bank deputies drove up and tried to break up the fight and arrest Tommy. The deputies approached with guns drawn. Tommy, whose street name was 'Crazy Tommy', drew his gun, killed one deputy and wounded another before the last deputy cut him down. Only Crazy Tommy would have tried that. Guess he was trying to live up to his name...or die by it.

Blackie parked on the restaurant side of the truck stop and thought, *there's a lot more cars out here than people in the restaurant. Wonder how many of them have walked across to the Holiday Inn.* Rolling up his sleeves as he walked, he was glad he left his coat and tie in the car, but he was not happy that it brought him down to the ankle pistol only. He felt half dressed without that .44 on his hip; plus, he bet he'd be the only guy at the pool in slacks, a white shirt, and his sleeves rolled up.

As Blackie sat there dozing in a lounge chair, he felt someone walk up beside him and murmur, "Hon, come put your bathing suit on so we can go swimmin'."

Opening his eyes, he looked at Mary standing there in a pink string bikini with hardly enough string to accommodate the dye to make it pink. As she tugged at his arm, he said, "Yeah, yeah, I'm comin'."

As soon as they stepped into the room, Mary put her hands over her head, turned around and said, "pull on the little bow and see what happens."

When Blackie pulled on the bow, what top there was fell to the floor. She then turned sideways, poked a hip at him and said, "bow number two." Bow number two negated the necessity to pull on three because what was there fell to her ankles. Blackie thought, *she's basically a great set of tits, a terrific ass, and they're being run by a brain the size of a peanut.* Mary turned around, knelt in front of him, undid the belt, and pulled it out. Blackie said, "Hmmm, I think I've experienced this exact act by you before." She pulled back and looked up. "And I hope many more times."

After an hour, Blackie was able to ask, "You carry that bikini with you for emergencies?"

"Actually, I keep it in my desk drawer, but yes, for emergencies."

As Blackie ruffled her hair, he said, "Are you going to get us something to eat? I'm too weak to dress."

Looking up she said, "I better go get you some raw oysters, because you're gonna need a lot more energy before this day is over."

As Mary started to dress, Blackie grabbed her bra. "You don't need any of that stuff, just put your dress on, and if you don't button it too high, we may get the food free."

As soon as she was out the door, Blackie called Nanci to see if anything important was going on. Nanci, said, "First let me apologize for my smart crack when you were leaving. Your private line has rung three times since you left, so I know you must be at a business meeting. As far as other calls, they can all wait; they're just the usual requests for vacation time, leave time, etc. Do ya know how much longer you'll be?"

"Not sure darlin'. I'll try to call ya back." Blackie turned the TV on, but all they had were soaps and, just as he turned it off, the door opened. Mary brought two huge ham and cheese po-boys, a baked potato with cheese, and a large Frosty. She spread the meal out on the table and removed everything but her heels then sat down to join him.

While they ate, Blackie said, "What's your husband say about this press?"

"Fuck him. I don't want to talk about him."

"I don't think so; he ain't got any tits, and I ain't talkin about him. I'm asking what he said about me."

"He really hasn't said too much. He's pretty naive. I think he thinks you and Jim are the 'bad guys,' and the Commissioner is just kind of the 'victim.' The Commissioner's reputation is pretty passive until you push him into a corner."

"What do ya mean?" Blackie asked.

"When he ran against Lambert for the Central Railroad Commission post, he was getting pushed around pretty good over in the coon ass parishes, and a couple of guys who were tearing his big signs down got beat up. Rumor had it that he hired a couple of those tough union guys from Calcasieu Parish to handle it."

"Yeah, that makes sense, because Tucker Bertrand is from down there, and now he has a job with us. What do you think? Do you think I'm the bad guy or Jim Knotts?"

"I don't know. I don't really care. I like fuckin' ya both."

"What about the Commissioner? Ya don't like fuckin' him?"

"I don't know if he even fucks. When he calls me up there, I just blow him to keep my husband's job."

"Jesus! You puttin' me on?"

"No. I'm surprised your ole lady ain't blowing him for your job."

"You mean everybody's wife's blowing him for their jobs?"

"I know Charlie Darnell's wife, the one you call 'redneck Charlie' is and Jimmy Meadows' wife, too."

"I thought Meadows was his cousin!"

"He is. His wife's not, and the Commissioner wouldn't care anyhow."

"You think Knotts' wife is blowin' him? Why are you fuckin' him?"

"No she's probably not, and I started fuckin' him to protect my husband's job just like you. I figure you both have more clout than my husband. Just turned out that ya'll are both pretty good fucks, so now I'm doing it for two reasons."

"What's the deal with the newspaper guy, Jeff? I heard you were fuckin' him.

"God, I've been doin' him since high school. He doesn't have anything to do with a job."

Blackie laughed. "Whose blowin' him to keep Gerald's job, Gerald?" Blackie asked, adding, "we better get on with this 'cause I have to be back at the office by four."

"Are you kidding me?"

"No, I'm not kidding you. I'm not blowin' him to keep my job, plus I can't type. I need to do some work."

Walking into his office, Blackie wondered who had been calling his private line. Nanci was on the phone and Vicki was in the back. Nanci got up, walked into his office and asked, "How'd it go?" adding, "that private line's been ringing off the hook."

"Ya mind gettin'me some coffee, honey? I see Vicki's in back someplace."

"Not at all, " she said and she started down the hall. She hadn't gone two steps when the private line rang. Blackie picked up the phone and heard Jamie's voice on the other end. "Boy, you're hard to catch."

"Hey, I'm important. I'm runnin' a big outfit here."

"Yeah, yeah, can you talk?"

"Some, but I can listen good."

"Ok. They effected service on Westerlund about 1:15. They're going to serve you tomorrow morning about 8:30. I called the New Orleans paper and Channel Four here. I've called the Baton Rouge paper and their supposedly best TV station, and I told them to ask the people serving you in the morning, who was the important person that had been served in New Orleans this afternoon. That should rock his boat a little bit."

"Ok, darlin'. What's your fee and when is it due?"

"It's due whenever I can get it and it's never ending. Speaking of ends, if I was there right now you could bend me over the end of your desk and start paying it."

"Oh, you're so blunt," Blackie said, pausing to thank Nanci, who had just walked in with his coffee.

"When are you coming to Baton Rouge?"

"Well, I'd like to come tomorrow and spend the night. I can tell my husband I have to get you ready for court. Then I can call ya at home tonight and tell your wife that you're gonna come down here to spend the night to get you ready for court."

Honor vs. testicles. Blackie was always faced with that problem.

"When does court really happen?"

"The day after tomorrow," she said.

"So, who ya gonna sleep with the next night?"

"That night, I really have to get ready for court the next day."

"So, do I really need much preparation, or can we accomplish both things tomorrow night?"

"Yeah, you pretty much wrote the script anyhow. I'm just there to make sure they don't screw you over. Are the girls picking up on any of this bad press?"

"Naw, Lu's really too young to get into the newspaper scene, and Teri and Bitsie are too busy in school and too far away to worry about a newspaper over here. How's Lisa like her job?"

"She likes it a lot. Thanks for not making her do any 'extra duty' to get it."

"Hey, not a problem, she's like family." On that note, the call ended and Blackie dialed Connie. She answered on the first ring and Blackie said, "I got back from a meeting, put my hand on this private line, and the phone was so warm, I know ya been callin me."

"Oh that is so sweet. When can I see ya?"

"I don't know. We're gonna have to cool it, with these FBI people all over me. I don't want them to see us together and involve you." They chit chatted a few more minutes and Blackie hung up, buzzing Nanci to call Millie for him. Blackie told Millie to call him back on his private line and hung up. The phone rang instantly and, as he answered, he was surprised to hear Mary's voice. "I talked to my husband and he said there were going to be some major changes. I don't know if it involves you, but I wanted to tell ya and also tell ya that it's not going to change our relationship."

"Ok, darlin', thanks a lot. I'm in the middle of something. I'll have to get back to you." He barely got the phone in the cradle when it rang again.

Millie said, "I can't believe you! You tell me to call ya and then you get on the phone!"

"What can I say? Everybody loves me."

Blackie gave Millie the same stall story that he'd given Connie.

He got to his house in plenty of time to pick up the girls and take them to Wendy's for a Frosty before dinner. After dinner, as Blackie was playing in the pool with the girls, he heard the phone ring, and Sandy came out and said it was Jamie on the phone. He told her to see if she could take a message, that he was playing with the girls in the pool. In a few minutes, she came out and said, "She just said you needed to spend the night in New Orleans tomorrow to get ready for that business you got coming up," Sandy said, keeping the word "court" out of the conversation for the benefit of the girls.

While Sandy was still showering, Blackie drifted off. The last thing he remembered was the David Letterman show.

Chapter 39

Blackie made sure he was in the office before 8:00 a.m. He didn't want to get caught in the parking lot for service. It was nearly 8:45, while he was eating his second donut, when Nanci stepped in and closed the door behind her saying, "Oh oh, there's two guys in my office that look like cops and two more guys with a big camera that looks like TV. A couple of guys and two or three women holding pads look like they may be some type of reporters."

"Maybe it's two movie producers, camera man, and staff."

"I don't think so. I think it's my first guess, cops and TV. I think Paul Bartels is here too. I saw him once on TV. At least it's a guy that looks like him."

"Really? What do they want?"

"You."

"So? Did they say they want to put me in the movies or on TV?"

"The camera guys and reporters and the Paul Bartels guy didn't say anything. One of the two cop-lookin' guys said, 'I'd like to see Mr. Steece.'"

"And what did you say?"

"I said, 'Wait, I'll see if he's in.'"

"And what did he say?"

"He said, 'Thank you,' and rolled his eyes."

"What did you say?"

"JESUS! I didn't say anything else! I came in here and closed the door!"

Blackie took another bite of the donut. "Guess we'll have to see if I'm in, huh? I know what. I could run down the hall, out the back door, you could get my car, and I could lay down in the back seat, and we could escape, you know, like they do in the movies."

She rolled her eyes again looking flustered. "Where would we go?"

"I don't know. Las Vegas to make love?"

"You need to be serious; they're waiting out there."

"How you know I'm not? Aw, shit, my donut's finished; ya might as well go get 'em. Write down each one's name and what their business is and let 'em in."

Closing the door behind her, Nanci went back to her office. In a few minutes she opened his door and said, "Mr. Steece, these gentlemen are from the FBI and the rest are TV and newspaper reporters."

"WOW, which one of you is Ed McMann? Did I win the million dollars?"

Completely ignored by the entourage, the lead agent removed a paper from his coat pocket and, with his ID in his other hand, he said, "Mr. Steece." Just then the blinding camera lights came on.

Feigning blindness, Blackie said, "I can't see, I can't see."

The agent again said, "Mr. Steece, this is a subpoena to appear before the Unites States Grand Jury in the matter of the United States of America versus the Commissioner, Gilbert Dozier, at noon this Friday."

United States District Court
For The
MIDDLE DISTRICT OF LOUISIANA

UNITED STATES OF AMERICA   No. 80-2-B

v.

Gilbert L. Dozier

TO: Mr. David W. Steece
        3206 S. Carrolton
        New Orleans, LA

You are hereby commanded to appear in the United States District Court for the Middle District of Louisiana at 707 Florida Street in the city of Baton Rouge on the 2nd day of September. 1980 at 9:00 o'clock A.M. to testify in the above-entitled case.

This subpoena is issued on application of the United States of America

August 18, 1980   C. Lee Duspuis
Mitchell B. Lansden   Clerk
Assistant U.S. Attorney

352 Florida Street   **By Paige Noel /S/**
Baton Rouge, LA   *Deputy Clerk*
504-389-0443

Received this subpoena at   on
and on   at   I served it on the
within named
by delivering a copy to   and tendering to ....the fee for one day's attendance
and the mileage allowed by law.

                    By_____

Service Fees
Travel _____$
Services_____$
Total_____$

Fees and mileage need not be tendered to the witness upon service of a subpoena issued in behalf of the United States or an officer or agency thereof. 28 USC 1825 or on behalf of a defendant who is financially unable to pay such costs (Rule 17(b), Federal Rules Criminal Procedure).

"What do ya want me for? I'm not the Commissioner."

"You're one of the witnesses," he said as he walked out.

"Greysuit" and his partner were barely to the door when Blackie felt like the President of the United States at a press conference. Every reporter asked a question at the same time. "Have you taken bribe money?" "Are you a gangster?" "Did New Orleans politicians get you a job here?" "What are your qualifications to run the Department of Agriculture?"

Blackie raised his hand. "Whoa," he said, "the Commissioner has instructed, as far as I know, all AIG employees not to talk to the press." He thought, *I know corn is yellow and peas are green, does that count?* Unabated, the questions continued. Blackie raised his hand again and said, "Please, I'm gonna ask you nicely to leave. If you don't, I'll have Ms. Parker call the State Police. I bet they can get you to leave." It took four or five minutes to get everybody out of his office, then, after a few minutes, Nanci came back. "I think the last of them has left. They took pictures of the building, the parking lot, and I guess the sign, I don't know," she said exasperated.

Blackie leaned back and smiled. "Coffee."

As Nanci headed down the hall, Blackie thought, those little female reporters with short skirts and blouses unbuttoned low, really had a way of pushing their way through the crowd to the front. It occurred to him that he'd probably enjoy fucking every one of them, but as far as any information, he wouldn't trust them as far as he could spit a dead rat, so when they were around, he better keep his mind on their evil little plots and not their tits. Nanci brought him back to reality with the coffee. He told her to get Jamie on the phone while he dialed Connie on the private line. When she answered, he said, "Don't miss TV tonight, darlin'. Instead of being wrapped up in your gorgeous arms, I'll be at home being a family man. After you watch the news you'll understand."

"Oh no, I got a—!"

"Gotta go, hon. I'll call ya as soon as I can," he said and hung up the phone.

Nanci buzzed, but Blackie picked up the blinking light without answering the intercom. "They left about five minutes ago."

"Was it as big a splash as you wanted?"

"Two TV and half a dozen newspaper reporters. What time will you be here?"

"I've got a suite at the Belmont; the bitch wouldn't give me the room number, but I'm gonna leave in a few minutes, so I'll call ya as soon as I get there."

"Ok, I'm gonna go home and see the girls before I get there, but I'll be there before five."

With raised eyebrows, Nanci mouthed the word "Commissioner" and held up three fingers. Blackie motioned for her to close the door, opened his desk drawer, and took a suction cup out, stuck it to the telephone receiver and plugged it into his tape recorder and then picked up the phone.

"This is the Commissioner speaking."

Blackie wondered if he told his wife, "This is the Commissioner fucking you." What an ego. "Yeah?"

"The press was just here asking all kinda questions about you, how you got your job, what your qualifications were. They said you were going to appear before the Grand Jury Friday. What did you say to them?"

"I said what you told me to. Don't talk to the press." This drew a long exasperated sigh from the other end of the phone. After a moment or two, Blackie said, "Hello, are you there?"

"Yes."

"I thought you hung up."

"I think we probably need to meet."

"Why?"

"To discuss your testimony."

"You want to tell me what to say to the Grand Jury?"

"Well, no, I mean like, in general terms," he sputtered.

"I don't think that's a good idea, but my attorney will be here in a few minutes and I'll ask."

"You have your own attorney?"

"Yes, I know I've told you at least a half a dozen times."

"Oh, I guess I'll get back to you."

Blackie hung up, thinking, *if the Commissioner's brain ever heard what his mouth was saying, it would cut its own throat.* Two minutes later the phone rang, and it was Jim. Blackie was glad the tape was still on the phone when he answered it. "What's goin on?"

"I just talked to the Commissioner and he is really a nervous wreck."

"What's he nervous about?"

"I guess he's worried about what you might say to the Grand Jury."

"I'd be a hell of a lot more worried about what the rice growers and sugar cane farmers would say instead of worrying about me if I was him."

"I was only with you and him a couple of times when ya'll tried to shake people down." Jim obviously didn't like that statement.

"We really weren't' shaking people down, we were just checking violators."

Ah ha, Blackie thought. *CYA Jim, I'd been thinking you were heading that way.*

"I told him you were solid, that he's got nothing to worry about."

"I hope he don't think I'm gonna purge myself for him." Blackie said.

"Did you get subpoenaed too?"

"No. I'm at home. I've been talking to him long distance."

Blackie hung up and decided he'd go take Sandy to lunch so in case they were watching him, he'd look like a real family man. He called her to tell her to get dressed for lunch. As he walked out, he told Nanci he'd check with her later, but he wasn't coming back to the office.

As Blackie and Sandy were having a leisurely lunch at the Capitol House Restaurant, several members of the Jefferson delegation and other members of the State Legislature stopped by his table for a few words. Some had heard of the investigation.

Blackie and Sandy picked the girls up from school, and, after visiting a short time, he packed his bag and headed out for New Orleans, which of course was the Belmont, which was only ten minutes away.

As he pulled into the Belmont parking lot, he remembered that Jamie was going to call him at the office and give him the room number. Well, that wasn't going to work, since he wasn't going back to the office. He figured he'd just go in and try the house phone and, if she wasn't there yet, he'd try again later. Blackie's luck again prevailed when Jamie answered on the first ring. Hearing his voice, she said, "You're not at your office?"

"I know. I forgot. I'm in the lobby."

"I'm in the main building, suite 114, and I'm tired of waiting."

"Oh, did you bring your typewriter?"

"That's not what I'm waiting for."

"Ok, see ya in a minute." When Blackie tapped on the door, Jamie opened it wide wearing just high heels.

Blackie said, "Wow, what if I'd have been the bellboy?"

"I guess he'd have gotten a thrill."

Blackie thought, *this woman in her early forties still looked really good and she had a sex drive of a young mink.* Maybe it was true what they said, women peak in the late thirties or early forties. "Can I come in?"

"You better!"

"Why do I feel like if I didn't, you'd cut my balls off?"

"That's why we're not married. I'd have to cut them off."

"Wouldn't that defeat your purpose?"

"I guess, but your friends could still fuck me and you could watch and it would be your turn to suffer."

Blackie walked into the room, thinking, *I guess that would be a way to get some rest.*

About six o'clock, they dressed and drove the hour and a half to a quaint little restaurant in McComb, Mississippi, where there wouldn't be any reporters, or anyone spying on them.

Though Blackie didn't drink, on more that one occasion he had reaped the rewards from what a bottle of good red wine did to arouse an already sexy lady. Once again, he was enjoying the pleasure derived from the bottle Jamie had consumed at dinner as she sat with her feet under her, cuddling up to him caressing his upper body.

As they rolled along south on I-55, Blackie wished they had stayed at a motel in McComb. With her sex drive and the mood he was in, he much preferred the kinky things they did out of town, where nobody knew them, like sneaking into the pool late for a naked swim, or sending Jamie down the hall with just panties or nothing at all to get ice, having her meet the pizza boy nude. They couldn't do that stuff tonight in Baton Rouge. Too many people knew them.

At seven o'clock, they decided to enter the restaurant from different doors, like they were just meeting each other for breakfast. Jamie in a business suit and her briefcase could look like she was the ultimate professional, completely masking the whore Blackie much preferred. As Blackie came in and joined her for breakfast, he realized he'd completely forgotten to check in with Nanci the night before. After ordering coffee, he excused himself and went to a pay phone, hoping Nanci had come in a few minutes early because it wasn't eight o'clock yet. Vicki answered on the fourth ring and told him that Nanci hadn't gotten in yet. He told her to look on his desk to see if there were any important messages, as he was sure Nanci would have left them there in case he had come in after hours last night. She said the only message there was one from Jamie, his attorney. He smiled to himself, saying "I'll call her later," and hung up. He then called his girls to make sure they were okay and to let them know he'd made it through the night fine. By the time he got back to the table, Jamie was on her second cup of coffee and had ordered him eggs, ham, pancakes, and a side of cheese grits. As soon as he sat down, the little witch ran her foot up his leg. He said, "Ya know, if there's a midget in here, he'll see what you're doing."

She said, "If there's a midget in here, I don't give a shit."

After the breakfast dishes were cleared away, Jamie spread some papers on the table, thinking if anybody was around it would look like a working breakfast. About ten, they got into their cars and drove to Blackie's office. When they arrived, Blackie introduced her to his staff and asked Nanci for any messages. A half a dozen reporters, the Commissioner, and an Assistant US Attorney had called, and the private line had rung almost continuously.

Blackie told Nanci to return the Commissioner's call and tell him that he was in a conference with his attorney and that she hadn't been able to get into his office to give him messages, but when he'd asked for coffee, she told him that he'd called and Blackie had instructed her to call him when his meeting was finished.

About three o'clock, they wrapped up their bull session, because Jamie had to go to US Attorney's office to make sure everybody was on the same page tomorrow. Blackie left for home and his girls and told Nanci that if the Commissioner called back, tell him that she'd looked in his office and he must have gone out the back door, because there was nobody there. Also that she had looked in the parking lot and his car was not there.

When Blackie got home, he put his state car in the garage next to the Caddie and left Sandy's out in the driveway so it would look like she hadn't put hers away, and someone passing by would think he wasn't home yet. Sandy answered several phone calls during the evening. He took none of them. This allowed him to have a very quiet and enjoyable evening with the girls.

Blackie met Jamie at the Belmont about eight o'clock. A little after nine he had Jamie call Nanci to see what was going on. She said the Commissioner had called twice and, shortly after the second call, Jim

Knotts called. Shortly after that, they went back to Jamie's room, she said to hang out, but he knew that wasn't going to work. Sure enough her idea of hanging out was to straddle him and hang from the chandelier (had there been one).

A little after eleven, they both got in Jamie's car and headed for the courthouse. As they walked into the witness waiting room, dumb-fuck's attorney was there. He either recognized Jamie from the time she had run for judge or he could figure out she was a pretty smart counselor by her dress and demeanor and really didn't say anything except whatever he said to whoever he called when he scurried to the payphone in the hall.

A few minutes before one o'clock, a US Marshall came in and said, "get ready. Bob Westerlund's on the way in." Jamie took a chair, turning it around facing Blackie on the bench with her briefcase with some papers on top of it and, when Westerlund came through the door, Blackie said, "Now," in a very low voice, and Jamie said in a loud voice easy enough to be overheard, "Dave, you're going to take this deal. If you don't take it, they're going to give it to somebody else and then you'll go to jail instead of them. If you take the deal, you'll walk. No fine, no nothing."

Westerlund, sitting about four feet away was pretending not to hear as Jamie continued. "I have a pre-trial in another courtroom. I'll be back here at two-thirty. You better hope the offer is still on the table."

"Yeah, yeah. I'll be sittin here pickin' my nose," he said, pretending to notice Bob Westerlund for the first time. As Jamie was leaving, Blackie said, "Hey Bob, what's happening?"

Bob said, "I got a subpoena. What are you here for?"

"I don't know. Yours probably says the same thing as mine. I'm here for the Agriculture thing. Somehow they found out that I handled that ten thousand dollars you gave the Commissioner for his payroll business. I think he's trying to say I got the ten grand. The government really don't give a shit about the little people like us. They want to fry the bigger fish. In this case, the Commissioner. My attorney worked out a deal where I can walk if I roll on him."

Westerlund said, "I'm gonna tell them I don't know shit. What are you going to do?"

"Bob, I got two girls in college and three at home, and you and I have always been okay, but there's no chance I'm going to jail for you or the Commissioner. You think they're gonna believe you gave me ten grand in this envelope for me? He pulled the plastic encased envelope out of his pocket.

Bob looked a little surprised. "What's that"

"This is the envelope that the ten grand came in at the Monteleone that day and it's got your fingerprints, my fingerprints, and the Commissioner's fingerprints. Now, who you think got the ten grand, me or the Commissioner? Who you gonna think paid it to the Commissioner? Me or you? When my attorney gets back, I'm gonna take the deal."

Westerlund jumped up and said, "Fuck this! I ain't going to jail for the Commissioner," and ran out in the hall and pounded on the U S Attorney's door. An hour and a half later, the Assistant US Attorney and Jamie came back into the witness room and said that Westerlund had been immunized, and had testified that it happened exactly the way Blackie said it had. The Assistant US Attorney said, "you have one more phase to go through to complete our deal. You're going to have to be here every day of the trial, and each one of the Commissioner's defense witnesses that you know something about, we need to know it. With that, they all shook hands, and Jamie and Blackie arrived back at Blackie's office about four o'clock. Blackie had been wearing a wire all day to catch the Westerlund's conversation and was glad he still had it on, because the Commissioner's car was parked in the lot. When they walked into the office, the Commissioner motioned for Blackie to come outside with him. As they sat in his car, the Commissioner said, "you can talk to me because I'm your attorney. What did they ask you in the Grand Jury and what did you say?"

"Commissioner, I can't talk to you about the Grand Jury. We just left the courthouse, and the US Attorney knows that Jamie is my attorney of record."

He looked a little bumfuzzled, like he didn't know what that meant. Blackie pushed, "Ya know, even sitting together could be witness tampering, and I'm not going to jail for you or anybody else."

The Commissioner said, "But, a, but, but."

"No buts about it Commissioner, I can't talk to you." And Blackie got out of the car.

Blackie went back into the office and watched from the window with Jamie, Nanci, and Vicki, as it took the Commissioner about ten minutes to decide what to do, which, in the end, was simply to drive away. Jamie and Blackie went back to his office and discussed when they would meet for pre-trial work and go over the witness list so he could refresh his memory on what or anything he could do to help the prosecution. Jamie thought it best that Blackie take some time off and take his family out of town on a vacation to keep them from both the press and the Commissioner's tentacles. They formulated a plan, where Jamie would leave and call the private line from a pay phone; Blackie would scream and holler like he was being threatened, thus setting up his excuse to get out of town. Blackie called The Man and, after a brief discussion, he agreed on the plan. As soon as Blackie hung up from talking to him, the private line rang. After the pretense call was over, Blackie called Sandy and told her to throw some things together, shorts, bathing suits, enough for about a week, that they were going to go to Florida and Disney World, but not to tell the girls ahead of time. Blackie then called Uncle Paul and told him to have Zap and Patsy leave right away and come stay in Blackie's house while he was gone. If they got any inquiries, they were to say they were house sitters. With that, he filled out a leave slip for himself (the power of being a boss), gave it to Nanci to turn in to Personnel the next day. He then called Connie on her private line, told her there had been a threat on his life, and the US Attorney was moving him into hiding for a week or so. If he could escape the unwanted bodyguards, he'd try to call her. He also told her that Nanci would be bringing a leave slip up to her tomorrow. Connie said, "Have her bring it to me and I'll handle it." He then called Nanci into the office. "Ya want to stretch the truth a little bit darlin'?"

"You know I'll do anything for you. Well, maybe not anything."

"If somebody like Mary, Jim Knotts, or Millie calls, you can kinda let them know off the record that there was a veiled threat against me and I've been moved temporarily, so they can sort the facts. Anybody else, just tell them I'm on a vacation." Then to give the threat a little credibility he added, "I wonder how they got my private line number?"

"You mean someone called that number?" I heard you screaming and yelling. I thought you were just mad at somebody."

"Yeah, and when I answered it, they said, 'Are you the guy that just testified at the Grand Jury?' I asked them who was calling, and they said, 'Is this the guy that just testified at the Grand Jury?' I said, 'Listen asshole, who's calling?' His response was, 'I'd be careful who you're calling an asshole, and I'd be careful what I said at the Grand Jury if I was you. Have you forgot you got a family?' Now I'm screaming, 'I ain't forgot, asshole. You're pretty tough on the phone. Why don't you drag your ass over here and see how ya do?' Then the asshole said,

'You can't stay awake twenty-four hours, and you can't watch those kids twenty-four hours.' When I started to scream at him again, all I heard was a dial tone."

"Jesus!" Nanci said. "Is your house gonna be safe while you're gone?"

"Yeah, they've provided armed house sitters. They're already there. If you got a real emergency, you can call my house, and I believe it's a man and a woman. I don't know their names, but ask for the woman; tell her who you are, give her the message, and they'll know how to get a hold of me. If you do this, don't tell anyone you made that call."

"Ok, if it's something important, I'll call from my house to your house."

"Smart girl. You might make somebody a good administrative assistant some day."

"I was kind of worried about you a minute ago, but you would probably be telling jokes while they were shooting at you."

"I don't know. I'm gonna run, darlin'. You want to go start my car in case there's a bomb in it?" he said, laughing, as he walked out the door.

As Blackie pulled his state car into the garage, he toyed with the idea of taking the Caddie and Sandy's car, finally deciding the Caddie would be much more comfortable. He walked through the breezeway into the house through the sun porch and told Sandy to start putting things in the car as he changed into his driving clothes. As soon as he walked into the den, of course, the "Where are we goin', where are we goin'" came out in three different octaves.

"It's a secret," he told them.

"Come on, Daddy, tell us. Mom said she didn't know anything."

"Go get in the car, take something to read with ya. Lu, Al, and Rae, take something to put you to sleep, so you won't bug your sisters.

In less that ten minutes, Blackie wheeled the Caddie up through the subdivision, out Sherwood Forest Boulevard to I-12, and settled back for ten or eleven hours of "Daddy, I'm hungry," "Daddy, I gotta go to the bathroom," "Daddy, are we there yet?" Oh well, they were still his little angels.

It was well after midnight and the girls and Sandy had all been sleeping for hours, when Blackie turned the Caddie into his brother Lynn's driveway in central Florida. Lynn had only been home from the Marine Corps for a couple of years and, though he could have gotten into the life, a turbulent divorce had followed his discharge, and the second marriage had caused him to try a simple life in Florida. That also had its plusses for Blackie, since it gave him a straight haven to go to without any questions. Lynn's two tours in Viet Nam and short time home had his acute awareness still high. When the headlights had crossed his bedroom windows, he was up and out the door to greet his older brother with a hug, before the girls were completely awake. They each picked up one of the girls. Blackie designated Lynn to take Lu, the oldest and heaviest, because Lynn was the youngest. Blackie took Alley, and Sandy took the baby. They carried the three girls to one of the spare rooms and, while Sandy tucked them in, Blackie and his brother went back to the kitchen, where Sharon, Lynn's wife, still half asleep, was making coffee. Past experience told her that she and Sandy would be asleep long before the two brothers finished rehashing business, politics, sports, and just general bullshit. Blackie gave Lynn the short version for the visit, but surprisingly, because of the turmoil of the last several days, after only a couple of cups of coffee, decided they better continue tomorrow, and they both went to bed. It was only about ten o'clock when little voices started saying, "Daddy, we're at Uncle Lynn's. We want to go to Disney World." He thought, *damn, what was God thinking of when he gave all this energy to young people and money to the old?* The young couldn't afford to do much and the older people lacked the energy. Blackie struggled to the kitchen and thought Sandy looked pretty rested before he remembered she'd slept the last five hours of the trip. *Wonder if they would ever have cars that drove themselves while you slept.* They had boats and planes that ran on automatic pilot. Sandy poured him a cup of coffee and started to make his breakfast. The girls were still running around overexcited about going to Disney World, where they had been at least once a year since the park had opened. When they came into the kitchen the next time with, "When are we going to Disney?" and were told it was too late to go today, you would have thought he told them they were all about to get an enema. When he added, "We'll go get the tickets today and go early in the morning," the enema faces turned into happy, screaming little girls again. "Go watch TV till I finish breakfast, then we'll go get the tickets. When we come back you can play in the pool."

Blackie thought he needed to call Traffi as soon as possible to let him know he was in town visiting his brother and pay his respects.

Lynn had left Blackie his car, which would cause him not to look so much like a tourist. As they worked their way through the traffic on I-4 on the way to Kissimmee, Blackie was amazed as usual at the huge amount of traffic in Florida.

Tickets secured and back home, Blackie dozed in a lounger while Sandy watched the girls in the pool.

It was late Sunday afternoon when Blackie pulled into Baton Rouge. As he carried one of the sleeping girls back to their bedroom, he wondered why they called it a vacation. He knew he was at least twice as tired as he was before he had driven to Florida. He had spoken to Jamie two or three times during the week, and she'd informed him that the Commissioner was all "lawyered up" with one of the rich alleged "top" attorneys. Other than that, there hadn't been much going on in the big city. Nanci had reported to Zap through his wife Patsy, that the Commissioner had a cow when he found out Blackie was on vacation and had even gone to Connie to try to get him off the payroll. Connie had called Nanci and told her that she'd informed the Commissioner that Blackie could sign leave slips for anybody including himself. He had over 1100 K time (compensatory hours), plus his unused annual vacation time; therefore, he could be out for over twenty-seven days on "K" leave. Other than that, and one call from Jim Knotts, it had been pretty quiet. Maybe he needed to go out of town more often. Blackie thought, *what a smart ass.*

Zap and Patsy spent the night Sunday so Blackie could get a good night's rest before court the next day, and he wouldn't have to listen for little "gremlin" feet during the night.

Jamie called at seven the next morning from the Belmont and said she could pick him up or he could get dropped off, but she didn't want him to have his car. She would be driving. Blackie said, "Come on. I'll be ready by the time you get here."

The trial went pretty much as scripted, until they got to the character witnesses. Blackie noticed that Hawk Daniels appeared to always have a front seat saved on the aisle closest to the witness chair and that he sat strangely with his leg a little into the aisle. It suddenly dawned on Blackie that Hawk had, from time to time, worn a tape recorder on his leg, much like Blackie's ankle gun. Blackie got the US Marshal to go whisper in the U S Attorney's ear to come to the hall. They asked for a short recess, and Blackie informed the US Attorney of his suspicions. When court was back in session, they called Hawk Daniels to the stand.

Objections were voiced, a sidebar was ordered, after which two US Marshals who had blocked the door from anyone leaving, came forward and escorted Daniels to the witness chair. He was then questioned directly by the Judge. He was asked if he had told any witnesses that had not yet testified any statements that previous witnesses had made. He was then asked if he was, in fact, wearing a tape recorder. He denied that as he had the previous question. The Judge then asked him to raise both his pant legs above the knee over the objections of the defense attorneys and Daniels. The Judge overruled the objection, and ordered US Marshall's to raise the pant legs. This brought the tape recorder into plain view. The Judge ordered it removed, and ordered one Marshall to bring it to his chambers while the other took Daniels into custody. Both the US Attorney and the defense attorney accompanied the judge in the chambers. It was about twenty minutes before they returned and the trial proceeded.

Bob Wright was soon called as a character witness, a very respectable attorney, and a long-time friend of the Commissioner. Blackie, in pre-trial conferences with the US Attorney, had dictated verbatim a one-sided shouting match that had taken place in the Commissioner's office long before the indictments were handed down. Blackie stated that he had been sitting on Jeannie's desk about at about eleven on the morning in question when Bob Wright had burst through Jeannie's door and on into the Commissioner's office. He did not close the door behind him, but shouted in a loud angry voice, "a rice grower whose been a friend of mine for years told me you threatened him if he didn't give you ten thousand dollars for your campaign. Commissioner, if I ever hear of anything like this again, not only will I not support you, but I'll work against you."

Bob Wright had testified that he believed the Commissioner was an honest man who he didn't believe he had ever done a criminal act. The US Attorney, during cross examination, repeatedly asked Mr. Wright had he ever thought that the Commissioner had ever committed a criminal act of any kind. After receiving the negative response from Bob Wright, he then removed a piece of paper from his folder and read Blackie's statement, asking again, Mr. Wright, do you remember making this statement in front of David Steece as he sat on Jeannie's desk less than three feet from the door? Bob Wright dropped his eyes, and, after a couple of moments, in an absolutely silent courtroom answered, "Yes, Sir."

The US Attorney then asked , "Was that a true statement? Had your trust in the Commissioner faltered to where you drove the hundred-plus miles from Lafayette and charged through two doors, unannounced, in what was described to us as a screaming, or at the very least, a loud voice, made this statement?"

"Yes, sir, I did," Wright said, looking sheepishly at the judge. "I'm very sorry, I swear I'm sorry."

The US Attorney interjected immediately, "You've already sworn to tell the truth. Now, I'm going to ask you one more time, Mr. Wright. Have you ever questioned the veracity of this Commissioner?"

"Yes, sir, I have."

"No further questions, your Honor."

Everyone in the courtroom was staring at the Commissioner who looked completely shell-shocked as his attorney said, "Redirect, your Honor."

After a short huddle with the Commissioner, he said, "Never mind, your Honor, no further questions."

The trial broke for the day with final arguments to be held the next day. Blackie, loitering in the hall with Jamie, was near the exit door when the Commissioner came out. He smirked at the Commissioner, who looked back as mean as he could, and angrily said, "I'm going to get you."

Blackie laughed and Jamie nearly sprinted to the US Attorney to report the threat. A huddle ensued with Jamie and the US Attorneys. Blackie walked up and said, "Ahhh, don't worry about this, now. I think it's just sinking in that he's going to go to jail." That night, Blackie had one of his men slip into the Commissioner's yard to set a jar of Vaseline and a bar of Ivory Soap and a string attached with a note that read, "You'll need these where you're going," on the hood of his car.

The jury returned a guilty verdict, and the Commissioner was sentenced to ten years. During the appeal process, the FBI, who had a legal wiretap on Louisiana State Senator Gerald, had overheard a conversation whereby one of the mules delivered kick-back money on an asphalt project that was being controlled by State Senator Gerald in his district. The mule told Senator Gerald that the Commissioner was going to pay him a hundred grand to take out this guy David Steece because the Commissioner felt that he was more than instrumental in his conviction. When the agents brought the information to Blackie, with his usual flamboyant style, he more or less blew it off. They also said they intended to leak that threat in a report of attempted jury tampering that was investigated and was now being reviewed by the sentencing judge. The Commissioner later received a total sentence of eighteen years which, ironically, was to be served in the same United States Penal Institute in Fort Worth, Texas, that would later house convicted Senator Gerald.

Newspaper Article No 1:

The States – Item

Vol. 103-No.201   Wednesday, January 30, 1980   New Orleans, La.   15 cents

Charges are bribery extortion

Dozier indicted by U.S. jury

By Jack Wardlaw
States-Item Bureau

BATON ROUGE – State Agriculture Commissioner Gilbert L. Dozier was indicted today by federal grand jury on five counts of public bribery and extortion.

U.S. Attorney Donald I. Becker said the indictment charges that, from the date of his election to office in 1976, "Mr. Dozier has used the Louisiana Department of Agriculture to conduct a pattern of rackereeing actives in violation of the laws of the state of Louisiana and the United States of America."

If Dozier is convicted on all counts. Becker said, the maximum sentence is 100 years in prison and-or a fine of $65,000.00.

The indictment ends a six-month Investigation by Becker's office, the FBI and the grand jury. Becker praised what he called the "extensive" cooperation of state Attorney General William J. Guste, Jr. in the investigation.

Dozier wasn't available for comment. But he has denied repeatedly any wrongdoing, saying the allegations are the work of political enemies and Were timed to wreck his re-election. campaign.

* * *

Newspaper Article No. 2:

The Times - Picayune
The States - Item

Friday, November 7, 1980   144th Year No. 288   New Orleans, La.

Dozier Sentenced To 10 Years

By Bill Lynch
Capitol Bureau

Baton Rouge- Former Louisiana Agriculture Commissioner Gil Dozier, sobbing openly in federal court Friday was sentenced to 10 years in prison and fined $25,000.00 on his conviction of three counts of extortion and one count of racketeering.

U. S. District Judge Frank J. Polozola, who had been a student of Dozier's at Louisiana State University as well as a law school classmate, said in delivering the sentence that he had violated the public's trust.

Polozolo told Dozier that despite their long association, he was obliged to impose "stern punishment" for the former commissioner's actions.

"The trust of the people of the state of Louisiana was seriously breached," the judge said. "It is wrong, criminally wrong, to use a public office, in this case agriculture, in your own interest." Dozier attempted to speak to the court on his own behalf, but broke down in tears.

"I deeply regret any activities or ambitions I might have had that caused me to appear before the court today," said a sobbing Dozier, a handkerchief covering his eyes. "I also regret the emotion I am showing here today, but I can't help it."

Polozola said that the verdict of the jury was overwhelmingly supported by the evidence.

"I completely agree with the findings," he said "Instead of operating the office in the interest of the people, you operated to further Gil Dozier's wants and needs."

Newspaper Article No. 3:

Gil Dozier's bond is revoked after jury-tampering charge

BATON ROUGE(AP) – Convicted in 1980 of racketeering and extortion, former Louisiana Agriculture Commissioner Gil Dozier was jailed Thursday accused of jury tampering and trying to hire a contract killer.

U. S. Attorney Stan Bardwell filed a pair of lengthy motions which outlined Dozier's "**alleged attempts to hire a killer**, arrange a burglary of an office, and suborn the jury which convicted him."

Dozier, arrested without incident at his home, was taken before U S District Judge Frank Polozola.

Dozier had been free pending the appeal of his 1980 conviction on charges that he used the power of his office to extort campaign contributions from people who did business with his department.

He was sentenced to ten years in prison, plus five years on probation, and $25,000.00 in fines on three counts.

The Fifth U S Circuit Court of Appeals upheld the conviction and the case is now pending before the U S Supreme Court.

According to the government on or about the latter part of November 1981, or the first part of December, 1981, **the defendant made inquiries into the possibility of having an individual killed**:

During February, 1982, the defendant requested a contract price for having an individual killed.

The alleged jury tampering was apparently an attempt to get members of Dozier's trial jury to say that other jurors engaged in improper prejudicial conduct while they were trying to decide whether Dozier was guilty or innocent.

The Court papers say last November or December, Dozier allegedly solicited help from Huey P. Martin "to influence by any means necessary" the members of the jury that convicted him.

The U S Attorney's office said part of the scheme included getting jurors to write letters to Polozola and to Dozier's lawyers – Gravel and the late E. Drew McKinnis – about alleged jury-room conduct.

Newspaper Article No. 4

Dozier begins 18-year term in Texas prison

BATON ROUGE (AP) - One year and nine months after his conviction for extortion and racketeering, Gil Dozier has begun serving his sentence - with additional time for tampering with the jury which convicted him.

The former agriculture commissioner reported to prison Thursday night in Fort Worth, Texas, to begin serving a term that had been stretched from 10 years to 18.

After revoking Dozier's bond and probation Thursday, U S District Judge Frank Polozola ordered him to report by 8 AM Friday.

The attorneys said they would file notice of appeal with the 5th US Circuit Court of Appeals in New Orleans by Monday but the appeal could take months to prepare.

Dozier stood with his head bowed when the sentence was read, then motioned to his children, sitting in the front row, to join him in private in a room behind the courtroom.

"The only thing that saddens me in this case is that when you revoke probation, you're almost admitting to yourself that you made a mistake," Polozola said. "Maybe the original sentence wasn't right."

Newspaper Article No. 5

The Times Picayune

<u>June 26, 1982</u>   <u>New Orleans, La.</u>

Dozier, Gerald are neighbors in Texas prison

By The Associated Press

Gil Dozier, the former state agriculture commissioner convicted of extortion, is now sharing prison space with former state Sen. Gaston Gerald - an acquaintance convicted of a similar crime. Charlotte Barron, a spokeswoman said Friday the former elected officials probably had run into each other at the compound.

"They're both in general population. They have free access throughout the institution. So they would be in contact with the rest of the general population." she said.

Jamie prodded Blackie continually and the US Attorney's office, about these threats that now included both the Commissioner and Hawk Daniels, finally convinced him, if only for the safety of his girls, to move to at least a safer place, to give the Commissioner, Hawk Daniels, or anybody else, time to cool off.

Blackie moved Sandy and the girls to a quiet neighborhood on the Mississippi Coast, but with his "hormone problem," he continued to sneak back over to Baton Rouge to either Connie or Millie. Mary was completely out of the picture, since she had gotten pregnant by Jeff and actually named him as the father while still married to her husband.

After leaving a meeting one night on Airline Highway, Blackie felt sure he was being followed. He got off the highway and looped around through his old subdivision, came out on O'Neil Lane on I-12 and got home with no incident, thinking, *paranoia is ridiculous.* They wouldn't think of looking for him driving Sandy's Lincoln, not his signature Caddie.

A week later, leaving the same motel parking lot, turning onto Airline Highway, he was reading a love note from Millie under the dome light.

The first shot almost deafened Blackie, and the flying glass and blood in his eyes rendered him nearly helpless and blind as he wrenched the steering wheel and stomped on the brakes. The car careened into a church parking garage and came to a stop. He was trying to think, *am I on the seat or the floor? Why can't I feel my legs? Gotta get my .44*, not knowing it had fallen out of the holster when he had toppled over. He could taste blood in his throat and, when he touched his face to see where the blood was coming from, he could feel glass. He heard the door being wrenched open and a voice. "Oh, my God, he's been shot twice. GET AN AMBULANCE! Blackie, fading in and out, thought, *fuckin' Lincoln, if I had been in the Caddie, they couldn't have seen me with the black windows! Where's my gun? Shot twice? He didn't remember any second shot. Where's my gun? Shit, Teri's graduation's coming and Lu's leaving Jr. High School. I have to be there for those! Jesus, I don't want to die in this fuckin' Lincoln!* He could hear the ambulance siren, thinking, *is that the ambulance? God damnit, Jamie, why didn't I listen to you? Alley has a school play coming up. Who could have known I was going to be in Baton Rouge...Sandy?* The last thing he remembered was a finger on his throat. He guessed they were feeling for a pulse. What was this bright light in his face?

The End

The picture below depicts the traffic flow on Airline Highway in New Orleans, Louisiana at the time the shooting occurred.

The above picture show the police officers investigating the shooting with the police unit in the background in the church garage.

The above pictures show front of the victim's vehicle and the driver's door glass with the bullet holes

These pictures were taken off of a video taken by a local news reporter and copied off of a TV news report. (thus the poor quality)

Author's Credentials

David Steece began his writing career in the early 1960s as the Editor of the *Delta Lions Club Monthly*. He wrote speeches for the Governor, Judicial, and parochial candidates. He has written and presented bills before the Louisiana State Legislature, Municipal and State Police Retirement Board, and prepared multi-million dollar budgets in both the public and private sectors. In the early '70s, he was contributing columnist to *The Mamou Acadia Press* (a multi-Parish Central Louisiana newspaper), *The City News* of Kenner (a suburb of New Orleans), *The Star and Crescent* (a monthly local law enforcement periodical). In 1973, he co-founded *Louisiana Concerned Citizens Committee* and *Pulse*, the only totally political newspaper in Louisiana at that time. A year later, he became its editor, at which time *Pulse* was picked up as a supplement to the above captioned publications. He was a speaker at Governor Jimmy Carter's Presidential announcement breakfast. Chief Justice of the Louisiana Supreme Court, Pascal F. Calogero, Jr., appointed him to serve as a speaker/debater for the New Orleans Regional Citizen Conference on the Courts. He was appointed by a joint resolution of the Jefferson Parish Council to serve on the Sesquicentennial Commission. He was elected to two terms as a director and one term as President of Louisiana Concerned Citizens Committee, and additionally, served on the following boards as a director: Strategic Marketing, Inc. (a public relations company), Cash Register Sales, Inc., Astute Detective Agency, Inc., and as Treasurer for Reserve Adjustment Bureau, Inc. (a national collection agency), and too many other civic organizations to list.

During his long career in law enforcement, he was commissioned by the Louisiana State Police, the New Orleans Police Department, Harahan Police Department, Jefferson Parish District Attorney's Office, Slidell Police Department, St. Tammany Parish Sheriff's Office, and Delgado Community College Police. He held a Louisiana Private Investigators License #1166-080194-LA. In Mississippi, he was commissioned as a Criminal Deputy by the Pearl River County Sheriff's Office. In Texas, he operated under Texas State Licenses #C-04623 and C-6646, licenses #360657 and 367479, as a Private Investigator, Security License #388213 and an Administrative License #388658. In Arkansas, he was commissioned by the Baxter County Sheriff's Office. His narcotics arrest record earned him Gold Shield Detective badges in three of the parish/counties he served in. Additionally, he served as a Safety Driving Instructor for AARP Driver's Safety Program.

David 'Blackie' Steece, Author

Index

Camp LeJeune, North Carolina, 89
Capitol House Hotel (Baton
Rouge),147 149, 193, 235, 236,
328,
Capone, Al, 55, 247
Carter, Jimmy President, 165, 348
Cedar Lake Development Co.,
Biloxi, MS, 89, 228, 258, 309
Channel 4 TV New Orleans, 135,
139, 146, 320
Channel 6 TV New Orleans, 233,
245
Chicago IL, vii, 15, 55, 245, 247
Chinese Inn (Baton Rouge), 69,
279, 282, 287, 290
Churchill Farms, 56, 103, 185
Civil Service (Baton Rouge), 207,
208, 221, 238, 240, 273, 282,
285, 291
Colgan, Ed, 34, 154, 169, 187
Colgan, Heather, 187
Colgan, Patsy Steece, 34, 154,
157, 163, 165, 167, 169, 183,
187
Colgan, Stacy,164, 187
Confortos, 57, 161, 184
Cook, Charles, Lt (Slidell LA
Police Department), 175

D

D. H. Holmes Department Store,
259, 260, 261
D'Amico, Louie, 67
D'Gerolamo, Eddie (State
Representative, LA), 1, 2, 11,
47, 49, 148, 219, 220
Dairy Queen, Baton Rouge, 7, 85
Daniels, William 'Hawk', 267,
277, 279, 282, 283, 293, 297,
336, 345
Darnell, Charles, 43, 47, 51, 52,
70, 191, 205, 211, 212, 213,
216, 217, 319

Dauphin, Derbes (Lt. New Orleans
Police Department), 34, 35,118,
119, 120, 121
Day, James Dudley, Dr. 101, 304,
Dearmann, Mike, 104
Denham Springs, LA, 254,261,262
Department of Agriculture, LA,
78, 101, 203, 250, 257, 267,
268, 287, 297, 301, 302, 303,
312, 313, 326, 341
Despenzero, Elaine, 170, 216
Dickinson, Angie, 37
Donelon, James J.,27, 49
Dorignac, Joe, 109, 110, 111, 132,
133, 134, 135, 140, 144, 148,
162,
Double Cross, x, 189
Dozier, Gilbert L. Commissioner,
Dept. of Agriculture, LA, 2, 3,
7, 9-13,18, 20, 31, 33, 34, 36-
40, 43-45, 47-49, 51-53, 57-63,
65, 68,-72, 75 -77, 84, 87-89,
92-94, 101-103, 107-112, 115-
118, 121-126, 135, 136, 139-
141, 144-149, 160, 184, 190-
192, 200, 201, 204-206, 211-
214, 219, 221, 222, 226-228,
230, 231, 235-237, 244, 249-
251, 257, 258, 260, 267, 268,
270, 273, 274, 277, 280, 282,
283, 292, 293, 296, 297, 300-
304, 308-316, 318, 319, 324-
327, 330-333, 336-345,
Duplantis, Gina, viii, xi
Dupree, Cornelius(Cuz) II, 39, 40,
41, 45, 52, 53, 73, 277, 279, 281

E

Economical Supermarket, Joe
Zuppardo, 109, 110
Eden Isles, LA, 87, 88, 228
Edwards, Edwin, (Governor, LA),
78, 231